C000184777

Love Sets Y

(Liebe Macht Frei)
The biography of Janni Kowalski
by
Jeremy Harder

'Arbeit Macht Frei'
'Work Sets You Free'
Auswitz-Berkenau

First Edition 2004

Published
by
Old Forge Publishing
39 Backgate
Cowbit
Spalding
Lincolnshire
PE12 6AP
01406 381313
www.oldforgepublishing.org

ISBN 0-9544507-3-6

Printed for Old Forge Publishing
by

Woolnough Bookbinding Ltd
Express Works
Church Street
Irthlingborough
Northants
NN9 5SE

OLD FORGE

Foreword

It has taken over fifty years to pluck up the courage to recount this potted autobiography. My lengthy hesitation has been due to fear of inherent prejudices which have prevailed for such a long time but which have, in recent years, become more relaxed.

Most histories of this period tend to concentrate on the atrocities that were committed against the Jewish nation and others unfortunate enough to be regarded as 'untermenschen', (sub-humans). These included Gypsies, Russian peasants, Poles, Downs Syndrome children (referred to until recently, in even the most cultured societies as Mongols), homosexuals etc. No one escaped the fanaticism of the drive for racial purity and horrendous experiments were carried out on defenceless men, women and children in the relentless drive to achieve this goal.

Countless books have been written on these subjects including many personal accounts of individual survival in the face of terrifying odds. Survivors have been able to testify to the outrages committed, not only against them, but also to countless thousands of others who did not survive the excesses of The Third Reich.

My story is very different and it is only now, in these more enlightened, tolerant times that I feel able to recount my experiences without fear of condemnation. Although I hated our oppressors with the same intensity as everyone else, my survival was entirely due to love. This love came from the Jewish family who took me in and cared for me, a Polish woman and her son and a senior SS Officer who fell in love with me.

I am neither proud of this story nor ashamed of my conduct. I did what I had to do in the circumstances and, like so many others, used everything at my disposal to survive. Where others had unlimited financial resources to buy favours and delay the inevitable, all I had was a most unusual face and body. I should add that in publishing this book, neither my biographer, the publishers nor I wish to imply that we condone underage sex, quite the contrary, but, since this is a true account of my experiences and the fact that my willingness to participate in such activities undoubtedly saved my life, it would not have been possible to write the book without the inclusion of such details. Additionally, I must make it clear that I was not abused in any way or seduced against my will; quite the reverse since I was frequently the instigator!!

With a couple of major exceptions, all the names of the participants have been changed since there are those still living who would undoubtedly suffer embarrassment by the revelations. Similarly, some dates and locations have been changed for the same purpose.

When I left the MSLO (Mixed Service Labour Organisation), I swore that I should never speak Polish again and until I spelled out the names of the streets etc., to my biographer, I have neither spoken, nor written nor read a solitary word of it. This was fairly easy to accomplish since, although I spoke the language very fluently, as far as I remember, I have always been dyslexic, although in those days, it was called 'word blindness'. Whether the blow to my head, which brought about my amnesia, brought about this dyslexia I cannot say, but I could not read Polish since their alphabet was, and will always remain, a mystery to me.

I did not have the same problem with German since the words were spelt exactly as they sounded. However, when I left Germany for good in nineteen fifty-four, I decided never to speak that language again. This has proved more difficult since I have maintained friendships in Germany for many, many years but, even visiting, I use it only as a last resort. In effect, I have not held a conversation in that language for nearly fifty years.

When I started speaking English again I had the same dyslexia when it came to reading and I still fight a constant battle with this problem. It is for this reason that I opted to have a biographer write my story.

Like the Polish lady, Hedwig who features in this story, I developed the ability to recall conversations absolutely verbatim and in so doing; I have relived every incident recounted, even remembering the facial expressions during such conversations or confrontations. I accept that this ability, which I acquired, is a form of compensation for my dyslexia!

It has been a very emotional journey back in time and frequently during the many recording sessions, I had to stop for quite lengthy periods as the memories threatened to overwhelm me.

'Emil', the SS Officer is still alive, eighty-eight years old and in fine health. He still plays tennis and goes scuba diving!! He has never married and when I told him of my intention to allow this book to be written, but that I should change his name although even then, he would be relatively easy to identify he responded by saying that he was proud of our relationship and the fact that we had loved each other for almost twelve years and had sustained our friendship for sixty years. When he enquired as to my current status, I told him that following my divorce I had lived alone for the past twenty-four years and still had no companion in my life. In great fun, he suggested that I should go over to Germany, take up with him again and 'see if we could make a go of it this time!'

We both laughed a lot.

Like a diminishing number of very old friends, he refuses to call me by my proper name and still insists on calling me Janni.

Parts of the narrative are, out of necessity, extremely sexually explicit. These parts are not intended to shock nor are they included for gratuitous titillation. On the contrary, they are an integral part of my story without which, it would be impossible to convey the essential stages of my development or express the extent of my emotions, my innermost feelings and the depths of my commitment to the very few people with whom I had a loving, physical relationship.

Janni Kowalski, 2003.

CHAPTER ONE

JANNI

It is difficult to know where to begin this story since, for the most part, it is the story of Janni Kowalski.

Most of the story I heard from Janni himself but I should never have heard this remarkable tale if it had not been for my Staff Sergeant, Michael, who sought my permission to estab-lish Janni's identity and nationality and had set up a meeting one Sunday lunchtime between Janni, Michael, a Pay Corps sergeant called Tim and me.

It was nineteen forty-six and we were stationed in Osnabrck as part of the occupying forces in Germany.

At the time, I was a young captain, only twenty years of age and although I was superior in rank to my staff sergeant, he was ten or eleven years older than me and vastly more experienced in our particular kind of work. In addition to this, he was a very accomplished linguist, having taught modern languages before the war. He had refused a commission for reasons best known to himself and was content with his rank of staff sergeant which he happened to consider the best rank in the British Army if one wanted to do as little as pos-sible!

Out of necessity and I must admit, a certain curiosity, I duly met Janni, but, for reasons which will become apparent, Michael had not told me all of his story nor the extent of his involvement. In fact, he only told me, rather reluctantly, some months after that first meet-ing and he has made his own contribution to this story which covers his relationship with Janni and which appears later in the book in the appropriate chronological sequence of events.

I should point out, lest you become confused, that at the precise time in question, I had no knowledge of Janni's dual personalities and only knew of him from the brief report on his status as a displaced person but I was intrigued because he claimed to be English and Michael was absolutely convinced that this was indeed the case.

In the meantime and based purely on Michael's evidence, I had obtained NAAFI passes for Janni and a pass enabling him to exchange currencies at the Army Area Cash Office where Tim, the Pay Corps Sergeant worked.

THE MEETING

Michael collected me from the mess and we drove into town and parked in the hotel car park. Inside, we were ushered to a window table and the waiter took our order for cold beers and asked,

"Will you gentlemen be dining with us?"

Michael and I exchanged glances and I told the waiter that we were expecting friends to join us and that we should let him know later.

He went away and returned with two chilled goblets of pale, golden beer.... wonderful.

We had been sitting for about ten minutes when a sergeant came in, accompanied by the most beautiful girl I had ever seen looking as though she had just stepped out of the pages of the most exclusive fashion magazine. She was quite stunning and to her credit, seemed totally unaware of all the turning heads. Indeed, there was nothing in the least bit conceit-ed about this breath-taking, lovely girl who was totally oblivious to the admiration she was receiving from all and sundry.

To my surprise, the sergeant looked in our direction, smiled, waved to Michael and guided his companion towards our table.

Michael and I both stood up as they approached and the girl put an arm round Michael's neck, kissed him lightly on the lips and said,

"Hello Michael. I'm so glad you came. I was worried that you might have had a change of heart."

She smiled a strangely sad smile at Michael, the significance of which was lost on me at that time.

Michael turned to me and said,

"Arthur, I'd like you to meet Tim. Tim, this is Arthur."

I shook hands with Tim, made the appropriate noises and turned back towards Michael as he said,

"This is the person I've been telling you about. Arthur, Janni Kowalski, Janni, Arthur."

For a moment or two, it didn't sink in as I said.

"I am delighted to meet you Janni, I've heard so much about you."

I was glad that it hadn't registered immediately and when realisation came, I was able to cover my confusion by telling myself that I should be having serious words with Michael for pulling such a stunt.

Janni broke into my thoughts by saying,

"Arthur, you have been very kind and I am indebted to you for obtaining my passes. By way of appreciation I should like to treat you all to lunch but only on the condition that we all sit down and one of you ill-mannered bastards orders me a drink!"

She grinned widely, showing her perfect, small, even teeth and Tim and Michael roared with laughter.

Tim held a chair for her as she sat down and Michael, in a sort of theatrical aside, said, "I should have warned you about Janni's command of the language, including all the swearwords which she uses with unbecoming frequency."

I laughed along with them and I was intrigued by the way in which both of them referred to her as she, without any form of embarrassment and treated her exactly as they would have done any very attractive young lady.

Janni showed no sign of self-consciousness; in fact, she was completely natural, so natural that I was sure Michael and Tim were having fun at my expense. She must have been in on the joke and I thought she must be a good sport to go along with it. I'd already decided that I liked her and her willingness to participate in a charade, which took the piss out of a senior officer, was quite daring and added to her appeal.

I smiled at her and said,

" I am quite used to other ranks playing practical jokes on their officers, but never with such a beautiful accomplice."

Her smile faded and she turned to Michael and Tim and said, "You two. You really are despicable. You haven't told the poor man have you and the pair of you just thought you would have a good laugh if and when Arthur became flustered. You lousy pair of bastards. Didn't you stop to think that by not telling him, you were going to make the situation equally uncomfortable for me? I came here convinced that Arthur would know about me in advance and that no further explanations would be necessary at this stage. I'm not very happy with either of you. If you will excuse me, I have done what I came here to do, that is to thank Arthur and now I should like to leave. Don't bother getting up Gentlemen."

She uttered the last word so contemptuously that it hung in the air for a long moment, which seemed to stretch into eternity as she picked up her bag and head held high, walked away from the table looking extremely elegant with her longer than usual, quicker stride. She was incredible.

At the table, there was a deathly silence; Tim and Michael looking suitably crestfallen and at this point I noticed an expression of what I could only describe as heart-breaking despair

4

on Michael's face as he said, "Oh Shit! I've made an absolute balls-up of that. I had better go after her and apologise."

Tim stood up and said,

"No Mike, you are far too involved. It's better if I go and explain that we thought it would be better if Arthur met her as she is, just as you did on the first occasion Mike and since it worked out well on that occasion, we saw no reason to think that it would be any different this time. Now, while I'm gone, you have some serious explaining to do Mike. Make it quick and make it thorough. If I find her, I'll keep her away for about half an hour. Make the most of it."

He excused himself and left in a hurry.

Michael, who had been very quiet, turned to me and said,

"I'm sorry Arthur, I should have told you but I wasn't sure what your reaction would be. I remember in the same circumstances, Tim saying to me that he doubted I should have agreed to meet, to quote him, 'a pretty little transvestite' and in retrospect, he was probably right. Anyway, now that you know, does it change anything?"

He looked at me imploringly and my suspicion grew that he was interested in more than just establishing her identity.

Fortunately, I am by nature, a compassionate soul, so I responded to his plea by saying,

"Michael, I am not sure how I should have handled such an unusual situation, but, in military terms, one should be briefed with all the information at one's disposal in order to form a balanced judgment and plan accordingly. I am a little put out to think that you considered me incapable of an unbiased reaction to such revelations. As it is, I was very impressed with your Janni and the realization of the truth has done nothing to alter that opinion. I shall continue to address her as a female and show her respect, because she certainly deserves it. I liked her and her spirit very much and I should advise you to mend your bridges very quickly. She obviously has a great affection for you and feels that she has been made the butt of a joke, just as I have by you and Tim. I know you meant well, but she is very feminine and very sensitive and although she is all bravado with her cheeky impertinence and swearing, underneath, she is insecure, frightened, nameless, stateless and in need of the kindest, most loving friends. Put it right Mike, then, use your inborn common sense and extract yourself slowly without causing the poor child any more grief."

Later, much later, I would be surprised by own intuition and I think Michael was equally surprised.

Michael broke in on my thoughts by saying.

"You are a shrewd bugger Arthur. Now I know why it is that you made captain so young. In that young breast beats a heart of pure gold and in that head, a brain capable of spewing forth gallons of bovine effluent."

We both laughed, the tension eased and Mike told me all he knew of Janni's past. There were huge gaps which he explained by saying that Janni was not ready to tell anybody about the full extent of her experiences for a long time to come and that for now, we should just have to go along with her reticence.

Mike couldn't hide the look of sheer relief which spread over his face when Tim and Janni appeared arm in arm and made their way towards us.

We both stood up and I held a chair for Janni. I was astonished by the sudden change in her demeanour as she kept her wonderful eyelashes lowered and muttered,

"Michael, I am sorry Darling. I'm far too sensitive and Tim had made me realise that you did what you thought was right. I apologise for embarrassing you in front of your boss. Please forgive me Darling."

I wanted to applaud. Not only had she made Mike feel like an absolute shit but also, playing the ingenuous child, she had seriously compromised him. She raised her eyelashes to reveal the deep, inviting pools of her wonderfully expressive eyes, draped her arms around

Mike's shoulders, virtually defying him to be anything other than extremely affectionate, pressed herself against him and said,

"Please tell me you still love me."

I clapped my hands thinking, 'small wonder she survived, she's marvellous' and said,

"Round two to Janni. Well done dear girl. Now can we dispense with all this crap, have something to eat and all get pissed."

It seemed to break the ice. They all laughed heartily and Janni moved the others out of the way so that she could sit beside me when I announced,

"I haven't had such an interesting day in years and Janni, if you don't mind, I'll foot the bill by way of reparation for the appalling behaviour of my subordinates, God bless 'em. If it hadn't been for these two bastards, I should never have met you."

She put an arm round my shoulder and said,

"Thank you Arthur. You are a perfect gentleman, I am only a small percentage of one and these two are the grungy residue in the bottom of the barrel. From now on, if it doesn't embarrass you, I shall love only you. You may kiss my lips, but the others can kiss my arse."

Bearing in mind my suspicions of Michael's feelings for her, I didn't think that this was such a good idea!

The meal and the rest of the afternoon went wonderfully, there was never a dull moment and with the consent of the management, Tim persuaded Janni to play the piano. She played some light music followed by a delightful recital of classical pieces all so cleverly linked that it was a continuous, unbroken performance, made all the more remarkable because she had no sheet music, playing everything from memory. My admiration grew in leaps and bounds.

Amid spontaneous applause, Janni stepped down from the small stage and made her way back to the table. The management sent over a bottle of their very best Deinhard sekt (champagne) in an ice bucket by way of appreciation.

I watched her as discreetly as possible, noting every movement, every expression, unable to detect the slightest hint of masculinity. I sympathised with Mike. She was truly captivating.

We finished the evening in Tim's quarters with plates of sandwiches cobbled together by Tim and Janni and a mind-boggling choice of alcoholic beverages. I made a mental note that these chaps were far better off financially than I was and began to appreciate Mike's decision not to take a commission with all the additional expenses involved.

Despite the earlier setbacks, it had developed into a most memorable day, none of us wanting it to end but, common sense prevailed and finally, Michael and I took Janni home.

Once at her flat she flatly refused to let Michael drive any more, which made a good deal of sense and the three of us climbed the stairs to her homely, but tiny flat.

I sat in a well-upholstered armchair with a large brandy in my hand conscious of the electricity flowing between Mike and Janni, aware of some insurmountable barrier between them and feeling desperately sorry for them both. There was no doubt in my mind that they had very intense feelings for one another and that heartbreak, for one or both, was just around the corner.

It came as no surprise, therefore, when, the next morning, Mike asked if he could be transferred somewhere else for a time.

In view of the situation, I arranged for him to go on temporary detachment to the American sector to clear up some cases in which both occupying powers had serious interest and where his linguistic skills would be of benefit to both powers.

Whether it was due to the absence of Mike, the desire for improvement, or any number of other things, Janni left Osnabrck shortly after his departure and moved to Hamburg.

Both Tim and I had cards from her on a regular basis and the three of us, Tim, Mike, (who had returned from temporary detachment) and I visited her on numerous occasions when we were in that city.

During my many visits, she became more and more trusting and no longer hid behind cheeky shock tactics. She became more open and confiding, recalling in an astonishing series of very detailed, no-holds-barred revelations, without sense of embarrassment or guilt, her road to survival. She admitted to amorally seducing the SS Officer who became her lover and protector, as a means to an end long before she actually fell in love with him.

I was in no position to criticise. On the contrary, bearing in mind that she was so young at the time and that discovery would have meant certain death, it would be impossible not to admire the fact that, despite all the fear-inducing, horrendous acts of barbarism going on around her, all day, every day, she had used the weapons at her disposal to survive. I felt very proud to know her but worried about her obsession with finding her SS boyfriend because I had learned a lot about the love-hate relationship which can develop between captor and captive.

During the early years of our friendship, and I am pleased to say that we are still friends to this day, she told me the part of her story in relation to Emil and Auschwitz. I have met Emil on a number of occasions and he has corroborated every detail.

It took a long time for the whole story, dealing with the periods before and after her incarceration, to come tumbling out and Janni and I have laboured, often into the small hours of the morning, over the intervening years to record every last detail. I have no doubt of its authenticity and I have seen seven or eight very valuable diamonds and three larger emeralds which she says she will never part with. She will one day erect a headstone somewhere in memory of the Jewish Lipschitz family who took her in and a similar one in memory of Hedwig, the Polish lady and her son Alex who were such an integral part of her life in Warsaw.

This is Janni's story as it emerged and if, in the reading, you experience the emotions of sadness, happiness, love, devotion, disgust with oneself and with others, serious questioning of your own sexuality, passion, lust, gentleness, forgiveness, generosity and understanding, abject terror, compassion, betrayal, in fact the whole gamut of human emotions which Janni endured for the most part of her life, you will know what courage, what strength of character, what sheer determination to prevail against all the odds, it takes to be a survivor on such a scale.

I for one feel quite humbled but you must make up your own minds.

Janni wrote the foreword and postscripts and the main story was recorded on an old Telefunken tape recorder during our meetings over many weeks and months throughout the years.

CHAPTER THREE

JANNI'S STORY

I have no idea how long I had been unconscious, but my first impressions on regaining any form of cohesive thought will remain with me forever. I was totally confused and bewildered with no memory of where I was and, although there was frantic activity going on all around me, smoke, flames and the acrid smell of explosives in the air, I could hear nothing except for the persistent ringing in my ears. I became aware of people bending over me, looking anxious and then presumably, upon recognising signs of life, urgently clearing away lumps of masonry and rubble. Feeling was returning and with its return came the first shocks of pain. I was relieved to hear someone saying he didn't think anything was broken, only severely bruised. The same man, I think, held my head and looked directly into my eyes and asked something, not very audibly at first. He must have realized that I still had hearing difficulties. He held my hand and with his other hand, wiggled his fingers, indicating that I should do the same and once we had established this simple means of communication, he checked the movement of all my joints. Eventually, he managed to get me into a sitting position then he carried out some more very basic tests before encouraging me to stand. I accomplished this with great difficulty and not inconsiderable pain and although I trembled all over and felt as though I should fall over at any moment, I felt inordinately proud of this very minor achievement. The man put an arm around me with his hand firmly under my armpit and walked me very gently and slowly to where a youth was sitting, a blanket around his shoulders, his face and dark, curly hair covered in dust. He clutched a mug in both hands and looked as bewildered as I felt. Someone thrust a steaming mug towards me but I could not grasp it. The curly-headed youth put his mug down, took the mug that had been offered to me in one hand, put his free arm around my shoulder and held the mug to my lips. Somehow, he managed to smile encouragement and I tried to acknowledge my thanks in a similar manner. I have the feeling that the ensuing result of my efforts was closer to a grimace, but it nevertheless prompted my new-found companion to a bigger smile, almost a grin, as he helped me drink the first coffee I ever remember. By any standards, it was probably the worst coffee in the world, but at that moment, it was the nectar of the Gods.

Gradually, as we sat there, still unaware of what had happened but nevertheless, watching with some interest the frantic efforts of people scurrying about, responding to shouts and rushing to pull yet another limp bundle from the mounds of smouldering rubble, I caught the more distinct sounds of voices. At first they sounded very distant, the ringing in my ears had given way to a whistling sound, making the voices sound like a badly tuned radio. As the whistling subsided and the voices became clearer, I had this instant conviction that, although I could understand every word, this was not the language in which I usually communicated. For the next few minutes, I tried to remember who I was, where I came from, what was my normal language and what I was doing in this strange place amongst people I had never seen before. I searched all the faces, hoping to see one that I recognized, some clue to help me regain my faculties, but all to no avail, and after a few more fruitless efforts of concentration, I gave-up, temporarily to concentrate on my companion. He seemed to have recovered from his ordeal much better than I had and had an air about him of calm composure and an acceptance of our instant and violent change of circumstances. His eyes ranged back and forth over the hellish vista and it was a joy to watch the waves of relief that spread over his face as he acknowledged with a wave and huge grin, someone shouting or waving to him.

"It must be a wonderful relief for you to see so many of your friends have survived," I said.

He turned to face me, his dark eyes suddenly brighter and a smile spreading over his face, he exuded genuine warmth and concern and I suddenly felt very close to him and very grateful for his presence. "I'm glad you're back with us. Are you feeling O.K.?" He asked, putting his arm around my shoulders and pulling me against him in a friendly, comforting way.

I grasped and squeezed the hand on my shoulder and said, "Yes, I'm O.K., I think. Thanks for all your help."

He gave my hand and shoulder another friendly squeeze and withdrew his arm.

We sat in silence, staring with awful fascination at the ever-increasing number of bodies being laid out side by side, their faces temporarily covered with scraps of any available material, the soles of their feet towards us, some barefoot some with only one shoe, the twisted limbs straightened as best as circumstances would allow. It was a sobering sight and for the first time since regaining consciousness, I became aware that something terrible and violent had happened and it was apparent that my companion was experiencing similar thoughts. His ready smile had vanished, to be replaced by one of fear and agony as he rose to his feet desperately raking the living with his eyes, calling out

"Mummy, Daddy, Rebecca, Isaac."

He ran to the line of bodies, frantically pulling away the covers from the upturned, lifeless faces, palpable relief showing as he neared the end of the line without having discovered the face of a loved one in that awful identity parade. I could not move as fast as he did because of my badly bruised legs but eventually, I caught up with him and this time, I took his hand as we searched together. His grip was so tight that I thought he would break my fingers but in the circumstances it didn't seem to matter.

These were the first dead people I could recall seeing and I remember thinking, with shocking honesty, that these corpses looked totally empty, useless shells, no longer individuals, no longer capable of anything except to cause an embarrassing guilt because I had no other, more worthy emotions. I could only hope that I should have been touched more deeply, moved to sorrow, to experience the more generally acceptable reactions on being confronted with sudden death, no matter whether from natural causes or sudden violence if those involved had been loved ones or acquaintances.

CHAPTER FOUR

MY NEW FAMILY

Suddenly, someone shouted "Aaron!" It was more like a scream and my companion yelled

"Mum! Dad!" and ran, still holding my hand and dragging me with him towards a little group of people. He let go of my hand and was enveloped in the love, warmth, joy and tears of reunion with his family and I stood, momentarily forgotten as they all cuddled each other, patted one another and realised that they were all alive, together.

Eventually, at a command from the man I assumed to be Aaron's father, the ragged, dishevelled family fell silent, they all bowed their heads and the father intoned a prayer, probably of thanks for deliverance in what I imagined was Hebrew.

When they had finished, Aaron tugged at his father's sleeve and said something to him whilst he turned and pointed to me. He beckoned me over and I went to them slowly and stood beside Aaron.

"This is my father, my mother, my sister Rebecca and my young brother Isaac and my name is Aaron", he said. I shook hands with all of them and suddenly felt terribly lost and alone.

"What's your name and where do you live?" Rebecca asked.

I thought very hard and very long, for so long in fact that I'm sure they thought there was something wrong with my hearing. I was aware that they were all looking at me very intently and eventually I mumbled very quietly.

"I don't know my name, and I don't know where I live."

Aaron's mother put her arm round my shoulder and said,

"Don't worry child, we'll find out later but for now, you had better come home with us. It's dangerous out here."

As she said that, I became conscious of the sounds of other explosions and the rattle of machine-gun and rifle fire. We ran along the street, away from the dead bodies and turned down so many side streets that I completely lost all sense of direction. We arrived at a tall, elegant house and went inside. Aaron's father took us all down to the cellar while his mother and sister collected food from the kitchen.

We remained there for several days. We thought it would never end as the hours dragged by and the sounds of bombing and shelling grew louder and louder. We could hear buildings collapsing. There were some tremendous bangs, which shook the whole house and made us put our hands over our ears and heads. Glass was breaking and we could hear and feel pieces of masonry falling on the floors above us.

It seemed that we had been there for an eternity when the noise stopped abruptly, punctuated spasmodically by single shots or the occasional burst of machine-gun fire.

Finally, that stopped too and a deathly, eerie silence prevailed, not a solitary sound until suddenly we heard an ever-increasing rumble.

"Tanks!" exclaimed Aaron's father. I didn't know what he was talking about; all I did know was that we were all very frightened.

Aaron put his arm round me and said,

"Don't worry, they won't kill us, they only kill the soldiers."

"Who are they?" I asked.

Aaron and his father looked at each other in a quizzical way before Aaron replied, "The Germans, of course."

Further discussion was halted by the sound of someone shouting through some amplified sound system. Aaron's father opened the cellar door, climbed over the fallen plaster, up the stairs and opened the front door. We all started to follow, but he held his arm out behind him, the palm towards us, indicating that we should stay where we were. With the doors open, the voice from the loudspeakers was more audible............ " further resistance is totally futile, the town is now completely occupied by our forces and we have just received news that your government has formally surrendered. We have no wish to inflict any unnecessary casualties. You have one hour to bring all your weapons to any of our units stationed throughout the city. In the meantime, no acts or threats against the German occupying forces will be tolerated and anyone perpetrating any such act will be shot on sight.

Notices, telling you what you must do, what you may not do and what will be expected of you will be placed at strategic positions throughout the city. Be sure you read and understand them.

This way we can restore order and some degree of normality as quickly as possible. In the meantime, it is essential that all doctors, nurses and hospital staff report to their respective departments immediately. This is essential for the treatment of the wounded, both German and Polish."

I had heard all this quite clearly and understood every word, without having to think about it and it was something of a surprise to me to realise that I could speak both Polish and German with equal fluency. Nevertheless, both languages felt alien to me but I could recall nothing to give any clue as to the other language in which I seemed to do my jumbled, erratic thinking.

Aaron's mother and father were both doctors and what had been their surgery was on the ground floor. On a brass plate, I saw that their surname was Lipschitz. They both looked very agitated and they held a heated discussion in a strange mish-mash of languages which I now know to be Yiddish. They had decided that initially, only Dr Lipschitz would report to the hospital and his wife would stay behind to look after us. We should have plenty to keep us occupied trying to make the place habitable, salvage whatever we could from the wreckage and, as best we could in the circumstances, make the place reasonably secure.

We worked hard for what must have been three or four hours clearing the kitchen and two big downstairs rooms, where, apart from broken glass and a lot of fallen plaster, the damage was quite minimal. Upstairs was a totally different story and Aaron and I were dispatched on a series of tortuous journeys through twisted timber, masonry, roofing slates etc., up and down, up and down, to fetch mattresses, bed clothes, towels, clean clothing and anything else that was of immediate importance. Meanwhile, there was no gas or electricity but mercifully, we could still obtain water from the taps and fortunately, their kitchen had a coal-fired stove. Mrs Lipschitz made some hot soup and we were able to retrieve some bread from a badly battered bread bin.

I had been studying all their faces and thought that they all looked very nice, despite their dusty, matted, bedraggled appearance. They all had the same dark eyes and eyebrows and, apart from Mrs Lipschitz, whose hair appeared to have a very slight reddish tinge, the others all had jet-black hair. They were all very good-looking; in fact, Rebecca was, although I could remember no one to use as a comparison, strikingly beautiful.

It struck me that I had no idea what I looked like and hoped that my appearance was as pleasing to them as theirs was to me.

Before we were allowed to take our bread and soup, Mrs Lipschitz made us wash our hands and said,

"You all look very nice, but you shouldn't have bothered to dress in such fine clothes for Isaac's birthday." She leaned forward, and took me gently by the shoulders, then looking at Aaron, said,

"And who is this pretty girl you have brought to your brother's party?"

Aaron caught-on immediately and said,

"Mother, this is my mystery guest; I told you she was very beautiful but would only reveal her identity on the stroke of midnight." This banter between them was good for us and we all started to laugh. From that moment on, the tension and fear that we had all felt seemed to fall away. It was only later that I found out that it was, in truth Isaac's twelfth birthday.

It was as if, at identical moments, they all remembered the importance of bodily functions, and, with huge grins they tried to race each other to the toilet. Fortunately, there were two, one in the surgery, for patients and one downstairs for the household. There were probably more on the upper floors but no one wanted to risk negotiating the obstacles on the staircases solely with the aid of a flickering candle, which might blow out at any moment.

For my part, I had probably peed myself when I was first blown-up and had certainly peed myself a couple of times during the heavy shelling and dive-bombing. For that, if for no other reason, I didn't need to go.

CHAPTER FIVE

LEARNING

The talk of birthdays had set me wondering; I hadn't the faintest idea of my age and, since I had no idea of what I looked like or how old Aaron was, there was insufficient information available for me to make even an educated guess. I was almost as tall as Aaron but much slimmer; my hands and feet were much smaller. It suddenly occurred to me that it was very strange to be observing my feet and it took a few minutes for the truth to sink in..... I had on neither shoes nor stockings and I had gone through all the preceding turmoil without noticing their absence.

Apparently, none of the others had noticed or they would have mentioned it. When we had all settled down again, Mrs Lipschitz said that we children should all have a proper wash. She would sort out nightclothes for us and bring them to us in the kitchen where we should wash, two at a time. First Rebecca and me, then Aaron and Isaac.

Mrs Lipschitz had four big pans of water on top of the coal stove and there was a big stone sink with a scrubbed, wooden draining board under what remained of the window. In the middle of the floor stood a big table and upon it, to one end, a large, blue and white patterned porcelain bowl with a soap dish beside it.

Mrs. Lipschitz gave us our instructions. I was to wash Rebecca's hair in the bowl with hot water from the stove and to rinse it under the tap, then she would wash mine. When we had completed this first part, we would strip off and have a complete wash. Mrs Lipschitz would bring us some clean clothes. After dressing, we would all go into the lounge.

All started well and the hair washing was completed without too much difficulty and lots of laughter. Then without embarrassment, Rebecca began removing the rest of her clothes, saying that she would wash first and I should follow.

She was standing completely naked, drying herself and looked very pretty. I can remember to this day how lovely she looked: tallish and slim with a narrow waist, beautifully formed breasts jutting upwards, the nipples hard from the cold water and brisk towelling and a dark triangle of pubic hair glistening in the flickering candle light.

She smiled and said, "O.K., Your turn."

I took off the rest of my clothes and began to walk towards the sink when I heard a gasp, a quick intake of breath and I turned to see Rebecca looking at me with an expression combining both amazement and horror. She covered herself very quickly with her towel and called,

"Mummy, come here quickly."

Her mother came in, responding rapidly to Rebecca's near-shriek.

"Whatever's the matter child?" she asked.

Rebecca, barely able to get her words out, pointed at me, and with all the excitement of announcing the birth of a newborn child, she almost shouted,

"Look Mummy, it's a BOY!"

I don't know who was the more startled by this revelation, Mrs Lipschitz or me, but she looked very hard at me and I followed the direction of her eyes and saw that I was not built exactly like Rebecca. True, I had a very girlish figure, but no breasts and my pubic hair was not as prolific as Rebecca's, was much softer and a sort of mid-brown in colour and protruding from this was an appendage. I was totally bewildered because I had accepted their initial reaction when Mrs Lipschitz had called me a very pretty girl and since, at that time I had no idea of who or what I was, or where I had come from, until this moment, I'd had no reason to question her assessment of my gender.

Mrs. Lipschitz was very kind, she came over to me, put a towel round me and put her arms round me.

"You poor child, didn't you know that you were a boy?" she said in such a soothing voice that I thought I was going to cry. I managed to hold it back, but could not prevent a couple of "gulps and sniffs".

"I didn't know; I can't remember anything and it all feels very strange and you said that I was a very pretty girl I stammered."

Rebecca came to her rescue and said,

"That's very understandable, we were all very disorientated by what happened and Mummy's right, you do look like a girl, you're far to beautiful to be a boy", and with a smile, trying to lighten the situation, she said,

"It's not fair is it Mummy; no one should be that beautiful."

We all laughed and Mrs Lipschitz said,

"Come on then let's get this beautiful child washed and dressed so that the others can get ready. Even though you're not a girl, you'll have to wear this nightgown tonight and we'll sort something else out tomorrow."

We went through into the other room and as we went in Aaron looked at me and his eyes almost popped out of his head.

"Wow! You look nice and you smell a lot better than you did when I first met you."

We all laughed, but poor Aaron had no idea that my gender had just undergone a complete transformation in a cold kitchen, in full view of a beautiful naked girl, without the aid of hormone treatment, breast implants and genital re-assignment. I must stress that I was incapable of such flippant thought at that time, not only because of my mental state, but because, at that time, over sixty years ago, no such treatment had been invented and I was very, very confused.

CHAPTER SIX

THE FIRST HINTS

When the boys had gone into the bathroom, Mrs Lipschitz held me at arms length and in very gentle tones she asked,

"Had you no idea that you were a boy?"

"No, the question had never crossed my mind amidst all the confusion although I was beginning to wonder if I looked as nice as the others, but, it was at that moment when all the bombing and shelling started and I was too frightened to think of anything else." I replied.

"Can't you remember what you look like?" she asked and when I shook my head, rather miserably and again close to tears, she stood up, went to a drawer from which she took an oval backed, silver framed mirror.

"Come and see for yourself, I'm sure you'll be very pleased with what you see."

I took the mirror in both hands and went closer to the candles. I didn't recognize my own reflection; all I saw was an unusually girlish face, with big brown eyes, long eyelashes, delicately shaped lips, even, white teeth and a longish mop of tousled brown hair and, despite the current limitations of my knowledge, I knew instinctively the male of the species should not look like the face staring intently back at me from the mirror. Had I been able to foresee the future and realized the difficulties and dangers my unusual looks would create, I think I should have contemplated taking my own life. But, in those early moments of my "rebirth", I was only concerned with finding out who I was, where I came from and what was going to become of me.

"I don't know that face, I can't remember anything, nothing. Will I remember; will it all come back to me?" I pleaded with Mrs Lipschitz.

"I'm sure it will eventually and tomorrow we'll see if there have been any enquiries about you. It might be a bit difficult due to all the upheaval, but there will be a centre where people will go to make enquiries about missing relatives, and we'll start there. There has been far too much excitement for one day, so we'll leave it till tomorrow before we tell the boys about you."

The boys came in from the kitchen, freshly scrubbed, their skin glowing against the white of their nightshirts and I noticed for the first time that their skin was a sort of olive-brown whereas, mine was more of a golden, sun-tanned hue.

Mrs Lipschitz said she would make us a drink then she would wash and change, then we must all try to get some sleep as tomorrow was going to be a very busy day.

For that first night, the sleeping arrangements were quite simple; there were two double mattresses and one single one, which we had brought down earlier, together with ample bedclothes. Mrs Lipschitz and Rebecca would sleep on one of the double beds, Aaron and Isaac on the other and I would sleep on the single bed.

I lay awake for hours, fighting against overwhelming tiredness, trying to find some clue, some trigger to help me remember at least some tiny part of my former life. It was all to no avail and eventually I could fight the tiredness no longer and drifted into sleep, made fitful by strange, nightmarish dreams and the products of my subconscious imaginings.

CHAPTER SEVEN

MY NEW NAME

I awoke still confused and because of my strange dreams, wondering if the whole thing was not one continuous nightmare.

Mrs Lipschitz said, "Oh, you're awake at last; my word, you did have a long sleep. Julius is back and I've told him all about you. We'll see him in a minute, all have breakfast and then we'll see if we can find out something about you."

"Who's Julius?" I asked

"Oh I'm sorry, Julius is my husband. He has to go back to the hospital fairly soon but he will help us to get things started," she replied. Then, she handed me some clothes, saying,

"These were Aaron's and we were keeping them for when Isaac had grown into them. They should fit you, but I can soon alter them if they don't. When you are dressed, come through to the kitchen."

She turned and left, leaving me a shirt, short trousers, underpants, dark grey pullover and grey socks. There were several pairs of shoes to choose from. The first pair fitted very well because my feet were quite small.

I went into the kitchen feeling like an outsider, but they all smiled warmly at me and chorused,

"Good Morning."

Mrs Lipschitz handed me a toothbrush and comb and pointed to the sink. It seems silly now, but I couldn't even remember what these items were for and Aaron, spotting my confusion, came over, picked up his toothbrush and with largely exaggerated movements, cleaned his teeth, for the second time and then, looking in the mirror, combed his hair. Having ensured that I understood, he winked, smiled and returned to the table. I loved him for that, for easing my discomfort and the cheeky wink that made me respond so readily with my own poor attempt to emulate it.

We ate strange- shaped bread, like it had been rolled very thin and tied in knots; it tasted very pleasant when I followed Aaron's lead and dunked it the hot coffee before putting it gingerly into my mouth. I couldn't remember tasting anything so good and although I could have gone on eating for a long time, I took my cue from Aaron and ate only as much as he did.

When everything had been cleared, washed and put away, Dr Lipschitz took me by the arm and led me along to his surgery and once there, did a lot of tests, examining me all over then looking down my throat, then my eyes and ears with funny looking instruments, which had lights inside them. Finally, he felt all over my head, very carefully. When he had finished, he said,

"Well, apart from severe bruising and a few abrasions to your legs, a lump and bruise to the side of your head and a small cut on your hairline, there doesn't appear to be anything physically wrong with you. We'd hoped that after that long sleep, you might be able to remember something."

I told him all about my efforts of the previous night, my strange dreams and the fact that in my dreams, I spoke and thought in a different language.

"Oh!" he said, "Can you speak to me in that language now?"

I thought for a moment and in the "other" language, I said:

"Why did you all think that I was a girl?"

Doctor Lipschitz looked at me with what can only be described as incredulity and at first, I couldn't tell whether he couldn't understand what I was saying, but could recognize the language or perhaps he did understand, was amazed that I could speak three languages

16

with almost equal fluency and needed time to decide how to answer what was for me a question of some importance. Finally, after what seemed like an age, he said;

"You were speaking to me in English and very beautiful English too; I myself studied medicine in England and in Edinburgh and you speak English with just the hint of a Scottish accent. This explains why my wife and children thought you were a girl."

"I'm sorry, I don't understand what you mean," I replied and I must have looked rather puzzled because the doctor looked at me, smiled, took hold of my shoulders and said:

"When Aaron brought you over to us, you were pretty dishevelled, you had a blanket round you, no shoes or socks, they must have come off in the rubble, and you were wearing what looked like a skirt? In fact, it was a kilt."

He must have seen that I was still none the wiser and he was very patient explaining to me that the kilt was an important part of Scottish traditional dress, worn by both men and women and much admired and copied the world over.

I was quite happy with this explanation and thanked him for explaining everything in such detail, to which he replied:

"In addition to the kilt causing confusion, you are also exceptionally beautiful for a boy, unusually so, and the fact that you wear your hair rather longer than the boys do in this country only served to further confuse us."

He sat very quietly, looking pensive and then, in very grave tones, he said:

"In the present, very dangerous circumstances, it is better if we do not tell the others that you are from England. You must never speak English again for as long as you are here. The Germans are also at war with England and if they were to find out about you, you would be taken away, probably to Germany and placed in an internment camp. This is going to make it extremely difficult to make enquiries about you through any official channels although I shall make some discreet enquiries through trusted friends. From now on, you will live with us as one of the family. In a moment, we'll join the others, I'll tell them of my decision, and then we shall decide upon a name for you."

I put my arms round his neck, gave him a hug and said:

"Thank you Doctor Lipschitz, I'm glad that Aaron brought me to you. If he hadn't, I'd have been very frightened by now and I don't know what would have happened to me."

He returned my hug, smiled and said,

"Let's go and join the others."

We went into the large living room where the others appeared to be waiting to see if I had regained my memory under the doctor's ministrations.

The doctor spent a few moments telling them that, physically, I was all right, but that he had no idea when I should be able to recall anything of my past. He informed them of his decision regarding my immediate future and then, to their obvious delight, invited them to think of a suitable name for me.

After lengthy deliberations, they decided upon Jan, the equivalent of John in English. Strangely, none of them ever called me Jan, in fact, for all the time that I knew them; they called me either Janni (they pronounced it Yanny) or Janek. The whole family welcomed me into their fold with great warmth and affection and, despite the strangeness of my predicament, I was very happy to be with them and came to love them all very dearly.

That day, we all set to work to make the house more secure and to effect as many repairs as we could so that we should have better sleeping arrangements.

It was decided that the top floor would be abandoned, the roof made as weatherproof as possible with the aid of tarpaulins and some of the damaged timbers and it was during the time spent affecting these repairs that I took Mrs Lipschitz to one side to ask her what was for me a matter of some importance. I chose Mrs Lipschitz because she was a paediatrician and would be better qualified to answer.

She could tell that something was bothering me and I was, without doubt, somewhat hesitant in my approach, but she smiled her lovely, warm smile and said:

"Come Janni, you have been very quiet and you want to ask me something. What is it you want to know child?"

I smiled back and replied,

"It might not seem very important to the others because they all know how old they are, but I don't know how old I am and I hoped that you would be able to give me some idea."

She laughed and said:

"Yes, I can see that it is important for you to know and although theoretically, you've asked the right person, I can only hazard an educated guess because, to be very honest with you, I've never met anyone quite like you before. Let me explain."

She thought hard for a moment or two formulating her thoughts; it seemed that my question had caused her some difficulty. However, as I was to learn, both Mrs Lipschitz and her husband always took the time to answer questions fully, explaining everything, so as to make sure we were fully satisfied with the answers they gave.

She took hold of my hands and said,

"Firstly, you have to understand that you are most unusual in as much as although you are undoubtedly a boy, you have a lot of female characteristics. You have a very beautiful face that any girl would be proud of, your arms are slim, your hands and feet small and delicately shaped and your bone structure is more like that of a girl than a boy. You don't have any appreciable muscle definition, although I've watched you working and you seem quite strong and tireless. Your mannerisms too are more girlish than boyish."

She paused for a moment, seeing that what she had told me so far was causing me obvious concern and continued,

"Because of all this, you are very special and we are so happy to have you with us. Now then, I had to tell you all these things about yourself so that you will understand why I can't be too accurate about your age. You see, girls mature earlier than boys and start to acquire evidence of puberty, such as pubic hair, breast development etc sometimes as young as twelve years but more often from about thirteen onwards. True, some boys mature earlier than others but mostly they trail behind the girls. In your case, I would say that if you were a girl, I would put you at twelve or thirteen but since you are a boy, somewhere between thirteen and fourteen. I'm sorry I can't be more accurate than that," she concluded.

After a moment or two, during which time she had obviously been collecting her thoughts she continued,

"During adolescence, and, often long after, many people have conflicting feelings and emotions about their gender and can become very confused about this strange mixture of both male and female in their make-up, neither being entirely dominant. Some, comparatively few, have the mixed physical characteristics of both sexes and because of this they can be both attracted to and attracted by both sexes and this too causes identity problems. At the moment, you have enough problems with your normal identity, without having to confront any other crisis, should it arise. But Janni, you must promise to come to me to talk about anything and everything should you ever feel the need to."

Frankly, I hadn't really grasped what she had been talking about, at least, not all of it and even though she had been quite open and serious, I didn't feel that anything of what she had said applied to me. I just smiled my usual impulsive smile, squeezed her hands and said,

"Thank you."

During the next few days, there was a semblance of normality slowly returning to everyday life. The schools were still closed, some shops had re-opened and great efforts were being made to get the trams running again. German engineer units had cleared away a lot of the rubble from the main areas and telephone lines were being restored with what we had come to recognize as German efficiency. Both my new-found 'parents' worked three days at the hospital each week and held surgeries from home during the remaining days, except Saturday and Sunday. They were very popular and the surgery was always full; a lot of the 'patients' only came to talk making the surgery hours extend until quite late.

When their parents were at the hospital, we would continue with improvements to our living conditions, do some shopping, play games and learn the process of acquisition, scavenging and scrounging. We all became quite good at this. Occasionally, we would talk to the soldiers, only to make an enquiry about something affecting our everyday life and in these cases, they responded, in general, kindly enough unless there was someone more senior present, in which case, they would be very terse, hurl abuse at us and sometimes, cuff our ears. I couldn't understand this attitude to perfectly harmless children and it was only after Aaron explained to me about the German hatred of the Jews that I began to understand.

It was shortly after one such encounter that the first of our real difficulties began. All the families had to register with the German authorities and all those of Jewish descent had to wear a yellow Star of David, predominantly displayed on their clothing. Mostly, this took the form of a black armband, bearing the star, but often it was emblazoned on the backs of jackets and overcoats or on the breast. This was quickly changed to a white armband with the Star of David in blue emblazoned thereon. It soon became apparent that this not only signified that the bearers of this identification were Jews, but non-persons, sub-humans to be treated on a par with animals. This treatment, practiced at first solely by the occupying Germans, soon became the order of the day for the indigenous, non-Jewish population and people who had once been friends, had enjoyed good, caring relationships with their Jewish neighbours no longer acknowledged them on the streets, looked the other way if there was the slightest chance of an encounter, although it must be said that not all of them became such appalling turn-coats. Indeed, many of them remained faithful friends, despite severe penalties and repercussions and in an untold number of cases during the years to come, carried out acts of incredible, selfless bravery on behalf of the Jews as a whole. These, however, were the exception rather than the rule. At least, in the initial stages, those who looked the other way or refused to acknowledge a Jew had the good grace to look ashamed or embarrassed. This later turned to indifference then to sneering and finally, outright hostility. Whether they had always harboured this hostility or only acquired it to display a form of solidarity with their conquerors and thus incur lesser punishment for some infringement of the new regulations, one can only speculate, but what can be certain is that they always looked after number one and any overt show of anti-Semitism stood them in good stead with the occupying forces.

It was decided that, since I had no name under which to register, it would be safer not to register me at all. This was a great mistake, which only became apparent many months later, but at the time, none of us could foresee the appalling events that the future held in store for us.

Notwithstanding the decision not to register me, I made a point of showing solidarity with my 'new' family and always when we were out together, I also wore a Star of David armband.

There was also the consideration, that not to have done so in their company would have drawn attention to us and invited considerable curiosity, then intensive questioning, which we would have been hard put to answer convincingly.

As the weeks, then months went by, life became progressively more difficult; we suffered more and more abuse, both verbal and physical and the number of shopkeepers who refused to serve us increased day by day. It was at this point that I decided, despite the protestations of the rest of the family, to shed my Star of David and shop alone. At first, this worked very well and I used to converse with the shopkeepers and customers in either Polish or German and we all became very friendly. They soon became accustomed to seeing me and were always kind and cheerful with me. In addition, I became a familiar sight to the German soldiers and on the surface, I became very friendly with a number of them, in fact most of them treated me with good-natured affection. Some were affectionate in a way that certainly made me question their motives, but I was learning quickly that my girlish appearance and ready smile had an undesirable effect on some of the soldiers and I had to play very carefully and tactfully in such encounters, feigning complete ignorance and innocence. But, if I'm completely honest, I enjoyed this sort of attention from some of the good-looking younger soldiers; it gave me a sense of power over them and I was totally in control of the situation.

Sometimes, I would ask the soldiers for a few cigarettes because these were excellent bargaining material and in these circumstances, I would pick out the soldiers who had made advances to me, knowing that if I looked them straight in the eyes with my eyes wide open, then allowed my lashes to fall slowly as I asked them for a few cigarettes, they almost always gave me some without hesitation, reading more promise in my look than I ever intended. It was a dangerous game, but I was enjoying it whilst I could get away with it.

I should add that at this time in my life, to my knowledge, I had had no sexual experience of any kind, no one had ever discussed the subject with me and any reactions or feelings that I may have harboured in this direction, came out of natural instinct and curiosity rather than from practical knowledge and experience. This situation was to change very quickly during the next few months in both the acquisition of knowledge and practical instruction. Tuition in these matters came from totally unexpected sources. Needless to say, I was an eager pupil, extremely happy with my tutors, quick to learn, always impatient for my next 'lesson' and quite happy to have 'exams' to ensure that I had reached the required standards of proficiency in the various techniques! I welcomed extra-curricular activities with open arms on the basis that practice makes perfect and that it was, therefore, incumbent upon me to get as much of this as possible in order to please my tutors with my progress. Apparently, I graduated with honours, achieving something approaching star-pupil status in record time.

My teachers were very quick to point out, that to maintain this high standard, I had to attend frequent refresher courses when it was explained to me that even higher grades could be achieved by inventiveness, experimentation and consideration for the needs, excitement and satisfaction of one's partner. The fact that neither of my teachers knew that I was receiving tuition from the other only served to add to the excitement of my schooling!

CHAPTER EIGHT

The weather had worsened considerably. The heavy snowfalls and blizzards causing massive snowdrifts. These, in turn, had frozen hard and long icicles hung from the gutters. Where the vehicles had laboured along the streets, the snow had been turned into a blackish-brown slush and the wheels of the vehicles sprayed some of this onto the pavements making the compacted, frozen surface like a skating rink.

In the house, it was fiercely cold since we could no longer obtain coal or much in the way of wood to maintain any degree of warmth over any extended period. We wore almost as many clothes indoors as we did outside and we were fortunate in as much as we had large quantities of bedding. Strangely, the telephones were still working, and this became very important in light of the restraints we all suffered after the imposition of the curfew. I had become friendly with a young Polish boy whose father had been killed in defence of his country. In my scrounging role, minus my yellow 'Star of David', we had crossed paths on more than a few occasions and eventually banded together in our quest for food, combustible materials and anything else that could be traded profitably and beneficially. He was of German/Polish origin, with the typical blond haired, blue-eyed look of the Teutonic ideal. I shall call him Alex and his mother Hedwig. On a couple of occasions, we had sailed very close to the wind in relation to the curfew and, since the distance between his house and mine was too far to cover in the available time, rather than risk being apprehended, after curfew, without any papers, I stayed the night at their house. We would telephone to my house to let them know that I was safe so that my 'new' parents would not worry.

On the third such occasion, Alex and I arrived at his house almost blue with cold. We had been out all day, buying, trading, scrounging and had acquired sausages, cheese, potatoes and cabbage, which we proudly displayed to Hedwig. Very fairly, she divided up our acquisitions in proportions appropriate to the size of our respective households and, this done, gave us bowls of thin hot soup and coarse bread to warm us through whilst she made up a bed for me in Alex's room.

Their 'house' was, in reality, a very small flat comprising one large bedroom, Hedwig's, with a double bed, Alex's with a single bed, small bathroom...a misnomer since there was no bath, only toilet, wash hand basin and temperamental shower, a miniscule kitchen with French doors leading to a balcony measuring one and a half metres by half a metre and a living room come dining room with similar French doors and balcony. There was a tiled stove in the living room, which was the only source of heat in the flat and to step out of this room, was akin to an arctic adventure but, being young and resilient, once in bed, we soon generated warmth. However, this particular night was the coldest we had ever experienced and our teeth were chattering, our bodies shivering and despite all our efforts, knees drawn up, hands between thighs, curled up in a protective foetal-crouch, the bitter iciness seemed to penetrate our bones.

Sleep was impossible and I was too enveloped in my own misery to attempt any form of conversation. It came as something of a relief, therefore when Alex, who was at least two years my senior, said, "Janni, you must be freezing down there on the floor. Come and get into bed with me, we'll be much warmer together."

I thought that this was a splendid idea and hastened to do his bidding, flinging one of my blankets over his bed before jumping in beside him.

Immediately, he drew me towards him, putting his arms around me and vigorously rubbing my back; it felt very good and I responded in kind and we soon began to feel the benefits of our mutual ministrations. The initial frantic exertions subsided into a leisurely stroking, which, became both comforting and exciting. I felt a sort of sleepy, languorous warmth creeping over me and with it, the desire to hold Alex even closer, my head against his chest and one arm round his waist. With this, his leisurely stroking moved from my back, first to my side, and then, after he pushed me slightly away from him, his hand moved over my shoulder, chest and stomach, gently moving his fingers in a light scratching motion, ever lower into my groin and up and down the insides of my thighs. Finally, when I thought that I could stand it no longer, he drew up my nightshirt and followed the same routine on my bare flesh.

I heard a sudden intake of breath, like a sharp gasp and Alex said, "God Janni, your skin is just like a girls, it's amazing." Before I knew what was happening, and by now, we had forgotten all about the cold, he had lifted my nightshirt up to my shoulders and was suddenly kissing my stomach, nipples, groin and inner thighs. He ran the tip of his tongue all the way up my stomach, chest and throat, continued under my chin and whilst I lay there in this amazing new world of excitement, eyes closed, mouth wide open and breathing very deeply, he brushed his open lips over mine, so very lightly, drawing in his breath at the same time. The effect was the most amazing combination of cool tingling and a bolt of lightning, which completely took my breath away. After a few seconds, I said, "Do it again!" I shall not go into further detail of how the night progressed, but this was to set the pattern for many nights to come and about which I make no apologies nor do I feel any embarrassment or sense of guilt.

The days passed by with Alex and I going about our everyday routines and I would make a point of staying overnight with him on two or three nights each week, but at home, Rachel was showing signs of concern over the number of nights I was spending away. At first, I thought she was worried over the risks I was taking travelling the streets and dealing with all sorts of shady characters until well after dark, but it was apparent that there was a deeper underlying concern for my welfare. She was a very perceptive woman and had noticed quite a sudden change in my demeanour. I was now quite obviously much happier than I had been and had acquired a newfound confidence, which, due to my experiences had been sadly lacking in the last few months. She asked a lot of questions about Alex, his age, what his mother did, how much I liked him, what their flat was like, where I slept when I stayed there, at which point, I thought "She knows."

My answers were truthful about most things, but deliberately vague about anything that was heading in the direction where I suddenly feared any deeper probing. It made me feel deeply deceitful and very guilty because the whole family were so kind and loving towards me and I knew deep in my heart that it was only Rachel's desire to protect me from all things evil that was prompting her questions. I felt wretched about the whole thing, which dampened my soaring spirits and I became more subdued and introverted. For several days, I saw nothing of Alex, not because of Rachel's shrewd questioning, but because he just did not turn-up at our usual meeting places. I was becoming very anxious and missing his company dreadfully. Suddenly, the prospect of "doing my rounds" without his cheerful companionship was no longer the happy-go-lucky prospect that it had been and it was, with an overwhelming sigh of relief, that I spotted him hurrying towards me with his lazy smile turning into a wide grin as he saw me. He ran the last fifty metres and put his arms around me, kissed me lightly on the forehead and said, "Hell, I've missed you." "You've missed me?" I said, holding his hand very tightly, "Where have you been these last few days, I've been worrying like hell about you."

He looked at me very steadily and said,

"Our relationship will have to change."

Suddenly, I felt very cold and started to shake; I thought to myself, "How can he stand there with his beautiful, lazy smile, so nonchalant, unaware that he is tying my inside into knots." "Don't look so worried Janni, I've got a job that I start on Monday at the bakery. I have to work from four o'clock until twelve noon each day so I shouldn't be able to see you until the afternoons."

The weights lifted from my shoulders and my mind cleared of all the horrible feelings of despair that had engulfed me. I hugged him close to me and held on for a long time. I think I must have embarrassed him because he laughingly broke away and said, "Come on, Janni, we've got work to do; let's go and scrounge some fags." We had quite a successful day and Alex was surprised when I said that I could not spend the night with him. He said that he had been missing me very much and was looking forward to being together again tonight.

"Why?" he asked, with a perplexed look on his face, "Don't you want to sleep with me tonight?"

"Of course I do, it's just that my parents are getting very suspicious and I don't like being evasive and having to tell them lies."

He said that he understood and that in the circumstances, it might be better if I didn't stay that night.

"Well, stay with me on Saturday", he said.

"I can't", I replied, "Saturday is the Sabbath and a family day in our household and since they are now my family, I'm trying very hard to learn their ways and to celebrate with them, but I'll see you on Sunday if that's O.K. with you."

"That's fine", he said, "except that I shall have to get up very early to be at work for four". He grinned broadly and added, "We'll just have to go to bed a lot earlier". Julius and Rachel were pleased to see me home early, before curfew, for the fourth night in a row and after supper, the whole family settled down to take advantage of the dying embers of the cooking fire. It was very cosy and Julius was very pleased when I handed him five cigarettes.

"You've had a good day then Janni. Did you see Alex today?" "Yes", I replied, as casually as possible, "He's got a job at the bakery and he starts on Monday. He has to have a special pass because he has to be at work at four in the morning. Isn't he lucky", I added.

"Oh, that is good news; how lovely. His mother must be very pleased", Rachel said and I thought I could almost detect a muted sigh of relief.

Without looking at either of them, and stooping to undo my shoelaces so that they could not see my face, I said, "The days won't be the same without him. I always felt a lot safer when there were the two of us".

I meant what I'd said, but in a way, it was rather mean, as if I was placing the blame on them for putting me at risk in the future by letting me go out without the protection of someone of whom they disapproved.

There was a prolonged, subdued silence until dear Aaron, who had no idea of the significance of what had just been said, offered to come out with me on my expeditions as my guardian.

This was one of those moments I dreaded. I was too young and too inexperienced to be able to handle it with tact. How could I tell him that he looked too obviously Jewish; that his very presence would make it virtually impossible to trade with anyone, that his Jewish ness would alienate all the contacts I had so carefully nurtured, that they would no longer trust me and in all probability we would get a sound beating. I didn't know how to reply without causing offence to the whole family and I turned and looked very imploringly at Julius without uttering a word.

Julius stared long and hard at me for what seemed ages and I was almost willing him to read my mind. Eventually, he stood up, walked over to Aaron and rested his hand on his shoulder.

"You know that is not a very good idea, but it was very brave of you to offer and your concern for Janni's safety does you credit. No, Janni will be better off doing what he does alone", and looking me straight in the eye, he continued, "except that he must conduct his activities in daylight and be home early, especially since he will no longer have Alex to look after him when it gets dark".

He looked right into my eyes as he uttered these last few words, but rather than show any anger for this obvious clipping of my wings, I smiled at him in a way that could only be interpreted as gratitude for his coming to my rescue and for his concern over my well-being. I hoped that my enthusiastic acceptance of the new restrictions would, in some way, allay the suspicions which Julius and Rachel had displayed in their earlier questions to me.

In bed that night, I thought back to the strange talk that Rachel had given me when I had asked her to estimate my age. At the time, I didn't understand the implications of what she had been saying. Now, I knew only too well and I slept very badly that night trying to make sense of my very girlish character, body and mannerisms and I remember thinking that they should not reasonably expect me to behave any differently. It just wasn't fair, there was so much missing in my life and I needed love and companionship, reassuring cuddles and more, and although I got all of this from my new family, the intense love and physical contact with Alex was far more exciting and I knew that if there was going to be a show-down over this with Julius and Rachel, my feelings for Alex would get the better of me. To prevent this waywardness and to maintain the happy relationship with my 'family', I need-ed some outside influence to divert me from the collision course which I saw looming before me.

The diversion, when it came, was from a completely unexpected source and although it saved me from embarrassing confrontations, it only served to make my life even more complicated and create much greater problems. All in all, I was very gullible, easily led and extremely naive. Combined with these factors, I was very young and had remarkable physical characteristics, which seemed to excite some very basic instincts in other people. My experiences with Alex had aroused both curiosity and desire to know more about sex and to indulge quite shamelessly in anything that brought pleasure in this exciting new world of development.

Friday had been a good day for me. Alex and I had managed to buy some very good sausage and some eggs and later, some heavy, coarse-grained bread. The market had re-opened and I found that if one was prepared to pay the right price, cheese, butter and veg-etables were also available, although quantities were restricted. I spent all my money and then scrounged some cigarettes from a young, good-looking corporal. I borrowed some money from Alex and bought some coffee at an exorbitant price. By now, I was pretty well loaded down since I was shopping for six whereas Alex was shopping for two. We made the decision that Alex would help me to carry my shopping home but that on no account was he to show any undue familiarity or behave in any way which might give away the true nature of our relationship. This established, we headed to my home. I let us in, closed the door behind us, and, indicating that Alex should follow, headed along the passage to the kitchen. Rachel was folding newly washed clothes and the kitchen was filled with the smell of clean, fresh linen.

She looked up as we entered and there was a momentary expression of surprise on her face when she realised I was not alone.

Before she could say anything, I said,

"Mum, this is Alex and he's helped me to bring all this shopping home. Oh, and I owe him some money. Alex this is Mrs Lipschitz."

Alex smiled in his lazy, charming manner, extended his hand and said,

" Hello Mrs Lipschitz, I'm very pleased to meet you, Janni has told me so much about you all."

Rachel responded very warmly but I could see that she was studying him in every detail. "Hello, Alex," she replied,

"I've heard a great deal about you too and I have been eager to meet you and to thank you, particularly for looking after Janni for us in these dangerous times."

Alex made the right, deprecatory replies and Rachel motioned us to sit down. "Give me a moment to put this washing away then we'll have a cup of tea and look at all these wonderful goodies you've brought."

She gathered up all the neatly folded washing in her arms and I opened the door for her as she left the kitchen.

"She's very nice, just like a real mum isn't she?" Alex said. "It's very clean and cosy in here, you're very lucky."

He was about to continue when Rachel returned and set about making tea. While the tea was brewing, she unpacked all the shopping, expressing both delight and surprise at the quantity and diversity of our haul. She paid Alex what I had borrowed from him and set about pouring the tea.

"Mum", I said, "I don't know anything about kosher food except that it is not available now so I had to take what was on offer. I hope it's alright."

Rachel came over, put her arms round me and gave me a big kiss on the cheek and still with her arms round me, she said, "Janni, it's all wonderful and you are so thoughtful. But don't worry about whether or not the food is kosher, we'll all have to learn to live with all sorts of very different things now if we're to survive." She let go of me and we both sat down at the big table with Alex who was politely waiting for us before he started to drink his tea.

"Janni tells me that you are starting a new job on Monday Alex; you and your mother must be very pleased". Before Alex could reply she continued, "Does your mother work?" "Yes," Alex replied, "She works three afternoons per week as a typist and translator in one of the new government departments, she had to work after dad was killed and it's no longer possible for me to go on to university with things as they are so it made sense for me to get a job, any job until things get better, I was very lucky to get this one."

Rachel took all this in and then, quite casually, she asked,

"Have you finished school?" and without waiting for a reply, she continued, "You don't look old enough to go to university."

"I'm seventeen, nearly eighteen and I was due to attend university last September", Alex answered.

I had never asked Alex his age and hadn't consciously thought about it but I was quite surprised to learn that he was so much older than me, especially as his mother looked so very young.

Alex, for all his outward, self-assured demeanour realised that there were likely to be more questions and decided to leave before they were asked. He was shrewder and cleverer than I'd realised. He stood up and looked at the clock saying,

" I really must get home to have things ready when mum comes home from work", and with a wry smile he continued,

"She'll go mad if I haven't tidied my room, emptied the waste bins and lit the fire by the time she gets home."

He turned to Rachel and extending his hand, he said,

"It's been very nice meeting you and thank you very much for the tea." He turned to me and said,

"Oh, by the way, I almost forgot, Mum's giving me a sort of 'last day of freedom' party on Sunday and she's asked you to come round for tea, then I'll teach you to play chess. Mum will make-up the spare bed for you. I'll have to go to bed early but you can stay up and play the piano for mum, she'd like that; Dad used to play, but not as well as you and until you came, nobody else played."

He turned to Rachel and said,

"Oh, I am sorry Mrs Lipschitz, how very rude of me, I should have asked you if it's O.K. for Janni to come. He told me that you were worried about him being out after curfew, but don't worry, we'll take good care of him."

It was a masterly performance and Rachel knew that it would be churlish to refuse.

"Just this once Alex, we really do worry when he's not here with us, these are such dangerous times and Janni is still very young." she added rather pointedly. I stood up and said, "I'll just see Alex to the door."

Rachel said goodbye to Alex and he walked with me along the long passage to the door, neither of us saying anything until we were well out of earshot of the kitchen, and once we had pulled the door to, he put his arm round my shoulder, brushed his lips over mine in that breath-taking way he had and with a huge grin, said, "Easy, wasn't it?" he squeezed my hand and said, "See you Sunday." With that, he was gone, walking quickly and quite jauntily down the street. I'd have laid bets that he had a self-satisfied grin on his face.

I went back inside the house and returned to the kitchen.

"Is there any tea left?" I asked Rachel.

Rachel nodded and poured us both another cup and she positioned herself directly opposite me.

"Alex seems a very nice, well brought-up boy and very good-looking too," she added, all the time studying my face.

"Yes, I suppose he is", I replied, and before she could ask anything else, I said, "I hadn't really thought about it."

I think Rachel realised that I was feeling pressured and changed the subject quite abruptly. She took hold of both my hands and praised my shopping achievements, then asked me to play the piano while she was getting the evening meal ready. I breathed a deep sigh of relief and hastened to the piano before she had any second thoughts.

Saturday was the usual close, warm family day, and after our meal, during which Julius had blessed the food and uttered words in praise of me and my contributions to the household, which made me feel both proud and humble in the face of these good people, I gave Julius the, by now, usual five cigarettes.

"I don't know how you manage it Janni, you're spoiling us," he said. "Come here", he gestured with sweeping movements, palms down and as I stood before him, he pulled me towards him, kissed me on both cheeks and said,

"Thank you so much Janni, you're very special and we are so lucky to have you here with us as part of our family."

CHAPTER NINE

Sunday morning was bright but very cold and I pottered about the house doing whatever household chores had been allocated to me. Dusting here and there, plumping-up cushions and finally cleaning the fireplace.

By now, I was nice and warm and I asked Julius if it was all right for me to play the piano and practise a few pieces for the evening. He nodded his assent and I went into the big front room where the piano stood and played for about an hour and a half. I enjoyed it very much and hadn't noticed how quickly the time had passed, I would have carried on had not Rachel called me in for lunch. They all made some complimentary remarks about my choice of music and I was in high spirits as I went to wash and change, excited at the prospect of seeing Alex again and sleeping with him.

It was about half past three when I left, with the usual entreaties to be careful ringing in my ears.

The earlier brightness had given way to a very heavy sky. Large snowflakes began falling before I was halfway to Alex's house and I was covered in a white mantle by the time I arrived. When Alex opened the door, I took off my coat and shook it outside before entering. No sooner had I done this, and before we mounted the stairs to the flat, Alex gave me a big hug and his, by now, familiar, naughty kiss. He gave me a huge grin and I took off my wet shoes and together, we went up the stairs two at a time.

Hedwig came over and kissed me on both cheeks and said,

"My word, your face is very cold, it must be blowing a blizzard out there." Then, noticing the wet shoes in my hand, she took them from me and put them near the stove to dry. We all sat at the table and played card games for about an hour. Alex won everything and as he won each hand, he smiled gleefully and made some good-natured, derogatory, but witty remarks about our respective skills. I could hardly take my eyes off him, he looked so relaxed and confident and quite strikingly attractive. I caught myself staring at him in what must have been an adoring manner and looked away quickly in case Hedwig noticed all the obvious signs.

Hedwig and Alex went to the kitchen, and after several trips to and fro, they had set the table and brought in plates of bread, butter, cooked meats, smoked sausage and cheese. It was a lovely meal, followed by coffee.

Alex left the room and returned moments later with three small, stemmed glasses and a bottle of what looked like blackcurrant juice.

"It's all right just this once isn't it Mum?" he asked.

His mother looked at him long and hard and then, with a delightful slow smile, she said. "O.K, but just this once and only one glass."

Alex poured the three glasses, handed one to his mother and one to me. As he picked up his own, he said, "Here's to my new job. .... Cheers"

Before I put my glass to my lips, Hedwig cautioned me to sip it slowly. I watched her sipping hers and noticed that Alex was doing the same and I copied their actions. The first sip was truly amazing, it tasted wonderful, but it made me cough and then, when my bout of coughing had subsided, I was suffused with a warm glow that seemed to reach down to my toes. I grinned at Alex and said, "What a fabulous drink; it must be some sort of magic potion." "Magic potion is right," he replied, "Its very strong plum brandy. We also have damson flavoured vodka and apricot brandy which you can try another day. Two or three glasses of this and you'd be flat on your back, so just make this one last."

"Will you play the piano for us now?" Hedwig asked.

I nodded and went to the piano, sat down and ran through the keys. It was still well in tune and the keys and pedals responded perfectly. The tone was excellent so I played some

Chopin, Johann Strauss, Waldteufel, Sinding, Beethoven and Brahms. When I had finished they both clapped and said how impressed they were that I had played them all without any sheet music.

"Lift your bum", Hedwig ordered, and when I had done so, she lifted the lid of the piano stool and took out a pile of music. She sorted through them and handed two to me. "Do you think you could play these for me," she asked.

One piece was called "Ain't Misbehavin'" and the other "Body and soul." I can't be absolutely sure, it was so long ago.

I studied the music for a few moments and said,

"I'll try, but I've never played music like this before so you'll have to excuse me if I'm a bit hesitant."

I started to play and once I'd become used to the strange, new, exciting rhythm, I began playing with more assurance, although some of the left hand accompaniment was hard work for my small hands.

By the time I started the second piece, my playing was more fluent and I really began to enjoy this interesting new music.

When I'd finished they both clapped again and Hedwig said, "That was lovely Janni, will you play for us again sometime?" I said that I would love to and asked if I could borrow some of her interesting songs to practise at home so that I could play better for them next time.

Hedwig agreed readily She stood up and said,

"I'm just going to make some hot chocolate. Who'd like some?"

"Me please" both Alex and I responded in chorus and we all laughed.

When his mother had left the room, Alex whispered,

"We'll go to bed when we've finished our drinks if it's O.K. with you."

I reached across and squeezed his hand and said, "I can't wait." Hedwig returned with a tray bearing three steaming mugs and we sat, sipping another drink that was also new to me and tasted very luxurious.

"This is lovely", I said to Hedwig. "Thank you very much, it's been a smashing party."

Hedwig stood up, and with an exaggerated curtsy, added,

"Thank you kind sir, and yes, it has been a lovely evening. Its a shame that it has to finish, but Alex has to be up very early and I think its time you boys went to bed. Don't forget to clean your teeth and Alex, don't forget to set your alarm clock." Alex and I went to the bathroom; both had a pee and cleaned our teeth. When we'd done, we went to say goodnight to Hedwig.

"Goodnight Mum, and thanks for everything," Alex said, hugging his mother as they kissed each other.

Hedwig came over to me and gave me a hug and a kiss and then said,

"Off you go then, Oh, and by the way Janni, you don't have to get up with Alex, I'll call you later." With that, Alex and I headed for the bedroom, got undressed and climbed naked into bed. We experimented a great deal that night and when I eventually fell asleep, I was thinking that it was the best day I'd ever spent. I felt enveloped in love and warmth and very tired! The alarm clock was very loud and insistent and it took me a few moments to realise where I was. Alex did not stir and I had to reach across him to find the light switch and to turn off the alarm. Before I could return to my side of the bed, Alex grabbed me with one arm round my back, the other holding the cheeks of my bottom and we lay cuddling each other for quite a few minutes. I could feel the customary reaction down below and knew that the same thing was happening to Alex as our bodies pressed together. "Stop it Alex, you'll be late for your new job", I said, without much conviction.

"You're right, damn it, I don't want to go, but it would be stupid to be late on my first day."

So saying, he pushed me off and rolled out of bed and started to get dressed. "I'm going for a pee, a quick wash and then I'm off", he said, "and you had better do the same ", he added.

I pulled on my nightshirt and followed him to the bathroom. Before he left, we had one quicker cuddle, made arrangements to meet at our usual place the following afternoon then he pulled on his topcoat, scarf and gloves, pulled me to him and gave me a brief peck on the cheek.

"Love you", he whispered, then, before I could respond, he was gone. I felt extremely happy and Alex's parting words had filled me with delight, as I snuggled down in the still warm bed I revelled in the feeling of joy that overwhelmed me every time I heard them, over and over again in my mind, It was a very happy Janni who finally sank into a contented sleep, but then, I didn't know what fate had in store for me in the morning.

CHAPTER TEN

Someone was shaking my shoulder and saying,

"Wake -up Janni, come on sleepy head, Wake-up"

It was Hedwig and she continued to shake me and exhort me to wake up until, rubbing at my eyes, I sat up and said,

"Hello, what time is it?"

"Half past eight," Hedwig replied.

I pulled the pillow up behind my back, made myself comfortable and took in my surroundings. The first thing that I noticed, with great misgivings, was the fact that my own bed lay completely undisturbed and it was therefore quite apparent that I had spent the whole night in Alex's bed.

If Hedwig had noticed, she didn't say anything about it.

"I've brought you a mug of tea, and I'll bring you some toast in a couple of minutes." With that, she was gone, only to reappear a few moments later with a large plateful of hot, buttered toast and another steaming mug.

"You don't mind if I join you for breakfast do you Janni?" and before I could answer she went on, "It's nice having company at the start of the day, someone to talk to, don't you think?"

I made some appropriate noise through a mouthful of toast and Hedwig just kept chatting away about all sorts of inconsequential things, punctuated by me with the occasional "Yes", "No", or "I suppose so."

All the time she was talking, I was studying her in detail and if she was aware of it, she affected not to notice. She was very pretty with sort of smoky-black, curly hair, quite thick eyebrows of the same colour above large, flecked-grey eyes. She had nice cheekbones and small ears and a long, graceful neck. She was quite slim and I estimated about five feet five or six inches tall. She was wearing a dressing gown over her nightie and had fluffy slippers on her small feet. She looked very nice and far too young to be Alex's mum now that I knew that he was seventeen.

I became aware that she had stopped talking and looked up to see her looking at me in a strange way and biting her lip in a slightly nervous manner. I smiled at her and said,

"Great breakfast, I never get breakfast in bed at home. I must come here more often."

We laughed and Hedwig said,

"Oh, you are lovely Janni, no, in fact you're beautiful, truly very beautiful."

I was a bit embarrassed and said,

"I can't look that nice with my hair all mussed-up, butter all round my mouth and crumbs on my nightie."

She smiled, showing her even teeth and said,

"But you are, I don't think I've ever seen anyone quite so beautiful, boy or girl." She had been running her fingers through my hair while she was saying this and quite impulsively, I squeezed her other hand, only because I couldn't find appropriate words.

She squeezed back and in a rush, she said,

"Look, it's a bit cold out here, do you mind if I jump in with you while we finish our tea." I think I must have said O.K., because, the next thing I knew, she had taken off her dressing gown and slipped into bed beside me. She snuggled-up against me and shivered, just for a moment or two. I was still sitting-up in the bed and she almost commanded, "Come down here and give me a cuddle and help me to warm up." Slowly, I complied with her wishes and I was conscious of the fact that my nightshirt had ridden up over my body. As I desperately tried to pull it down, Hedwig said, "Don't bother about that, come here." With that, she rolled me towards her and put her arms around me. I responded by putting my one free arm round her waist. It felt very nice. She was suddenly doing the same things that Alex was doing on that memorable first night and I reciprocated. We were becoming very warm, in fact it was quite stifling and as I raised my head for air, Hedwig said, "Take your nightshirt off." I began struggling out of it and was aware of movements beside me. When I emerged from my nightie, Hedwig was naked beside me. We put our arms round each other and I felt her breasts pushing against my chest and my iron-hard willy pushing against her.

She half-rolled away from me and I followed with one arm behind her neck.

Instinctively, I kissed her on the mouth in the lightly, teasing way that Alex had taught me.

I heard a sharp intake of breath and felt her body tremble. She pushed me away. Looking directly into my eyes, she said,

"My God, who taught you that?"

"I don't know, it just came sort of naturally", I replied.

She pulled me back on top of her, stroking all over my body with her soft hands and all the time, she was breathing quite heavily. Then, as her hands were moving over my waist, hips and bottom, again there was that strange, sharp intake of breath and she said, almost in awe, "You really are so beautiful Janni, your skin and body are amazing. It's just like going to bed with another girl and it's very exciting."

Whilst I was digesting this, to me, hitherto unknown fact that girls could get pleasure out of going to bed together, just as Alex and I did, I indicated to Hedwig that she should turn onto her tummy and when she had complied, began another Alex speciality which I enjoyed very much and saw no reason to think that she would be any the less appreciative. I knelt astride her legs and began massaging the backs of her thighs, upwards, pushing up against the cheeks of her bottom, thumbs running up the deep cleft and outwards in circling movements. Sometimes, I would delve deeper with my thumbs and brush gently over her anus.

She was obviously enjoying this very much, and, when I continued as Alex did by wetting my thumbs with spit and running the tip of one thumb in little circles over that very sensitive part, she was gripping her hands tightly and saying all sorts of wild things. She was beginning to moan to herself, very quietly and I bent down and began to kiss and lick the cheeks, pushing them apart with my hands until I could get my tongue inside, then, when it was moist enough, I inserted the tip of one finger which I moved in and out very, very gently.

"Stop .Oh Stop", she murmured and started to turn onto her back.

"That was incredible and wicked. Where did you learn tricks like that?" I gave a sort of 'How the hell do I know ' shrug and lay on my side, very close to her with my upper hand feeling her breasts which were very firm. It was yet another totally new experience for me and I was intrigued to note that her nipples went hard, just as mine did when Alex kissed and played with them.

She took my hand and placed it firmly down between her thighs and I realised that from now on, everything was going to be pure guesswork. I'd never discussed the female anatomy with anyone before and hadn't much of a clue as to what was expected of me. I needn't have worried. Hedwig placed my fingers on the most sensitive area and, still holding my hand in hers, began to move my fingers in a circular movement. I was fascinated.

After she took her hand away, I started to explore this fantastic, moist world. I could slide my fingers up and down and penetrate the most secret depths, then slide them up again to that very sensitive spot and begin gently rubbing. All the time, Hedwig was lightly squirming, forcing her body upwards against the movements of my fingers and making noises, which I assumed must be indicators of her pleasure.

After quite some time of this, she indicated that I should position myself between her legs, which she had opened accommodatingly.

As I propped myself up with straight arms, she reached down and got hold of my willy, which, by this time, was almost at bursting point. Then, before I knew what was happening, she had put it inside her and at the same time, brought her knees up, thighs against my waist and was using her heels, like spurs on the cheeks of my bum to indicate how I should move and what the tempo should be.

I didn't require much encouragement or instruction from this point on. It was the same as Alex did to me only in a different place! However, unlike Alex, I couldn't control my excitement and I knew it would be all over within seconds. Hedwig must have anticipated this and as she moved her heels to make me go faster, she put her hand down between her legs and began frantically massaging that vital spot. She started shuddering and moaning, writhing like an eel and as I seemed to explode in great, intense waves of pleasure, she clung tightly to me, letting out a long series of deep sighs.

When the heavy breathing and our heaving chests had quietened down, we lay, side by side, our bodies covered in perspiration, Hedwig holding my hand in hers. Eventually, to cool down, Hedwig trampled the bedclothes down and then propped herself up on one elbow and smiled down at me.

"That was terrific, wasn't it?" she said, more a statement than a question, and when I nodded, and without opening my mouth, just made a long mmmmm sound, she ruffled my hair and said, "You are absolutely incredible, so exciting and far too beautiful to be a boy, especially with your lovely girl's figure and skin."

Before I could reply, and quite nonchalantly, yet very disconcertingly, she said, "No wonder Alex loves you so much."

It was as if someone had struck me dumb and at the same time, punched me in the stomach. I was totally paralysed, incapable of movement or speech and lay, inert for what seemed like an hour, but which was probably only a few seconds. Eventually, I said, "What do you mean?"

Hedwig turned to face me and said,

"Oh, come on Janni, you can't fool me, nor can Alex. I'm his mother for God's sake. I've seen the way you look at each other and I know love when I see it. Did you think I hadn't noticed that you sleep together?"

It wasn't said in an accusatory manner, just a pure statement of fact, but I felt that some defence was necessary and probably expected, so I stammered, "We only sleep together to keep warm. It's very cold in here as you have found out", I said, turning to look at her.

I had expected to see a very serious face staring back at me. Instead, there was a lovely smile, almost bordering on a grin and very reminiscent of Alex. "I'm not scolding you, in fact, I think it's quite nice, you and Alex."

Then, with a very impish grin, she said,

"I promise not to tell him about you if you promise not to tell him about us." After I had nodded my agreement to these terms, and I must have shown my amazement at her equanimity, she pulled the bedclothes over us once again and started to tell me something about herself.

It was her father who was German and her mother was a polish Jewess. She had inherited her mother's colouring and her father's features. They had been reasonably well off and she had been a happy child. She attended a good school in Leipzig, which, in addition to its academic curricula, boasted a very highly regarded music and dance facility. She won a scholarship to a college in Danzig (Gdansk) and the whole family moved there.

Hedwig had started dancing from the age of four, concentrating principally on ballet, until, in her sixteenth year, she ventured into modern dance as a logical extension of her training. Before completing her last year, tragedy struck when both her parents were killed in a train crash.

There were no other close relatives to turn to and her father's side of the family had virtually excommunicated him following his marriage to a Jewess.

To keep her head above water, Hedwig tried to obtain work in the ballet, the theatre, the chorus line, in fact, she was prepared to dance almost anywhere within reason because, although she still had a roof over her head, it was rented and cost quite a lot to run. All this on top of having to feed herself, find bus fares and buy clothes more appropriate than the school clothes she'd worn all her life.

She got in with some other girls at the theatrical agencies and one of them moved in with her so that they could share expenses. She also got Hedwig a place in the small combined theatre-cum-nightclub where she worked with a troupe of dancers. Hedwig was well liked and her dancing was more than good enough for the numbers they were expected to perform.

The friendship grew and, as Hedwig told me this part she was smiling indulgently at me and holding my hand, the two girls started sleeping together. This continued until a new musician joined the orchestra and he and Hedwig fell deeply in love. Within no time at all, she became pregnant, two weeks before her seventeenth birthday.

She continued dancing until it was too obvious and then left. By this time, her boyfriend, Alex's father, had moved in with her and his money was just enough for them to scrape by.

Hedwig had an old typewriter of her mother's and she went to evening classes to learn to type, take shorthand and familiarise herself with general office and secretarial duties. They were married in a registry office just two weeks before Alex was born. Several months after that, they moved to Warsaw where Hedwig had located a relative of her mother who was not only prepared to put them up, but would also look after young Alex if and when Hedwig got a job.

In fact, she got a job before her husband, working for the registrar of births, marriages and deaths for three days per week and shortly afterwards, her husband, Lech, joined the army as a bandsman playing trumpet as well as piano.

Lech had been stationed in the Capital during all his Military service. He was a popular soldier and ran the dance band side of the orchestra in addition to his more formal duties. The band was in great demand for many functions.

They enjoyed nearly seventeen years of happy, blissful, fulfilling existence until Germany invaded their country and then, every able bodied man, regardless of what branch of the service they were in had to take up arms and fight for their country. Lech died within the first three days of fighting and after the funeral, Hedwig moved into the smaller flat that she has now, and, as she did after the loss of both parents, set about rebuilding her life. Very cleverly, and with a great deal of forethought, she had taken steps to substitute the records of her parents within the registry and in so doing, had erased all traces of any Jewish blood in her family. She and Alex would be free of any persecution on those grounds.

When she had finished this potted history, I moved closer to her, cuddled her and said, "How awful. You've had some awfully bad luck."

"I'll get over it", she said, and turned towards me, putting a limp arm round my neck and shoulders.

I felt two things, first her breasts pushing against me and then, the by now, familiar stirrings of arousal in my naughty bits. Hedwig giggled and said, "My, my, aren't you the eager little beaver."

We did it all, and more, all over again and this time, I learned all the other things one could do with ones mouth apart from eating, whistling, kissing and spitting. Finally, when we got down to the 'end-game', I was determined to make it last longer than the first time, but not for my sake; I had quickly learned that the pleasure of one's partner was equally, if not more important than one's own.

To delay the inevitable, every time I began to experience the tell tale build-up, I would stop, hold my breath, think about something as far removed as possible from what I was doing, and even, on one occasion, I asked Hedwig if she would teach me to dance. After she had agreed to this and after a few more energetic moments, it all ended as before, but this time, I had inserted my middle finger in Hedwig's bottom, and the combined in and out movements, both front and rear caused her to go absolutely wild, moaning and writhing and shuddering like mad until she finally subsided in a series of diminishing tremors. "You are really very wicked, but you're lovely. That was sheer bliss, I just went somewhere up into the sky and it took a long time to come back down to earth. Was it as nice for you?" she asked.

"Fantastic", I said. This was my new word and it seemed very appropriate.

"Honestly though, I've never done it before", I continued, smiling into her lovely eyes. "Well, you've either got a very inventive, imaginative mind or a good teacher and I suspect it's a bit, no, a lot of both."

In view of the fact that everything seemed to be quite open now, and there was no longer any point in denying my relationship with Alex, I said, "I've got two super teachers now, haven't I?"

"Come on, we'd better get up and have a shower. I'll have to wash and dry these bed-clothes too, before Alex gets home". Hedwig was saying all this as we headed, naked to the bathroom.

The fire had not yet been lit and the flat was quite cold, Hedwig's nipples were standing out from the chill whilst my, not over-generous appendage had almost withered away out of sight and I couldn't help thinking that willies have a very definite mind of their own. For no reason at all, in potentially, very embarrassing situations, they will spring to attention as though to get a better look for possible, compatible company. Then again, I was to learn later, they would refuse to stand when urgently required to do so and could become quite sulky if the cajoling and attempted inducements were not to their liking. Putting all further such thoughts out of my mind, I showered, dried myself briskly, cleaned my teeth and then dressed.

I felt great. Then, I noticed the time, it was half past eleven. Panicking, I rushed in to the big living room, put on my dry shoes, overcoat and scarf, picked up the sheet music and shouted to Hedwig to tell her that I had to go home. She had dressed and came out to see me looking very anxious. "Don't worry", she said. "I'll phone your mum and tell her that you got interested in this new music and wanted to play more and more, that the time passed without us noticing. I'll apologise for not keeping an eye on the time. That should fix it". Before I could say anything she said, "I'll be very humble and contrite, really convincing. Now then, off you go, and promise you'll come and see me again on Tuesday and Thursday mornings." Her expression left no doubt as to what she had in mind and I was more than happy to give my promise.

As I left to walk home, I walked along with a very bouncy stride at first, but my thoughts of Alex took all the cockiness out of my gait. I felt terrible. Firstly, because I had betrayed him, secondly, and much worse, with his mother.

I tried to persuade myself that it wasn't my fault that I'd been led astray, but in reality, I had been a very willing participant. In honesty, I can't say that I resolved there and then not to repeat the morning's activities on any future occasion, but I did solemnly promise that I would love Alex even more and make him as happy as possible, always providing that he remained unaware of what had transpired between his mother and me. I must stress, that at that point in time, I had no idea that what Alex and I were doing was illegal, nor that the German authorities meted out very severe punishments for anyone caught perpetrating these acts. Furthermore, Hedwig's seduction of a minor was also a criminal offence. All in all, we were really taking terrible chances. Fortunately, neither Alex nor I were of a promiscuous nature and we confined our demonstrations of affection for one another to the safety of our own homes, and Hedwig was hardly likely to tell anyone what she and I had been up to. I arrived home, all smiles, apologised for being so late and launched into an explanation. Rachel stopped me in mid flow, told me that Hedwig had very kindly telephoned and taken full responsibility for my lateness and had apologised profusely. "She sounds very nice and she was very complimentary about you, your good manners and your piano playing. You'll have to play some of this new music for us this evening, Hedwig made it sound very exciting". Rachel stopped talking for a moment and gave me her customary hug and kiss followed by all the family in turn. This warmth, the way the whole family always greeted each other, was something very special. It wasn't a ritual learned by rote, which was just another duty, but a real, genuine expression of love and affection. It impressed me greatly and I considered myself very lucky to have been included. Needless to say, my response was just as loving and sincere.

I promised to play for them later and to tell them all about the party, with some notable omissions, and then said, "I must change, go to the market and the shops and do a few of my usual rounds. I'll be home by four o'clock, certainly no later than half past", I continued, over my shoulder as I mounted the stairs to my bedroom.

"I hate you having to do this Janni, Please do be careful. I'll leave some money on the sideboard", Rachel called after me.

CHAPTER ELEVEN

My shopping and scrounging were reasonably successful, but the situation was becoming serious in terms of individual allowances and the shopkeepers were restricting their wares and produce to everyone. No longer could you buy as much as you could pay for, although most were opportunist enough to 'find' a little, or in some cases a lot more, if one was prepared to pay exorbitant prices. Sadly, this became the norm and with few exceptions, those Jews who still managed to do their own shopping, were often asked to pay as much as ten times the amount paid by non Jews. Such is the baseness of human nature that there will always be those who seek to make vast profits out of the misfortune of others. There seemed to be very little evidence of compassion, good neighbourliness or pity in the face of rampant greed.

The market traders were altogether a better bunch to begin with, but it wasn't long before they too descended into the same mercenary ways. Since our German Overlords condoned, even encouraged this behaviour, there was no avenue of complaint. We were being systematically bled dry, but, if we were to survive, there was no alternative. Having completed my shopping, I hurried to meet Alex, fearful of the fact that due to my dalliance with his mother, I would be late and that he might have given up and gone home. My fears proved groundless. He was waiting, as usual, outside the little cafe and held a brown paper carrier bag in one hand. As he spotted me, he waved with the other and smiled his fabulous smile.

He handed me the carrier bag inside which were two large, still warm loaves of bread. "Perks of the job", he said, and continued, "I've already taken one home for mum". We went into the cafe and Alex bought two hot drinks, which we took to a small table by the window.

"I was going to suggest that you came home with me, but its late and mum will be home at four o'clock", Alex said with obvious disappointment.

Thinking ahead, I said,

"In future, I'll do my shopping early and I'll be waiting outside your house when you get home. That should save a lot of valuable time."

"Good idea", Alex enthused, and with a huge grin, he went on, "I'll bring you some more bread, but you'll have to earn it!"

We chatted cosily, making our drinks last, but the time seemed to pass far too quickly. It was time to go to our separate homes.

When we came to the place where our paths diverged, we scrambled into a derelict building and held each other very close. Alex kissed me in the way I never tired of, and then, quite suddenly, they became longer, more exploratory, more passionate, interspersed with slower, more tender, gentler kisses. I was trembling and tingling all over; breathless and speechless.

He cupped my face in his hands and brushed his lips over my forehead, my eyelids and finally over the tip of my nose and said, "Christ, Janni, I'm totally potty about you. I love you like mad. Promise me you'll always be with me and tell me that you love me too". As he said this, he looked imploringly, deep into my eyes.

I blinked away the tears that had suddenly welled -up in my eyes and said, "Oh yes Alex, I do love you very much, and yes, I promise." We held each other very closely until our emotions were under control and then, left the building, said our farewells, and headed for our respective homes. On my way home, I was filled with conflicting feelings of guilt and great joy and my normally cheerful mood escaped me as I approached the house.

I must have appeared quite surly and pensive because, almost immediately after depositing the shopping on the kitchen table, Rebecca came in followed by her mother.

Rebecca, took me by the shoulders and said,

"Whatever's the matter Janni? You really look down in the dumps". I remained quiet for a few moments to gather my thoughts and then I heard myself blaming the attitudes of the shopkeepers for my depression and ranting about the unfairness of it all and what a lousy bunch of opportunists they all were.

I was astonished at my own performance and the fact that my outburst was delivered with such obvious, intense loathing for those who were exploiting us. Possibly, some of this loathing was directed at myself for my own duplicity.

Rebecca put her arm around my shoulders and made comforting gestures while Rachel brought us hot drinks and said how sorry she was that I had experienced this unsavoury side of human behaviour after nobly accepting the very responsible role, at such a young age, as provider for the whole family. She said how guilty they all felt for exposing me to the worst in people.

Surrounded as I was by these loving, caring people, my mood didn't last for long. In no time at all, I was telling them about Alex's party, the plum brandy, over which Rachel lightly scolded me, but with an indulgent smile on her face.

"It seems you had a great time", she said, and then, as if she had already given the matter some deep thought, she continued, "Hedwig seemed very nice when I spoke to her on the phone and it sounds as though you like her too". I nodded and she said, "If we could arrange it, and when they are both available, it might be nice to invite her and Alex over for tea."

This was a totally unexpected development and I was pleased at her apparent acceptance of my friends.

"That would be really nice, Mum", I said and I was thinking, how readily and naturally I called Rachel 'Mum'. Earlier, I only called her that when I wasn't thinking, and I suppose that Rebecca, Aaron and Isaac must have thought it strange at first, but now, they seemed to accept it as quite natural.

Julius arrived home and we all greeted him then he and Rachel went into the sitting room, presumably to discuss the events of the day.

Later, we had our evening meal, during which, Julius asked me to thank Alex, on the family's behalf for the bread and then said, "Right ho, let's clear these things away, get them washed up and then we can hear some of this new-fangled music Janni is raving about."

He smiled indulgently at me and said,

"I hope this doesn't mean you're going to neglect your classics." "No chance", I said, "But all music is interesting and it deserves a hearing, then the listener can decide whether its good, bad or indifferent. Their conclusions will not necessarily be the same as other people's."

Julius looked at me with a combination of respect and amusement and said, "My my Janni, it almost sounds as though you fear we may not like it and are defending it in advance". With that, he ruffled my hair and said, "You should know by now that we are all very open minded and tolerant about most things."

"Is it O.K. if I go and sort out my music then"? I asked, and when Julius agreed, I went to the front room and scanned quickly through some of the music that Hedwig had lent me. I was looking for something easier to play than those I had played the night before. There was a good selection, including songs from films and musicals, even some numbers, which had been written for, and performed by Marlene Dietrich. I ran through a couple of pieces quite quickly and found them relatively easy, but it was the music of Fats Waller which really took my fancy. This was more difficult, but I thought that if I played it a little slower, nobody would notice and it would make things easier for me. When they all trouped in and made themselves comfortable, I stood up, gave a mock bow and began playing.

Fortunately, all went well, without too many hiccups and after playing two Fats Waller numbers, I was mentally congratulating myself when, to my astonishment, after they finished clapping, Julius said, "That was very, very nice Janni. I particularly liked the way you played the Fats Waller numbers at a slower pace!"

My flabbergasted expression must have amused them, but Rebecca came to my rescue, saying, "Papa didn't want to make you nervous or spoil your evening by telling you beforehand that he collects Fats Waller records. In fact, he's got original recordings of the songs you just played."

Julius interposed, saying,

"And you played them very well, especially considering that you'd never played anything like this before yesterday. Perhaps you'd like to hear some of my records tomorrow evening." "That's a nice idea, it'll give me the chance to hear how they should be played." I replied.

Rebecca stood up, came over and gave me a big hug and said,

"Now then Janni, seeing as this is a musical evening, perhaps you would like to accompany me whilst I play something for Mama and Papa."

When I had agreed, with the proviso that I could play the particular piece of music, Rebecca opened up a neat little black case and took out a clarinet. Having fitted it all together, she came over to the piano, struck a chord, fiddled about with the mouthpiece and reed for a second or two. After striking the same chord again, all the time sustaining the chord with the loud pedal, she played a scale on the clarinet. Apparently, she was satisfied with her tuning.

She opened her leather, music case and handed me the sheet music. As soon as I saw it, I knew that I had heard this before somewhere, and, with mounting excitement; I hoped that this might be the first indication of returning memory. Alas, this did not prove to be the case, but at the time, my joy at actually remembering something from my past, seemed to inspire my playing. Rebecca responded with such clarity of tone, wonderful phrasing and a beautiful, haunting quality that her rendition of Mozart's Concerto for Clarinet will remain in my mind forever.

When we had finished, there were emotional tears of joy running down my cheeks and a great lump in my throat, which was proving hard to swallow. I stood up, took her hand, bent over and kissed it. Having regained my composure, and with it, my voice, I said, "That was the most beautiful thing I've ever heard. You're a wonderful musician Rebecca and a very dark horse to boot."

I'm sure that I saw a tear in Julius's eye as he stood up, and, after expressing his pleasure for the quality of the entertainment we had provided, suggested that we all have a warm drink and then, the younger children should go to bed.

It was a sentiment with which I heartily concurred since it had been very long, tiring and emotional twenty-four hours for me.

Once in my bedroom, I collected my nightshirt and went to the bathroom where I stripped off and had a stand-up wash, cleaned my teeth and combed my hair. I stood looking at my naked reflection in the mirror, turning this way and that in order to inspect my body and face from every angle. The constant references, more so today than any other day, about my facial beauty, my extremely girlish figure and the texture of my skin were very much to the forefront of my mind and to improve my shopping capabilities, the nucleus of an idea had been slowly taking shape in my head.

I appraised myself slowly and critically, paying great attention to detail. My frame had increased proportionately to my height during the past twelve months or so, and what I saw convinced me that my projected plan would work admirably. What I saw was indeed a very girlish figure, slim arms, small hands and feet, flat tummy, narrow waist and the typical, unboylike rounded hips. Turning sideways, I could see that the small of my back curved gently inwards from the top and then curved outwards more sharply over a distinctly girlish bottom. With the aid of a hand mirror, I looked at the reflection of my rear and found confirmation that my rounded bum, with the cleft running almost from the small of my back, should, most definitely have belonged to a girl. I was not disappointed; on the contrary, I was well pleased. Another turn to the mirror, this time to examine my face in detail. My hair was longer than it had been and it was thick, brownish black and hung in gentle curls. My eyebrows were clearly defined arches of the same colour above large brown eyes, the whites of which were very bright and clear. Extraordinarily long eyelashes made the eyes look even bigger. The nose was straight, narrowish and small set in highish cheekbones above quite a full mouth with very precisely defined lips, almost as if someone had drawn round the outline with a slightly darker coloured pencil. I parted my lips and looked at small, even white teeth and then down to the delicate chin. All of this was perched on a slim neck. I pulled my nightshirt on thinking that although it must be very unnatural to possess such an unusual body and looks, I was very happy with what I had seen, not the least bit worried or sorry about my appearance. In fact, I now knew that my plan would work. In bed, thoughts about the whole of the last twenty-four hours persisted and it was impossible to sleep right away. Young as I was, I knew instinctively that my relationship with Alex would be regarded as, to say the least, unnatural and by some as downright disgusting. But, to me, I felt more like a girl than a boy and seemed to have more feminine mannerisms, emotions and reactions than any male of the species. It was, therefore, very difficult for me to believe that what I was doing was wrong. I reasoned that if God had built me this way, he should expect me to behave accordingly. As for my dalliance with Hedwig, I felt no guilt over that since I had not instigated proceedings. From this latter consideration came the question that required an honest, no reservations answer. Did I prefer going to bed with Alex or with Hedwig?

After reliving my experiences with both of them in my mind, I decided that although both were very, very exciting, my love for Alex, the passion, tenderness and emotions we aroused in each other, combined with his caring, thoughtful, intensely protective attitude towards me, left me in no doubt that his love and lovemaking were more important and more satisfying than the hectic, frantic, wholly physical sex with Hedwig. Having reached this happy conclusion, after very lengthy and deliberate consideration, I drifted off into a deep, almost exhausted sleep.

CHAPTER TWELVE

Monday was the usual hectic round of shopping and scrounging and it took much longer than usual with the result that I was fairly tired and had loads to carry. It seemed silly to carry everything over to Alex's house, and then have to carry it all the way home. So, I decided that although I should miss him and he would undoubtedly be disappointed, I would telephone him and let him know that I would see him the following afternoon instead. I awoke early next morning to find the sun streaming through the window and, upon looking out, I saw that although it was very bright, the people on the streets looked well wrapped up and all walked very carefully, placing their feet with precision to avoid slipping. The snow still appeared hard and crisp and there was little sign of any thaw. After I had washed, dressed and eaten breakfast, I too wrapped up warm, collected some of the money that I had saved, money from Rachel for such shopping as I could acquire and left to do my rounds.

Shopping went fairly well and I was soon hurrying for my morning appointment with Hedwig.

My decision to meet Hedwig, in spite of my conclusions of the previous night, had more to do with the plan I was formulating than the prospect of an erotic morning. Hedwig's assistance was vital in the implementation of my scheme.

Experience had taught me that it was always better to ask for something after giving something first, and in this instance, the giving was very pleasurable and fulfilling for both participants. As we lay in our post-sex contentment, I initiated the first part of my plan. We were in the shower together and I made a point of looking very deliberately at Hedwig's body then carefully studying my own. After a few moments of exaggerated movements, the better to make comparisons, I said to Hedwig, "I really have got a very girlish body, haven't I?"

Hedwig, realising what all the strange movements had been leading up to, just as I had intended her to, replied, "Yes, you have Janni. But, it's not just your body; it's everything about you, from your slim arms, small hands and feet, beautiful shoulders and legs, a stunning face, to your general demeanour and mannerisms. You're very exciting."

When we were thoroughly dry, I said,

"I know this is going to sound silly, but, out of curiosity, could I try on one of your dresses and a pair of high heels? I think our feet are about the same size."

She seemed quite excited by the prospect and said,

"What fun. Of course you can."

The next half hour was spent trying on different clothes and shoes and, if I'm completely honest I must confess to enjoying and being excited by the transformation that the very feminine garments brought about.

While I was busy practising walking in high heels; something which, after only a few moments, seemed to come quite naturally to me, Hedwig returned from the bedroom and as she stopped in the doorway to look at me, her eyes widened in amazement and she said, "My God, Janni Darling, you even walk like a girl. No one could tell the difference. Wow!" She brought a box from the bedroom, put it on the table and indicated that I should go and sit on the chair beside her.

She opened the box and I was intrigued by the contents. There were all sorts of tubes, jars, things that looked like fat crayons, some finer, pencil like objects and an assortment of brushes.

"What are all these?" I asked.

"It's greasepaint; stage make-up from my dancing days," Hedwig explained. "Now sit still," she added.

With a look of intense concentration on her face, she spent the next twenty minutes or so applying make-up to me, using a variety of subtle shades to various features and finally, after carefully selecting a suitable lip colour, applied this, followed by the worst, most uncomfortable bit, which was the application of mascara and what she called 'eye liner'. She held me by the shoulders at arms length, examining her handiwork quite critically from all sides, and, judging by the expression on her face, she was well pleased with the outcome.

"Go and have a look in the mirror and tell me if you like what you see", she said and watched with obvious delight as I walked across to the mirror. The transition was quite remarkable and it was immediately apparent that Hedwig was highly skilled in the art of make-up. It was so beautifully done, with the tones so cleverly blended that it was difficult to tell that it had been done at all. She had accentuated all the best features of my face; my already large eyes looked even larger, the slight darkening of the lashes making the whites appear much whiter and the lashes much, much longer. The overall effect was absolutely brilliant and pleased me very much.

"I want to see myself in the long mirror", I said impatiently, and headed for her bedroom. She followed and stood beside me with a sort of wan, indulgent smile on her pretty face as I turned this way and that, examining myself in great detail.

I finally turned to her and said,

"That's fantastic, you'll have to teach me how to do it. Thank you so much Hedwig".

She looked me up and down, stared long and hard at my face and said,

"I really can't believe it myself Janni; it's amazing. Not only do you look so very beautiful but you also behave in a completely feminine way. All traces of masculinity have vanished as though they never existed. Come here", she commanded and, when I had complied, she put her arms around me and we cuddled each other for some moments before she pushed me away. Her expression was still soft but with serious undertones in her voice, she asked, "What made you want to do this all of a sudden?"

Although I had anticipated the question, it still came as something of a shock, particularly as I should have to answer with complete honesty, since Hedwig was a very keen observer of life and her own experiences had given her a deep insight into my problems. There was not the slightest chance of lying to her.

I took a deep breath and replied,

"Some instinct has been pushing me to do it for some time, but it always felt as though some stronger motivation than a basic desire was needed for me to take the initial step." What I had to say next sounded very mercenary, but I felt sure that Hedwig would understand my reasons and the dire necessity, which had hardened my resolve. "Hedwig, it's all to do with economics and increasing the chances of survival for me and my adoptive family. Let me explain", I began, and before she could venture any comment, I continued, "There are six of us in our family and because of the attitude towards the Jews, I'm the only one who, as a non-Jew, can shop, unchallenged. But, as a youngster, notwithstanding the fact that I speak both Polish and German, the shopkeepers and stallholders are only prepared to sell me a limited amount; they will sell more if I pay a much greater price, but this will soon eat up our meagre resources. So, I thought that I'd beat them at their own game and become two people, shopping independently". I paused for a moment or two to give Hedwig time to digest this information and then asked, "Do you honestly think that my appearance has changed convincingly enough for me to get away with it?"

Hedwig's response was very encouraging and she answered my question with such conviction that any doubts that I harboured about my proposed course of action were quickly allayed.

"Janni, you would convince anyone, effortlessly, right down to the voice. I don't know whether or not you have realised it yourself, but even though your voice has broken, it's not very deep and the moment you donned a dress, your voice-pitch changed, ever so slightly and now, you have a very sexy, husky voice. You don't even have the slightest trace of an Adam's apple. Do you realise that you're getting me all excited again?" she added with a mischievous twinkle in her eyes.

Fortunately, she happened to look at the clock and said,

"Oh hell, look at the time. I must fly otherwise I'll be late. I'd forgotten that I promised one of the other girls that I'd stand in for her this afternoon."

With that, she dashed about frantically whilst I stood there, wondering what to with my made-up face. After persistent enquiries, she handed me a pot of cream, which she assured me, would remove all traces of make-up.

"Let yourself out and slam the door after you and don't forget to come on Thursday morning", she shouted over her shoulder as she headed for the door.

She brushed her lips lightly over mine and then she was gone, leaving behind the delicate scent of her perfume.

CHAPTER THIRTEEN

After Hedwig had gone to work, I thought I should have about half an hour or forty-five minutes before Alex arrived so I spent ten of them examining myself in the long mirror, pirouetting and looking over my shoulder, watching myself walk towards the mirror and, with a hand mirror, examining my back view as I walked away from it. Next, with comb and brush, I changed my parting, combed the parting out and decided upon the most suitable style for my new personality.

I had become so engrossed in my experimentation that I had completely misjudged the passing of time and suddenly, quite panic stricken, I was brought back to reality by the sound of the key in the door.

There was nowhere to hide and before I had time to think, Alex was moving about in the living room.

Deciding that the best form of defence was attack and realising that this was a heaven-sent opportunity to try out my new persona, I summoned up all my composure, and, in my new voice called, "Is that you Alex"? adding, "I'll be with you in a moment." As I walked to the living room, with more nonchalance than I was feeling, I said, "Your mother told me you were very good-looking, but I think she should have said gorgeous."

The expression on Alex's face said it all. He stared in total amazement, looking me up and down with his look changing from one of surprise at finding someone at home, an apparent stranger at that, to one of growing interest and obvious admiration. "Er, who are you?" and, after closer inspection, he stammered, "My God. You must be Janni's sister, where did you spring from?"

I walked straight towards him in my new slinky manner, draped my arms over his shoulders, clasped my hands behind his neck and said, "Look closely at me Alex, I'm not Janni's sister, it's me ...Janni." He was quite nonplussed, struggling to come to terms with everything until I took his face between both hands and kissed him, first in his special way and then in the more lingering way we had done on the last occasion, pressing my body close to his and letting my fingers stroke the back of his neck and ears. In the first brief pause, I said, "Love you and I always will."

He began kissing me very passionately and his hands moved downward, lingering on my waist for a few moments before he took hold of the cheeks of my bottom. He was becoming very aroused and holding my bum much tighter when he suddenly gasped, "Christ, you've got nothing on under this lot."

He took my hand and almost dragged me to his bed where we spent the next hour and a half in extremely wild, highly imaginative, passionate lovemaking. Not once did he ask about my new appearance except to say that it was madly exciting. At that time, I don't think it was conceit, but I'm sure he believed that I had done it all as a surprise, just to please him! Whatever his reasons, I loved him for them. At that particular moment, it would not have been the right time to tell him the real reasons and later, after a good deal of reflection, it seemed better to let him think that my idea of the dual roles for shopping had sprung from my play-acting for his pleasure. Alex helped me to remove all traces of the make-up and then we showered together, my second of the day!

We arranged to meet outside his house the next day, hugged and kissed each other briefly and I headed for home, feeling both exhilarated and somewhat exhausted.

CHAPTER FOURTEEN

The pattern became firmly established, seeing Alex on Mondays, Wednesdays and Fridays and Hedwig on Tuesdays and Thursdays. On Sundays, I was allowed to stay over and did the shopping etc on my way home. Hedwig and I spent many a happy hour with her teaching me how to apply make-up and although I had asked her to help me to buy some new clothes, she wouldn't hear of it, saying that she had plenty that I could choose from, with some exceptions. The only things she did agree to buy for me were items of underwear and a couple of saucy berets.

We had a lot of fun when I had pressed her to teach me to dance and we would reverse roles from time to time so that I should become proficient in all aspects of dance. Sometimes, we would dance numbers from the shows she had been in and act out the parts of the individual dancers and the chorus. Often, on Sundays, I would dress-up and Hedwig and I would entertain Alex amidst hoots of laughter as Hedwig, in true music hall style, threw in some very hammy, one-line jokes. On a number of occasions, I would wear fishnet stockings and a top hat, sit at the piano and give an impression of Marlene Dietrich, which they both thought fantastic. Alex would take turns to dance with us for the conventional dance music and he danced very competently. It was during one such dancing session, when Alex and I were dancing a slow waltz that we got a bit carried away. I stumbled after catching one of my high heels on the edge of the carpet and as Alex grabbed me more firmly to stop me from falling, I put both my arms round his neck and snuggled closer to him. He responded by putting both his arms around me and we danced very closely, cheek to cheek until Hedwig, with a gentle, but slightly mocking smile on her face, suddenly interrupted our enjoyment of each other by saying, "Honestly, you two. Anyone would think you were madly in love." Poor Alex turned scarlet and Hedwig's face fell as she realised just how much she had embarrassed her son. She crossed the floor very quickly, put her arms round both of us and said, "Oh hell! that was a stupid remark wasn't it?" and before either of us could reply she rushed on, "You both looked so beautiful and natural dancing together like that and I said it without thinking. Please forgive me, both of you, for causing you any embarrassment, it was quite thoughtless of me."

Alex regained his composure, moved so that he had one arm round my shoulders and one arm round his mother's. He took a deep breath and with what I considered to be remarkable bravery, he said, "Mum, you've nothing to apologise for, you were quite right. I do love Janni very much and he loves me too. I was sure you must have noticed before now and to be honest, I have never kept any secrets from you except this one. I've wanted to tell you, but didn't know how, or what your reaction would be and I'm glad it's out in the open. I hope you're not too upset or disappointed in me."

I was so proud of him. I put both arms around him and as I looked over his shoulder, I caught Hedwig's eye and she blew me a kiss and gave me the most delightful, happy smile.

Alex and I turned towards her, still with an arm round each other's waists and Hedwig, still smiling said, "You know I love you both very much and I'm glad that you have told me. Yes, I have suspected for a long time. How could you think that I wouldn't notice that Janni's bed hadn't been slept in, even if you did make attempts to rumple it a bit. Hell, I'm the one who does the washing and after all these years, I can spot sheets that haven't been slept in".

She paused for a moment to let this sink in and then continued,

"Alex, I'm not the least bit disappointed in you, in fact I think you two are lovely together. And anyway, it's hardly surprising, Janni is so beautiful and so feminine that it would have been a miracle if you hadn't felt so strongly drawn to him and you are so strong and handsome that it would have been equally surprising if Janni hadn't fallen for you. I'm delighted, but please, both of you, remember these are very dangerous times and please keep any displays of overt affection within the confines of these walls."

She held us both tightly and then said,

"Phew, I think this is another of those occasions when we need something stronger than tea. Alex, bring the apricot brandy and three glasses."

When Alex left the room Hedwig whispered to me,

"We'll have to stop seeing each other. If Alex found out, it would break his heart and I know you would much rather be with him than with me."

She grinned impishly as she said,

"On second thoughts, perhaps we could just see each other once a week and sort of tail off gradually."

I grinned back, squeezed her hand and said,

"Sounds O.K. to me."

We had quite a few apricot brandies and I was feeling decidedly light-headed as I swayed along to the bathroom on my now unsteady high heels, where I started laughing to myself, imagining what people would have thought if they had seen what was, to all intents and purposes, a pretty young lady, hitching up her dress and peeing in a standing position! This was something I would have to think about if I was to go out dressed like this. I should no longer be able to nip into a bombed out building for a quick pee, after all, one was never certain that one wouldn't be caught unawares by someone on a similarly urgent call of nature.

I cleaned the make-up off my face and splashed it with liberal amounts of cold water before returning to the living room. In my absence, Hedwig had made the usual treat of hot chocolate which we sipped gently, lingering over each luxurious mouthful, sadly aware that soon, it would all be gone and would be virtually impossible to replace. When we had finished, Alex and I washed and dried the cups and glasses and put them away. We washed our faces, cleaned our teeth and went to say goodnight to Hedwig.

She held our hands and said,

"It's been a lovely, very happy day. Now, off you go to bed and don't forget the alarm clock." That night, still slightly tipsy from the apricot brandy and happy and contented, we just curled up together and fell asleep almost instantly.

We awoke to the insistent ringing of the alarm and after a few minutes, snuggled up for our usual morning cuddle, during which, we made our arrangements for the rest of the week. Alex made some tea and brought some to the bedroom which we drank as he dressed. He finished his tea, bent over and brushed his lips over mine, with a wave of his hand he said, "See you this afternoon. Love you", and then he was gone. I drifted back to sleep, but it was more catnapping than sustained sleep and I was already sitting up in bed when Hedwig came in to wake me. She had dressed already and I breathed an inward sigh of relief because, amongst other things, my nipples felt quite tender and sore and even the feel of my nightshirt against them caused discomfort.

We chatted, as usual and then Hedwig said,

"I must go. Let yourself out darling."

I arranged to see her the next morning with a view to making my first shopping expedition in my new identity.

Hedwig said to come early and after I had changed, she would come with me on my first tentative foray to make sure that no harm came to me.

I dressed, left the house and went shopping. The weight of my clothing was causing me real agony and I must have cut a strange figure, walking along with my back bowed and my shoulders hunched forward to keep my shirt from brushing against nipples. By now, it was very, very uncomfortable and I was relieved to get home, put the shopping in the kitchen and go to the bathroom, where I took off my shirt and examined myself in the mirror.

The brown circles round my nipples were swollen up like half golf balls and the skin round them looked inflamed. It was quite painful to the touch and I knew that I should have to get some help from Rachel.

I approached her with a certain amount of trepidation, wondering if this was the result of too much sexual activity and that the cause would be very apparent to an experienced doctor. After indicating that I wanted to see her privately, Rachel ushered me into the old consulting room and indicated that I should sit down.

She could see that I was in a state of some discomfort and without speaking or waiting to be told, I removed my shirt and just pointed to my nipples. Her eyes widened slightly, otherwise, she gave no indication of surprise, I suppose it was her professional training, and she came over to examine me. I flinched as she touched them and as I looked down to see what she was doing, I noticed that when she took her hands away, they were wet.

"What is happening to me? They are very sore and tender and I can't stand the weight of my shirt against them", I said to her in a puzzled, somewhat frightened tone. "Don't worry, Janni, it's nothing serious. It happens occasionally in some boys and I should think that you are more predisposed to it than most because of your genetic make-up. Believe it or not, you are lactating, that is to say, producing milk. It won't last for long and they will go back to normal fairly quickly. Now I'll just bathe them lightly and then we'll put some cool dressings on which will make you feel more comfortable. You don't need to say anything to the rest of the family about this, but we will need to change your dressings fairly often especially if you feel the need to."

She was extremely thoughtful and after she had dressed the offending articles, she cut strips of oiled silk, then taped over the dressings so that there would be no seepage and no telltale damp patches on my shirtfront, which I would have been hard-pushed to explain.

The patches, with their soothing ointment felt good and I was very relieved when my shirt no longer caused such acute discomfort.

"Thanks Mum, I was really in quite a state about it and I thought something dreadful was happening. They will be all right, won't they? I said, still not thoroughly convinced. She held me by the shoulders, at arms length in her customary way and said, "I promise you Janni, you've nothing to worry about, you'll be right as rain in a few days although the swelling may take a little longer to go down. Now let's go and have some tea and toast. Oh, and thank Alex for the loaves, I don't know what we'd do without the pair of you."

On that happier note, we retired to the kitchen and joined the rest of the family at the big table.

After dinner that evening, Julius and Rachel retired to the front room while the rest of us cleared-up, washed and put away the dishes. Rebecca and I had sort of gravitated towards each other over the last six months or so and we had become very close. On reflection, it was like the boys on one side and the girls on the other and we always supported one another in arguments with Aaron and Isaac. Mostly it was good-natured banter with plenty of derisive, sarcastic comments flying about and in these exchanges, Rebecca always came out on top. She had a very ready, quick wit and was never at a loss for a stinging response, but being the good-natured boys that they were, these ripostes only provoked more outrageous derision from them. It was great fun and the kitchen was always a very happy place, ringing with the sound of laughter.

Rebecca had noticed that I was not operating at my usual speed and that some of my movements were not as fluid as they normally were. She asked me, "What's the matter Janni? You're not yourself today."

I leaned closer to her and whispered in her ear,

"Don' t tell the boys, but I've got something wrong with my tits." She went into convulsions of laughter at my choice of word and it was obvious that my reply to her question had been taken as a joke rather than a serious statement of my problem.

She gave me a big kiss on the cheek and said,

"Janni, you are so funny at times, that was hilarious."

She put her arms round me to give me a cuddle and it was as I hunched my shoulders forward and arched my back to avoid contact that it obviously struck a chord and she suddenly realised that I hadn't been joking.

A look of sheer contrition appeared on her face and in whispered tones she said,

"My God, you were serious weren't you?" As I nodded, she continued,

"Oh Janni darling, I am sorry; I really thought you were just being funny, particularly when you said 'tits' "

We both smiled and she said,

"I suppose Mum has sorted it, er them, out for you, but you can tell me more about it later when the boys are not around."

Then, as though it was quite a commonplace occurrence and as if she were confiding in another girl, she smiled and said, "I suffered the same discomfort and tenderness when my tits started to grow". She smiled a huge smile and we both laughed at her daring use of the word 'tits'. We played silly board games and cards for the next couple of hours using buttons for money and the keen, competitive spirit of us against them was even more pronounced. I'm afraid to say that Rebecca and I were no match for Aaron's skill at bluffing and he and Isaac cleaned us out in a very short space of time at cards. Needless to say, they laughingly sneered and gloated and made some very uncomplimentary remarks about our combined ability.

Aaron, who no doubt had heard some of his older friends making similar comments, said, "Girls are only fit for one thing and that's..." He trailed off, blushing heavily in the process when he realised the enormity of what he was about to say, not to mention the fact that he had addressed both Rebecca and myself as 'girls'.

Rebecca pounced, not wanting to let him off the hook and determined to prolong his embarrassment.

"And what one thing would that be, dear brother?" she enquired with the most beatific smile on her face.

Aaron, striving to regain some of his composure, shrugged his shoulders and with an air of apparent nonchalance, replied, "Oh, you know washing up, cleaning, ironing. You know, sort of general housework". He paused for a moment before continuing, "I almost forgot, there is the important matter of child-bearing and looking after babies". He said this as if it was an afterthought, a throw away line of little importance. It was beautifully done and he had achieved what he had set out to imply in the first place but in more acceptable language.

Rebecca and I both hooted with laughter and clapped our hands in appreciation. Whether or not I had set the tone for the evening by my use of the word tits, I don't know but the next thing Rebecca said to her brother was, "Bloody hell Aaron, you are a conceited, arrogant bastard at times." We were all suitably impressed by Rebecca's choice vocabulary and we fell about laughing.

Julius and Rachel came in with indulgent smiles on their faces and Julius said.

"My my, you lot have been enjoying yourselves, you've hardly stopped laughing all evening.

It seems as though your mother and I missed out on all the fun." They walked over towards us, arms round each other's waists and Julius continued, "Come on, and make some room for us then we'll all have a hot drink. We made small talk for a while then discussed the more serious matter of the worsening situation surrounding us. What with public hangings, people being shot on the streets with little or no provocation and the bodies of those who had died from starvation, left for ages, unattended, where they had fallen, and given only a cursory glance from those passing by as the prowling dogs sniffed at their piti-ful remains, it was a very fearsome atmosphere indeed. Any excuse would be used for the administration of a severe beating by the ruffian element of the soldiers who appeared to have been employed for just such a purpose. Largely speaking, the average Wehrmacht sol-dier wasn't a bad sort of chap and if one was polite and reasonably friendly, they respond-ed in kind. There was, however, an ever-increasing presence of the dreaded S.S. and they were altogether a different species. Brutality was second nature to them. An evil, all per-vading brutality that struck fear into the hearts of most people, even those with little rea-son to fear. It was apparent that they revelled in their barbaric ways and enjoyed terroris-ing their victims. I can think of no cause which would allow any man, woman or child to descend to such depths of depravity unless they were subnormal. These brainwashed killers, who, along with their leaders, branded the Jews as 'untermenschen' that is mental-ly and physically sub normal, were without doubt, not only the most horrifically evil, vio-lent, depraved, fear inspiring animals it has ever been my misfortune to encounter, but were a total negation of Germany's claims to be the most civilised, advanced nation in the world. Some of their conceited, strutting officers, all of whom appeared to have the habit of striking poses, seemed to be permanently looking down their noses. They were always immaculately turned out and if one passed close by, the smell of cologne was noticeable. But then, I suppose they had to do something to mask the stench of the sewers from whence they had crawled.

We had all become quite subdued and Julius expressed sincere thanks for the central role that I was playing as sole provider and exhorted me to be extra careful and vigilant and not to do anything that could be construed as offensive or seditious. He finished by saying that we should all go to bed but first, we were all to join in a prayer of thanks for our good for-tune thus far. He said that he was sure that in some way, God had directed Janni to them and that they should all pray for my continued safety and well being. He placed his hands upon my head, closed his eyes and intoned something in Hebrew, bowing many times from the waist as he did so.

I could feel tears welling up in my eyes and I felt both proud and very humble. I loved the whole family very much and considered it not only my duty to help as much as I could, but very privileged to do so.

I undressed in the bathroom so that the boys couldn't see my dressings, which I wanted to examine for any traces of leaks. Fortunately everything appeared to be in order so I cleaned my teeth and scrambled into bed.

It was difficult to find a comfortable position and finally, I fell asleep on my back, only to be woken from time to time by the other two who complained that I was snoring. It was a very uncomfortable, restless night during which I slept only fitfully, recalling Rebecca's comments about her 'tits' growing and hoping that her mother's explanation was the true one, not just something to pacify me.

CHAPTER FIFTEEN

The next morning, the damp patches on my nightshirt told me that I had started 'leaking' again and I hastily pulled on my dressing gown to hide the evidence.

Rachel was already up and in the kitchen and when I told her of my problem, she took me and changed the dressings and I immediately felt more comfortable.

After I had washed and changed, I sipped my cup of tea and ate a slice of toast. When I mentioned my intention of going out shopping, Rachel showed immediate concern and begged me not to try to carry too much. I said that if necessary, I would ask Alex to carry things for me and with that reassurance, Rachel gave me permission to go.

I shopped successfully but I began to understand Rachel's concern; the weight of the bags was making the puny muscles on my chest very hard and this in turn was causing considerable discomfort to the tender, swollen area around my nipples. It was with great relief that I finally arrived at Hedwig's flat. She let me in and was a little surprised when I asked her if she would mind carrying the bags upstairs. Briefly, I explained the problem and she suddenly became all 'mumsy', took the bags and led the way upstairs.

She made coffee and when we were seated at the table, she suggested that it might be better to abandon our planned expedition with me in my feminine attire, but I insisted, saying that I couldn't put it off any longer.

She offered no further argument and I stripped to the waist, got the make-up box and set about the transformation under Hedwig's critical eye. Apparently happy with what she saw, she suddenly said, "I've been thinking. To give you some added protection for those tender areas, why don't you try one of my bras and we can pack it with cotton wool".

"That sounds like a brilliant idea and anyway, it would look more natural", I enthused. It worked very well, and by the time I had completed the whole transformation, right down to suspender belt and stockings, the overall effect was quite remarkable. Hedwig was delighted. She lent me one of her coats and a shoulder bag and I parted my hair in the middle, letting it hang down either side of my face and placed one of my saucy berets on my head at a rakish angle.

Hedwig grinned impetuously at me and said,

"Fabulous. Come on then. Any last minute doubts?"

I took a deep breath and said,

"It's now or never, let's go."

I very nearly came to grief at the first hurdle; I had never walked down the stairs before in high heels and almost fell. It took some moments to get the hang of it but progress was slow by comparison with Hedwig's assured movements and it was obvious that I should have to practise this technique. Once on the street, Hedwig linked her arm in mine and we sallied forth into the unknown. It was brilliant, we smiled a lot and chatted animatedly and I felt totally confident, as though I had been doing it all my life. It was even more encouraging when some German soldiers whistled at us. We bought some things for me, a bra, a suspender belt and some knickers and stockings. Then, to test the response of shopkeepers and traders, I bought as much food as I was allowed, without any challenge and a great deal of courtesy.

Finally, we sat in a bar and drank coffee while Hedwig smoked a cigarette. It was the first time I had seen her smoking and I expressed my surprise, to which she replied, "Oh, I have one every so often but I never smoke in the house. Don't mention it to Alex, he hates the things. It was just something to relieve the tension. I needn't have worried though, you are so completely natural, I defy anyone to tell the difference."

We returned home quite elated and I was still in all my glory when Alex arrived home from work. He was doubly surprised. Firstly, he hadn't expected me to be in the house and when we told him what we had been doing he became quite agitated, and berated his mother for condoning my actions. After lots of reassurances and cuddles, he calmed down and said, "O.K., but I've got to see this for myself before I'll agree to you doing it again". With that, I donned the coat and beret again and this time negotiated the stairs with greater success. Once on the street, I linked my arm through his, told him to stop scowling and we walked for half an hour during which time, we attracted many admiring glances, which lifted Alex's spirits, and by the time we got back home, he was all smiles.

After that, he agreed that it would be all right but he insisted that either he or his mother should accompany me and that under no circumstances was I to do this alone. His concern was very touching and I mouthed the words 'I love you' at him, Hedwig noticed this and smiled at me, both wistfully and indulgently.

Poor Alex, when I had cleaned my make-up off and was changing, he really wanted to engage in some very amorous contact and I had to tell him about my problem and the restrictions it temporarily imposed.

He was immediately very contrite and attentive and I absolutely loved it when he said, "Oh, my poor baby, it must be awful for you". He held me very gently and kissed me on the forehead. Tired as he undoubtedly was, he didn't hesitate and carried all the heaviest items of shopping all the way home for me. He added a couple of loaves to the already overflowing bags and when we presented Rachel with our acquisitions, she couldn't believe the amount we had acquired. We drank tea and Alex, looking really exhausted, thanked Rachel for her hospitality and got up to leave. Julius came into the room and said, "Oh Alex, I'm so glad I caught you, there is something I want you to have". He put his hand into his pocket and brought out a long, slim case which he handed to Alex saying, "This is from the family for all that you have done for us and for looking after Janni too; You are a very kind young man and it's a great comfort to us knowing that you are taking care of Janni. Please accept it with our warmest thanks."

Alex was caught off-balance, he stammered, "Thank you Dr Lipschitz, I honestly don't know what to say except that I shall treasure it always". He had opened the case whilst he was talking to reveal a beautiful gold wrist watch and he walked over to Julius, put his arms round his shoulder and touched his cheeks to either side of Julius' cheeks, murmuring "Thank you sir".

It was all quite emotional and I walked Alex to the door in silence.

At the door, Alex, still somewhat overwhelmed, said,

"Christ, they're wonderful aren't they, I don't deserve this."

I spent some moments reassuring him and telling him that he really had earned it, and then we made our arrangements for the next day, kissed and cuddled very briefly and he left.

CHAPTER SIXTEEN

The weeks passed quickly with little or no change in what had become something of a routine. Poor Julius and Rachel were becoming increasingly bored and restless having nothing to do all day of any significance.

After being required to give their help in the hospital to tend the wounded and seriously injured, they had been told to leave the hospital and to cease practising as doctors with immediate effect. If they were found to be contravening this order in any way, they would be dealt with extremely harshly. It wasn't just them; all Jews had been barred from working in any professional capacity and had been ordered to do the most menial jobs, emptying dustbins, cleaning the streets and toilets, in fact anything that the Germans could think of to cause the greatest humiliation.

It was sad to see all those talented brains being so needlessly wasted. Julius had anticipated some of these actions and, very shrewdly, had disposed of his most valuable assets prior to the invasion. He had kept a few small, portable valuables for trading purposes when and if the money he had retained ran out. So far, it was lasting quite well and my success at scrounging and dealing ensured that, unlike many others, we were not starving. We began to hear strange, harrowing tales of whole scale executions in places further north in Chelmno, Sobibor and Treblinka, but confirmation was almost impossible and mostly, the tales were regarded as scaremongering by people with fertile imaginations.

I mentioned this to Hedwig and Alex and although they reacted incredulously, they still thought it wise to be on the safe side and since they were very worried about me, having no means of identification, Hedwig decided to do something about it.

She took two photographs of me, one as a teenage boy and the other as a teenage girl. A friend of hers developed and printed them and, because of where she worked, Hedwig was able to provide two genuine birth certificates for me; with these, and the photographs, she managed to get me two sets of identification documents, all on the genuine forms. I kept these documents at Hedwig's and carried the appropriate identity card with me on each of my daily sorties.

These gave me greater confidence and on a number of occasions, I broke my promise to Alex and made several trips to shops and markets on my own, dressed as a girl. By now, everyone accepted me, I would even stop and chat with the soldiers and was highly delighted when some of them tried to make dates with me. I knew some of them by their christian names and for soldiers, on the most part, they were very polite. I would regularly wave to those whom I knew and with whom I felt completely safe and at ease.

Everything was great between Alex and me and Hedwig had long since decided that it was better for all concerned if she and I no longer dallied together, which was a great relief to me. We remained very, very close and I was welcome in their home at any hour of the day. I had taken to the life in skirts so happily that I enjoyed every minute of it and usually, I shopped in the morning dressed as a boy and in the afternoons dressed as a girl. I would drop off the morning shopping at home then dash to Hedwig's and either with her or Alex, shop again, scrounge cigarettes and coffee from the soldiers and do a bit of dealing with whatever goodies I could acquire in this manner. I suppose that I became over confident and in so doing, had lost some of my highly tuned awareness consequently I was not as observant as I should have been.

In all my sorties, never once had I encountered any other member of my 'family', in fact, the possibility had never crossed my mind.

It came as a great shock and surprise, therefore, when, on leaving a shop where I had just purchased some new undies and had stopped to cadge some cigarettes from a couple of soldiers whom I knew quite well, I came face to face with Rachel.

I don't know who was the more surprised. Rachel looked at me as if she had seen a ghost and the expression on my face must have registered instant recognition. We stared at each other, silently, both waiting for the other to speak.

Rachel was the first to regain her composure and she said,

"Forgive me for staring, you must think me very rude, but you look so much like a young boy who has been staying with us that I feel sure you must be related."

I was still incapable of speech and Rachel, perhaps feeling that some further explanation of her conduct was required, continued, "The poor boy was injured in the bombing and has no recollection of who he is or where he comes from and it would be wonderful if he could be re-united with his relatives." My mind was racing; it was apparent that my transformation had been so complete that Rachel only saw a girl who bore a remarkable resemblance to Janni... I was torn between perpetuating the deceit or coming clean about the whole thing.

After careful deliberation, I decided upon the truth and said, "Let's walk a little". I took her arm and we fell into step side by side. I led her towards home and when we were just a few paces away, in my normal voice, I said, "Mum, it's me, Janni."

She stopped dead in her tracks, turned to face me and looked at me with something approaching pity in her beautiful eyes. Her shoulders sagged and with a voice full of sadness and deep concern, she whispered, "Oh Janni" and fell silent.

We remained, silent and motionless for some moments until Rachel took my hand and said, "Come along darling, let's go into the house and talk about this. I'll go in first and you go straight up to my bedroom where we won't be disturbed. I don't want any of the family to see you like this." Five minutes or so passed by then Rachel appeared with two cups of tea. She closed the bedroom door behind her and we sat, side by side on the edge of the bed.

I decided that I would speak first and it was with a great deal of trepidation that I embarked on my explanation.

To have admitted that the whole thing had been carefully planned, not only for the shopping advantage it gave me, but also because I felt the need to dress as a girl seemed too much of a confession to contend with at one go. So, I told Rachel that the idea was born out of the games of charades we played when I stayed over at Alex's. How we dressed-up and with Hedwig applying the make-up, we all acted out roles from plays and mimed things for the others to guess.

It was during one such game, I explained, that with Hedwig's expert assistance, I dressed-up as Marlene Dietrich, played the piano and sang, and the possibilities occurred to me. I went on to say that I persuaded Hedwig, against her better judgement and without Alex's knowledge, to lend me her dresses, shoes and things so that I could put the plan into operation. I wanted to reassure her and showed her my identity papers, saying, "You don't have to worry Mum, honestly. Nobody can tell the difference and I'm totally accepted wherever I go and now you know how I've been able to acquire so much food and everything else for us." It had all come out in something of a rush and I hoped she could make sense of it. Rachel remained quiet for some minutes until finally, she said, "Just walk round the room for me Janni, please."

I complied, walking as casually as possible and I couldn't help it, I smiled at her.

I heard a quick intake of breath and Rachel said,

"Janni, I always said that you were very beautiful, in fact too beautiful to be a boy and I was right. I still cannot believe that I should have been so completely deceived by your appearance. But then, you walk and talk just like a girl and there is no trace of masculinity in your movements, the transformation is only superficial, but quite astonishing."

She paused and was obviously considering whatever she was about to say next with great care. She continued, "Accepting, for the moment, that you have gone to these extraordinary lengths for the sole purpose of being an even more efficient provider, I'm both humbled and extremely grateful, but Janni darling, you are playing a very dangerous game. I saw you laughing and joking with those soldiers and while it appeared light-hearted enough, there was no doubt in my mind what they thought about you. I'll bet some of them tried to make a date with you."

The expression on my face must have confirmed her suspicions and she nodded, saying, "I thought as much; Dear God child, you are playing with fire. Just look at yourself, you look incredible and any self-respecting young man would be very proud to be seen out with you. As a girl, you look about eighteen and whatever you've got on under that dress your breasts look very impressive." I think my face must have turned deep red with embarrassment and I stammered, "It started with me stuffing a bra with cotton wool to protect them when they were so very sore, but when the seepage stopped for good, the swelling didn't go down as you promised. All these months later, I've still got small breasts and at times, they are very tender and uncomfortable. It seemed the sensible thing to do."

"I had better take another look at them", she said and then took me completely by surprise with her next question.

"Do you like dressing-up and going out as a young woman Janni? Do you feel more comfortable in that role?

And do you enjoy the banter with the young men?" she asked.

There was no point in denying it and I nodded, not trusting myself to speak. Her tone was one of great concern as she asked, very quietly and very deliberately, "Have you ever done anything or wanted to do anything with these young men that you shouldn't be doing?"

Because I loved Alex so much, I never wanted to do any of the things that we did together with anyone else so that I could answer Rachel's question quite honestly, "Oh no Mummy."

The look of relief on her face was a joy to behold and she smiled as she took hold of me and hugged me saying, "Thank God. We all love you so much Janni and I couldn't bear the thought of you sinking into some seedy, sordid world. I don't think I need to explain to you what I'm talking about do I darling? "No", I said, "I promise you nothing like that has happened or will happen."

She sighed with relief, gave me another huge hug and said,

"Alright then Janni, but I implore you to exercise extreme caution, don't allow yourself to be drawn into any difficult situation and never allow any of those soldiers to escort you, either alone, or in any numbers. The possibilities frighten me to death. Now, we'll say no more about it and I'll not mention it to the children, but you must realise that I have to tell Julius and he may want to talk to you about it. But remember Janni; you can always come to me first if things become difficult for you in coming to terms with your preferences. You can rely upon me to listen sympathetically and to give you such support and advice as I can; is that O.K?"

I hugged her back and held her very tightly, I was so grateful for her understanding and compassion, and I could think of no words to say that would not have sounded clumsy and inadequate in the circumstances so I glanced at the clock and with something approaching urgency, I said, "Oh mum, just look at the time. I'll have to dash like mad to get back to Alex's, change and get back before curfew. To make matters worse, Alex will know that I've been out dressed like this, on my own and he'll go absolutely berserk."

I headed for the door as I was saying this, and Rachel followed quickly, saying,

"You had better let me go first to make sure none of the others is about", and so saying, she preceded me down the stairs, opened the door for me and indicated that it was all-clear." I adjusted my beret, gave Rachel a quick peck on the cheek and set off at a brisk walk for Alex's flat. Alex was furious when I turned up late and alone. He shouted and bawled at me and shook me hard by the shoulders and once, when I made the mistake of saying that he sounded like a jealous lover, I thought that he was going to hit me. I had never seen him in such a terrible rage. It took some time to calm him down and from his words and actions I deduced that in part, I had been right. He feared for me going out on my own without his protection because he had seen how the soldiers looked at me and he thought that I was becoming over friendly with some of them. This was my first experience of overt jealousy and possessiveness and the near-violence it provoked frightened me considerably. I promised myself that in future I should do nothing to arouse such destructive passions again. This would not be easy, because I was an outward going person, I made friends easily and because I never felt the least bit threatened or intimidated, I didn't appreciate that others might not feel the same way. Quite apart from this, Alex had never complained, when, dressed as a boy, I had behaved in exactly the same manner. What he had previously regarded as good fun and clever scrounging was now observed as sexually provocative behaviour. If I'm totally honest, he probably had some justification because I did enjoy the attempts of the soldiers to become better acquainted with me, even though I had no intention of allowing it to happen. It was just so nice to be the object of desire and attention and it made me feel very cheerful and perhaps a bit conceited. I should have to watch this very carefully because Alex's love and complete trust meant more to me than anything else in the world and I didn't want to alienate his affections in any way, shape or form.

Although I shouldn't have done, because Rachel would be very concerned and probably, a little bit angry, I stayed the night and, needless to say, succeeded in allaying Alex's fears as I fell asleep in the comforting protection of his arms.

Some months prior to this, the telephone line to the house had been disconnected, and my family worried about me until I turned up the next day. For this reason, I left the flat early and returned home before doing my rounds to reassure them.

On the way home, I noticed a substantial increase in the number of military personnel, among them, some very high-ranking officers and over the next couple of days, the numbers would swell considerably. We had no idea that this enormous build-up of military might was being duplicated in East Prussia and Hungary as well as here in Poland and that it was the build up to the invasion of Russia. At the time, we just thought that it was another rotation of troops. At home, as expected, Julius gave me a very stern talking to but made no mention of the previous day's events, for which I was grateful and I assumed that either Rachel had not mentioned it or if she had Julius had decided to let her continue to monitor and deal with the situation. That evening, as I had done many times in the past months, I played some of Julius' records and followed later with spirited renditions at the piano. The family were quite used to some of my impersonations by now and without the benefit of my girl's clothing, I did my Marlene Dietrich impression which amused them greatly but during this, I noticed Julius and Rachel looking at each other rather significantly and I resolved to do no more female impersonations in their presence. Some days later, I awoke early. It was a very bright, beautiful, sunny day and from first light there had been great activity with soldiers marching, tanks and great fleets of lorries making their way eastwards out of the city.

The incessant noise, the barked orders, the sounds of marching feet and the occasional snatches of the 'Horst Wessel' lied from the S.S. contingents brought us all out onto the streets to witness the scenes. It was a very impressive sight and many of the onlookers waved at the soldiers who smiled and waved back. They were all in very good spirits.

The troop movements continued throughout the day and the soldiers who remained seemed to be relieved at their good fortune. How right they would prove to be, but then, that was in the future and they had no way of knowing the ultimate fate of thousands of their compatriots. At this moment, they were part of the most powerful fighting force the world had ever seen who had brushed aside their enemies like flies and they saw no reason to doubt their continued success, convinced of their invincibility.

Finally, the rumble of the tanks and lorries died away and the city and its inhabitants settled down once again to face an uncertain future.

CHAPTER SEVENTEEN

Once again, we witnessed yet another build-up of troop numbers in and around the city, which we assumed to be reinforcements in transit to the front. Amongst these, was a large S.S. presence. These were, if anything more awe-inspiringly violent and callous than the previous soldiers of that 'elite' organisation. Beatings, hangings and shootings increased dramatically and the atmosphere of fear became almost palpable. People hurried away from any scenes of violence, avoided eye contact with any of the soldiers, adopting a peculiar, eyes-down attitude whenever they approached or were approached by this new breed of soldier.

The purpose of these increased numbers soon became very clear. All Jews were being driven out of their property at very short notice; being allowed to take only the minimum amount of possessions with them. They were then herded into a quarter of the city which became known as the Warsaw Ghetto. We were lucky in as much as we escaped the initial purge because our property had not been repaired in any way and was a pretty tumbledown looking affair. At first, we mistakenly thought we would be allowed to remain there, but to be on the safe side, Julius and Rachel sorted out and made up bundles of necessities in case we were forced to move. It was apparent that many things would have to be left behind and in the next few days, we disposed of as many items of furniture as possible for what were truly 'bargain prices.' Julius and Aaron constructed a reasonable sized handcart which was kept in the yard, behind double doors where Julius' car had stood prior to its confiscation. From the experience of others it was known that we would be allowed very little time to move when we were forced to join them in the, already overcrowded, buildings which comprised the ghetto.

The stress, the waiting, the whole uncertainty surrounding our future had changed our attitude completely. It was apparent in the change in demeanour of all concerned. Where, only a few short weeks before, we had counted our blessings to have fared relatively well and had been reasonably optimistic of our chances, that optimism had now given way to great anxiety and I was very touched when Julius and Rachel implored me to make use of the identity Hedwig had provided for me and to go and join her and Alex if it became apparent that we were to be herded in with the rest. I said that we would cross that bridge when we came to it but the thought of having to make a choice, which meant leaving them, hung heavily on my mind. I pushed it to the back of my mind, hoping against hope that I would never be forced to make that awful decision .I was still able to shop with measured degrees of success but, with these new soldiers about, I no longer dressed or behaved in any way provocatively and avoided, wherever possible, any contact with them. Any group of soldiers being marched purposefully through the streets usually presaged another episode of violence, which invariably culminated in beatings and shootings and it was wise to make oneself scarce at the first sign of any such detachments. If dogs accompanied them, you knew that they were doing house searches and the dog-handlers would take sadistic pleasure from allowing their vicious charges to savage anyone within biting distance to the great amusement of their equally thuggish companions. I had warned Alex and Hedwig of our imminent movement to the ghetto and promised them that I would be in touch if the worst came to the worst but that they should not worry if they heard nothing of me for a few days. I would have to work out new routines and assess the possibilities of egress from and ingress to our new 'accommodation'. From what I had seen, this was going to be very difficult since all access routes were heavily gated and guarded with everybody being checked in and out. Forced-labour work parties were marched out and back under guard and random access was impossible. It had been obvious to me during this period of foreboding that Julius and Rachel had come to a certain conclusion about my relationship with Alex and, whilst they showed neither approval nor disapproval, they allowed me to spend more time with him than ever before. Perhaps I had misinterpreted the relaxation of the house rules as a sign that they knew what was happening between Alex and me when in fact, it might just have been that they were unselfishly thinking of my safety and had decided that things would go better for me if I happened to be with Alex when orders came for them to move. Whatever the reason, I took full advantage of it and spent most afternoons and nights with Alex, making the most of the opportunity while it was there. It was not long enough. As usual, I stayed at home on the Saturday and, just like Aaron, Isaac and their father, on the Sabbath, I wore the yarmulke they had given me as we went through the normal ritual with which I had, by now, become familiar.

Quite suddenly, there was a deafening and persistent banging on the door and, upon opening it, Julius was confronted by two S.S. soldiers, one of whom had a vicious looking black, German shepherd dog on a leash, which bared its teeth, growled and barked incessantly. These two were accompanied by two members of the Polish police and a Jewish collaborator who had the odious, self-important manner of all his ilk.

The Jew, one policeman and one soldier barged straight into the house; one of them stayed in the room with us while the other two searched the remainder of the house.

Finally, they returned and one of them said,

"This is all of them. There's no one else here."

The soldier told us that we had exactly ten minutes to pack our things and get outside.

Similar operations were going on all over Warsaw. This was the final round up. There was no chance of me claiming to be non-Jewish, as I had been caught, wearing my yarmulke and taking part in a Jewish religious ceremony. In addition to this, I had left both my identities at Alex's flat.

CHAPTER EIGHTEEN

We loaded as many of our treasured possessions onto the sturdy little cart as we possibly could and it was decided that Julius and Aaron would pull the cart while Rachel, Rebecca, Isaac and I would carry the remainder of our belongings in an assortment of suitcases and bags. Other folk, similarly laden down with cases, bags and boxes joined the procession to the Ghetto. All the time, the guards, German, Polish and Jewish were ordering us to hurry up, cuffing, kicking and hitting with rifle butts or whips and the number of savage-looking dogs prowling the flanks of this pitiful column made any hope of sneaking away quite impossible.

It was quite a long march and few, if any, of us survived the trip without some sort of vicious assault upon our persons. It was as though they made a point of sparing no one from their brutality and once we had arrived at our destination, the guarded gates were opened and we were once again subjected to beatings as they herded us into the inner street. Here, we were made to line up in families and were allocated to our 'accommodation.' In our case, this proved to be two very small rooms, which we had to share between the six of us. They were at the top of three flights of stairs and we had to take extra care in taking our things up, always leaving at least two people with the cart in case any of our possessions were looted; this had become the norm according to one resident who gave us a timely warning. It was a strange place in which we found ourselves. This area, which was known as 'The Ghetto', had always been a predominantly Jewish area and now that it had been walled in, the walls reaching up to three metres in height, all non-Jews had been driven out. Jews from other areas, towns and countries had been crammed into the area and at some stage, the population within this walled area must have been close to half a million or more. Some of the original occupants retained their old, luxurious apartments, but as things became more and more crowded, families were crammed into totally inadequate accommodation. We were no exception.

At last, we had conveyed everything upstairs and had time to survey our surroundings. Apart from our two rooms, we shared a toilet- cum- bathroom with some eight or nine other families, a total of about forty people in all. At this juncture, we knew nothing of the cooking facilities, or rather the lack of them.

First, we had to decide on sleeping arrangements and prepare the rooms accordingly. What little of value we had been able to bring had to be carefully concealed; during the next few days, ingenious 'hidey holes' were constructed and the most treasured items carefully wrapped and secreted away in relative security. Honour appeared to be departing in pace with the loss of dignity. Within days, able bodied people were assigned to work details and would be marched out of the gates to do heavy, menial duties, returning exhausted each evening and having had little or no food to sustain them in their heavy labours.

Although there were communal kitchens where soup was distributed, the amounts were very limited and the only other foodstuffs available were potatoes and onions and occasionally, a few eggs. Food generally was very scarce and we had to ration what little we had very rigidly. Everywhere within the ghetto, the gaunt hopeless faces of emaciated people were shocking evidence of the slow, systematic starvation of the inmates and the death toll rose daily. The extremely unsanitary conditions caused outbreaks of contagious disease, dysentery and chronic sickness in general. Only the fit, with strong constitutions survived unscathed.

In one way, I was in a pretty unique position in as much as I had no papers and, due to this, I had not been registered so it was very simple for me to escape the work details. Together with some of those considered too young to do any useful work, we explored every inch of the ghetto and before very long, two of our number had discovered a means of leaving and returning without detection via the city sewerage system. Soon, maps were drawn up of the network to all parts of the city and outside communications were quickly established.

Details of these routes and outside 'allies' were restricted to a very few trustworthy people. In the general, rapid process of degradation. Morals had sunk so low that betrayal of whole families by those who had once been good friends, for the sake of one or two slices of bread, was not uncommon even though the betrayers knew that the result of their actions would invariably result in the execution of the 'guilty' parties. It was imperative that only those who were known to be completely trustworthy were party to our secret routes and we younger people deferred to the older and wiser members of our community in all matters of security and priorities in exploiting our communications network. As a result of this, it was some weeks before I could get a message to Alex and Hedwig and nearly two months before I was able to use the 'escape route' to visit my beloved Alex. I shall neither excite you nor bore you with details of our reunion except to say that it remains with me, despite all that was to happen in the future, as the most emotional, wonderful, loving experience of my entire life and to this day. I can remember and relive every incredible moment of it in sharp, accurate detail. My illicit trips to and from Alex's could not have been more timely since the foodstuffs which we had brought with us to this ghastly place had long since run out.

We still had plenty of money and those of us who could sneak out and either buy, scrounge or barter for food had to be very careful to temper our good fortune with common sense and bring in only a little food at a time which was all consumed at night out of sight and sound of others. Against all our natural instincts to help those less fortunate than ourselves, we had to refrain from offering any food from outside the ghetto to any of the hundreds of starving people who were our companions in this hell hole. Suspicions would have been quickly aroused and jealousy, greed and the thought in the minds of some inmates that, to report any such suspicion might bring a reward from our persecutors, made any such act of compassion a dangerous weakness. Human decency is soon eroded when self-preservation is the order of the day; selfishness and callous oblivion to the suffering of others in the game of survival were now the norm and only the strongest of friendships survived. Envy often leads to vindictiveness and acts of betrayal. Tempers were strained and outbreaks of violence between the inmates were becoming more frequent. In this frightening, electric, doom-laden atmosphere, eye-contact was now avoided with our own kind and the forces of evil were present everywhere, never more evident than in those Jews who had volunteered their services as 'Ghetto Policemen' and whose gratuitous violence to their own kind and crawling, obsequious subservience to their German masters was a sickening example of the depths to which the cowardly will sink to preserve their unworthy lives. To facilitate my comings and goings, I now kept my identity papers in a secret cache in the sewers, collecting them on my outward journeys and hiding them again on my return. I never stayed out for more than one night at a time because I could only go out and return at night. During the day, I would obtain sufficient food to see us through that evening and if I stayed at Alex's for a whole night, it meant that I couldn't get back until the following night.

After one such rare occurrence, I returned 'home' after two days and was greeted with relief on my arrival. This relief was tempered with a detectable undercurrent of fear and foreboding brought about by a frightening turn of events the previous day, when, without warning, at about seven in the morning, vast numbers had been dragged out of their rooms, clutching a few pitiful possessions and were marched to the accompaniment of the usual harsh beatings, whippings, blows from rifle butts and barking of dogs to waiting trucks into which they were crammed so tightly that it was only possible to stand, barely able to move.

The gates had been opened and the lorries driven away. They had not returned and enquiries elicited the reply that they had been sent to 'Work and Resettlement' camps and that, eventually, we would all be going to join them.

Julius and Rachel implored me to leave this place, to stay with Alex and Hedwig and look after myself. I flatly refused to do this saying that I would always be able to get away through the sewers if the worst came to the worst and that I would rather make sure that they were all right. They argued with me, but I was adamant. I loved them all very much and I couldn't bear the thought of being parted from them. I should have heeded their advice.

CHAPTER NINETEEN

It seemed that everyone was suspicious of everyone else, almost to the point of paranoia and because I was a rather strange, somewhat shadowy, non-Jewish person, I had been regarded, right from our incarceration in this awful place, as something of an oddity. It was not that I was perceived as a threat in any way; in fact, I was the subject of intense specu-lation. But the paranoia was working its will and questions were now being asked about my presence. Why would a non-Jew voluntarily stay in a place like this? Did I have an ulterior motive for being there? Had I been deliberately placed there by the Germans to report on any underground movements? Despite reassurances from Julius and Rachel, the inmates gradually distanced themselves from me and when I went to use the sewers to go to Alex's, my route was barred by four older, strapping youths who informed me that I was no longer allowed to use this facility.

I had known for some time that a form of resistance was being planned and that, from various sources, arms and ammunition were being smuggled into the ghetto via the sew-ers. Information was being sent out to, and received from, various pockets of Jews in hid-ing on the outside and also from other sympathisers. It was felt that although I had done nothing to incur this distrust, it would be prudent of them to keep me under constant obser-vation and to prevent me from contacting anyone on the outside. For the next three or four weeks, I had no option but to remain hidden within the confines of the ghetto, as a direct result of which, our food supplies quickly ran out and we began to feel the real pangs of hunger.

We began losing weight and because I was not on the work parties and was not official-ly registered, there was no 'official food' for me. This made our rations even smaller and I opted to take just enough to sustain me because it was important that Julius, Aaron and Isaac, who were all doing heavy, manual work, should have the lion's share of the food to replace their energy and not deteriorate to the stage where they had no resistance to illness. Rachel and Rebecca were employed recycling rags from clothing or any source, which was baled and then sent off to Germany. Over the last three years, Rebecca and I had become very close, almost, so her mother said, like sisters and the family had no reservations about the pair of us cuddling up very close and comforting each other since our behaviour was purely fraternal.

One morning, as usual, very early, the familiar shouts of 'Raus', 'Schnell' greeted us as yet another large batch was sent for 'resettlement'. The clearance stopped in the adjoining building and we knew that the next such transportation would include all of us.

We were very downcast that night, none of us knowing what to say, or even wanting to voice our thoughts. Our subdued manner and the atmosphere of foreboding became intensely claustrophobic and Rebecca took my hand, held it very tightly and said, "Come Janni, let's get some fresh air".

I nodded and we walked out, hand in hand, to the upper landing where we quietly opened a window and stood there taking in deep breaths of air, neither saying a word until our breathing returned to a more natural rhythm. After what seemed an eternity, Rebecca turned to me and asked, "What do you think will happen to us Janni?"

I honestly didn't know. Any answer would only have been pure speculation so I avoided a direct answer by saying, "I really don't know Becca, but we'll all be together to look after each other and I'm sure we'll be alright."

It was not very convincing but Rebecca accepted it and gave my hand an extra squeeze of acknowledgement.

She was so lovely, so pure and so vulnerable that my heart went out to her and I strove by words and actions to give her what comfort I could.

Naturally, therefore, it came as something of a surprise when she said,

"Janni, I'm twenty-one, coming up for twenty-two, I've never had a boyfriend, except when I was very young at school. I know nothing of love or sex, I've never had anyone apart from the family tell me they love me and we are about to be shunted off to God knows where and to a very uncertain fate. I need to know about love and sex and all the joys which I may never get the chance to experience where we are going."

There followed a long pause as if she was giving me time to let this sink in before she continued, "I know that we have been like brother and sister, but we are not really related and we really love each other don't we?"

I nodded my head and muttered wholehearted agreement and she went on,

"I've thought about it quite a lot recently and I decided that you should be the one to tell me and teach me all about it."

I was completely unprepared for this and was momentarily speechless. She was full of surprises and cut into my astonished thoughts, displaying remarkable intuition and powers of observation by saying, "It's obvious that you and Alex are lovers and that you have been for a couple of years and you always look so happy when you have been with him that at times, I envied you and almost felt jealous."

Whilst I was digesting this, she carried on,

"You know we all think you are very beautiful and I've never forgotten that first day in the kitchen when I discovered that you were a boy. I've fantasised about you ever since and I can't think of anyone that I'd rather have as my teacher. Please say you will."

I remained quiet for what must have seemed a very long time and I was suddenly aware that my long, pensive silence was causing Rebecca to have doubts about her very open attitude and perhaps, some regrets about her allusions to Alex and me.

I took a deep breath and said,

"Becca, you know I love you very much and I'm extremely flattered to think that you have been fantasising about me and that you want me to be your teacher. "You intrigue me immensely and any chap would be an idiot to turn down such a wonderful invitation. But first, there are lots of things to consider."

She was hanging on to every word, looking at me with her wide, fabulous eyes, which I found very disconcerting, making it very difficult for me to collect my thoughts and assemble them into some logical sequence. After yet another lengthy pause, I continued, "First Becca, two questions. What makes you think that Alex and I are lovers and secondly, if you believe this, what makes you think that I would be any good as a teacher in a normal, boy-girl relationship?"

She leaned back against the wall and with a rather wistful, almost faraway expression on her face, she said, "There are so many tell-tale signs between you and Alex, the way your expressions soften when you look at each other, your touches are more like gentle caresses, his face is a picture of love and pride when he watches you, whether you're playing the piano, talking or just simply being you, in fact, he hardly ever takes his eyes off you; he's totally besotted."

She paused and it was obvious that she was considering how to describe my behaviour towards Alex without causing any ill feeling.

"You are always very cheerful and you have brought an untold amount of joy and happiness to our family but, notwithstanding the fact that we all love you so much and that you return our love in so many ways, when Alex is around, we can all tell that the love you feel for him goes far deeper, it is palpably passionate."

I doubt if Alex had realised that we were so obvious and I know that I hadn't so it came as something of a surprise to learn that we had not been as clever as we thought we had been in concealing our relationship.

Whist I was digesting this uncomfortable revelation and wondering whether I ought to ask Rebecca about the family's reaction, she broke into my troubled thoughts, as though she could read all of them.

"The boys are not very worldly and don't really appreciate the situation, but Mummy, Daddy and I have been aware of it for some time and if it's any consolation to you, none of us is condemnatory; we understand that in so many ways, you are more girl than boy and that you cannot be blamed for having the feelings that you do. We also think that Alex is lovely and very honourable and protective towards you and in our way, although it is natural for us to harbour reservations, we are very happy for both of you. Before you ask, Mummy told Daddy and me about your two identities and the risks you have been taking to obtain extra rations for us. I think you are terribly brave and at the same time, I smile to myself when I picture you swinging along on your high heels being whistled at and chatted to by the German soldiers; I'll bet you enjoyed that didn't you?"

I nodded and she grinned widely and did a grossly exaggerated parody of me, walking along, swinging my hips and handbag, which sent us both into a prolonged fit of the giggles. We were almost helpless with laughter and since we had always been very tactile, we put our arms round each other until our mirth gradually subsided and enjoyed the warmth and close proximity of our bodies. I stroked her hair and brushed my lips over her forehead and said, "Becca, you're lovely and I do love you very much".

Her chin came up and she looked directly into my eyes and without thinking, I held her chin gently in my hand and kissed her lightly on the lips in the way that Alex had taught me. She trembled and took a long shivering breath, at the same time placing her arms firmly round my neck, eagerly searching for my lips with hers and I had to take her face in both hands, move our mouths apart and say to her, "Slowly, gently".

With my hands still cupping her lovely, delicate face, I caressed the backs of her ears and neck with the tips of my fingers and then brushed my tongue over her lips and murmured to her that she should open her mouth a little.

The kissing became more intense and she responded very quickly to her newfound pleasure. After a long spell when our mouths had been in constant contact, I moved my hands down to her small waist and then, slid my hands gently up and down her sides, thumbs, at the extent of the downward movement, stroking her groins and at the other extent, brushing the sides of her breasts. She squirmed against me, pushing her pelvic bone hard against mine and as she did so I became bolder with my hands, brushing her erect nipples with the ball of each thumb and then slowly downwards, further each time, the inside edges running down to meet between her thighs. Upwards again, this time with the balls of my thumbs rubbing, more urgently against her pubic mound and all the time kissing to stifle her sounds of delight and appreciation. As we continued, she stood with her legs further apart and with my right hand, I massaged the sensitive spot in the way that Hedwig had shown me whilst with my left hand I held her exquisite little bottom and explored the crevice with my fingers. Eventually, I took her hand and placed it on my erect willy and was rewarded with a little gasp, whether in alarm or admiration, I could not judge, but she did not let go! Finally, I raised both the back and front of her dress and slid my hands inside her knickers, continuing my previous ministrations both back and front. Unhampered by intervening material, the moistness facilitated my explorations and with the careful attention I gave to the most sensitive spots, it was not long before she was shuddering and gasping in what must have been a very prolonged orgasm.

She still held onto me very tightly as though afraid to let go, all the time her little gasps and involuntary shudders subsiding until gradually she was still.

We stood holding each other for what seemed an eternity without saying a word and I was conscious of the fact that I was still extremely hard and aching. With my left hand, I unbuttoned my trousers and got my stiff willy out of hiding. With my right hand, I took hold of Rebecca's hand and placed it firmly over the poor aching creature and once she had established a comfortable grip, I moved her hand backwards and forwards until it was apparent that she had mastered the required mechanics and was enjoying the sensation as much as I was so I replaced my hand in her warm, moist nest for the few moments that it took before I suddenly had to turn sideways to avoid ejaculating all over her dress. While I was going through my little period of shuddering, she made sounds conveying fascinated amazement.

Eventually, I dried myself with a handkerchief and wiped the telltale evidence from the floor. This task completed, we stood, side-by-side, arms around each other's waists, breathing deeply through the open window.

Every now and again, still without speaking, we would have a proper cuddle and she would hold her face against mine. It would have been all too easy to start all over again so I finally broke the silence and asked, "Was that nice and was it all you expected for a first lesson?" "It was fantastic ", she replied, "And it was a lot more than I expected for a first lesson as you well know," she added with mock severity which brought about another fit of the giggles and lightened the difficult aftermath of our actions, thus removing any feelings of guilt or embarrassment we both might have felt considering how wantonly we had both behaved.

It was fortuitous that we were standing apart, both laughing, because at that moment, Rachael came up the stairs to tell us that hot drinks were ready and it was a delight to see her smile so indulgently as she found us laughing fit to burst.

As I lay in bed that night going over the events of the day in my mind, I felt quite elated at first but it wasn't long before this euphoria wore off to be replaced by pangs of guilt and the profound certainty that I had betrayed my love for Alex, whom I thought about nearly every waking hour and whom I missed dreadfully. My emotions were in turmoil; whilst I had allowed things to get out of hand with Rebecca, and, it must be said, thoroughly enjoyed our encounter, I now felt somewhat ashamed and deeply, disturbingly, mixed up.

I accept that as Rebecca had said, I was in so many ways, more girl than boy. Although my breasts didn't 'leak' any more, the original swelling had not gone down; on the contrary they had increased in size and the aureoles surrounding my nipples had grown larger and darker and were like two small hemispheres, still about the size of half golf balls. The surrounding area had increased in size too and I now was the possessor of fairly shapely breasts. Apart from my very normal masculine appendages, my body was that of a teenage girl and I wore loose, oversize clothes to conceal this fact. Don't misunderstand me, I liked my body very much and was not embarrassed by it but, in honesty, I would have attracted less attention dressed as a girl than I did dressed as a boy, despite my baggy clothes and deliberate change of gait and posture.

Because of my very femininity, I found it very odd that Rebecca should feel so strongly attracted to me in such a physical way, then I thought of Hedwig and how she had said it was like going to bed with another girl and how excited that made her feel. After all, in terms of two people of the same sex being drawn together, Alex and I had been instantly attracted, even before my female characteristics had become so pronounced. Perhaps it was because of these, rather than their absence that Rebecca felt the way she did about me. Maybe my strange physical attributes made her feel secure, but try as I did to make sense of it all, the more confused I became.

I slept very fitfully, awoke very jaded and, for the first time, aware of the fact that I was very, very hungry. Food was barely enough to sustain us and it showed in the thinning bodies of Julius and the boys. Watching them returning from their arduous tasks, weak and exhausted, their stamina and resilience gradually being drained from them, I resolved that, one way or another, I would resume the role of provider, no matter the cost to myself.

63

CHAPTER TWENTY

As always happens in times of war, persecution, riots or any other form of disaster and disruption, the prevailing conditions bring out either the worst or the best in people. I had seen very little of the latter and plenty of the former with people, both German and Polish, taking advantage of the plight of the Jewish community. The homes that they had been forced to vacate were systematically looted of everything of value from valuable artworks to the lowliest teaspoon, from the precious and hallowed religious items to the relatively worthless pair of shoes, well-worn coat, umbrella or kitchen utensil. The voracious pillagers turned nothing down. It came as no surprise, therefore, that the overwhelming desire of these single-minded thieves clouded their judgement and lead to an involuntary relaxation of their normally strict, extremely efficient security in order that they might engage in, and encourage others to, exploit the plight of the ghetto's inmates. To this end, on certain days of the week, they allowed the inmates to man stalls, just like a market, where they could barter their worldly possessions for miniscule amounts of food, thread, toilet paper et cetera in exchange for items worth many hundreds or even thousands of times the value of the food on offer.

The Germans and Poles swarmed in, often their avaricious natures leading to violent squabbles between themselves over the acquisition of some item or other.

Security had become lax and it was apparent that by virtue of the very numbers involved, it was almost impossible to check everyone in and out of the ghetto on these 'market days'. After several days of observing the routine, I realised that this provided my best chance of leaving and returning at will and I made preparations accordingly.

It was difficult; I had no wish to cause alarm to my 'family' but at the same time I had reservations about revealing my intentions to them. Firstly, because they would undoubtedly have done their utmost to dissuade me and secondly because of the implicit danger to myself and the possible repercussions for them if I was unlucky enough to be caught. In the event, I just mentioned to Rebecca, as casually as I could that I was "working on something" and might be missing for a day or two! On the day of the next market, I got up early and set about putting my plan into operation. The normal work detachment was assembled amidst the usual shouted orders, mandatory beatings and barking of dogs and marched off to their various tasks. After a short pause, the remaining inmates went about the business of setting-up their stalls.

In the meantime, I had washed all over, washed and fluffed-up my hair, applied my make-up and dressed in my girl's clothes. I put some household objects into a bag so that it would appear that I had made 'purchases' at the market and waited with baited breath for a relatively large number of successful shoppers to leave the ghetto simultaneously.

The chance came when twenty or thirty women headed for the gates talking excitedly amongst themselves, proudly comparing their 'bargains'. As they passed me, I joined them, displaying the items in my bag and laughingly congratulating others on their exquisite taste. We came to the gate en masse and with barely a glance, the guards passed us through with good-humoured, knowing winks and assertions that they would no doubt see us all next time. We all answered enthusiastically in the affirmative and then we were out and heading for our separate destinations.

It was certainly wonderful to be out of the brooding, claustrophobic, frightening atmosphere of the ghetto and my soaring spirits gave me a wonderful lift, which involuntarily expressed itself in a very carefree demeanour, and a gait that attracted admiring looks from groups of soldiers. Some whistled at me and made expressive gestures of appreciation at which I could not resist smiling and some expressed their appreciation in German with coarse compliments such as "Nice arse" or "Christ, I could shag the arse off that!" Which

I chose to ignore by pretending not to understand although inwardly, I was both amused and very flattered.

For the next two hours I shopped and, to the shopkeepers who said they were happy to see me and enquired where had I been, I replied that I had been unwell but was now fully recovered and hoped to see more of them. It was just like meeting old friends and it gave my confidence a wonderful boost. If Alex was still working the same shift, he would be home by now and I approached his flat with a strange mixture of fear and excitement. I was trembling almost uncontrollably when I rang the bell. For a long time nothing happened even though I rang persistently and, just when I thought that he must be out, I heard the distant sound of a door opening and closing and footsteps on the stairs. It was obvious that he had been sleeping; his hair was tousled and he had the expression of someone who was still moving in a dreamlike haze. To me, he had never looked more beautiful and alluring and my heart was beating so fast it made my breathing very erratic. He opened the door wider, looked up and if I had harboured any doubts about his feelings for me, they were dispelled in that instant. Neither before nor since have I witnessed such an expression of pure joy, relief, love, elation, call it what you will, on any other human being's face and then we were hugging each other, mumbling incoherently between sobs of joy, tear streaked faces pressing together and silently, arms around each other's waists we climbed the stairs, holding tightly, too tightly as if we were afraid to let go.

We both went into the kitchen and made drinks which we took into the lounge where we sat, holding hands while I told Alex everything that had happened and why I had been unable to see him for what seemed like an eternity. Naturally, I omitted to mention my 'landing encounter' with Rebecca! He did not interrupt but squeezed my hands tighter from time to time throughout and when I had finished, he sat, staring into my eyes, looking at me with such deep love and compassion murmuring, "Oh Janni, my poor beautiful Janni, it must be terrible in there. How can you bear it?" Further discussion was halted by the arrival of Hedwig whose face broke into a huge, delighted grin when she recognised me and she rushed over to engulf me in her arms. It felt wonderful and at Alex's insistence, I had to recount everything that had happened since we had seen each other last. They were still both overawed and alarmed by the audacious way in which I had left the ghetto, a strange combination of fear for my well-being and profound admiration for my daring. It would have been churlish of me to say that I was not being brave but merely that I was terribly hungry and desperate to see Alex again, so I said nothing, just held them both very tightly. We ate an evening meal and almost simultaneously, they both said, "You'll have to stay here with us now. You can't go back to that awful place". This was going to be the difficult part and from the very beginning I had to be very single-minded, adamant, brooking no opposition to my intentions even though I knew that what they were saying, what they were imploring me to do, made complete and utter common sense and would have met with the full approval and encouragement from my 'family'.

I told them of my intention to secure adequate food for them for as long as it was a practical possibility and that I should only cease these operations when it became far too dangerous to continue. Above all else, I had somehow to retrieve my identity papers from their secure place in the sewers and this would involve regaining the trust of the appointed guardians of that route. I had already formulated a plan in my mind, which would be put into operation this very night and would require me to leave the flat for about an hour.

They listened intently, hanging onto every word, protesting vehemently from time to time and, apparently appalled by my determination to carry on despite the acknowledged dangers. Finally, they accepted that my mind was made up and that no amount of cajoling would make me change it.

Having accepted this, they decided that the best course was to work together to ensure that everything went without complications and aroused neither interest nor suspicions.

The overall plan was quite simple. I knew the routine and the exit points of the team who used the sewer route, precisely where and when they would emerge to meet their contacts. It was my intention to confront them there as a sympathiser, bent only on helping their cause. Initially, such help as I could offer would only be the provision of food, other essentials and any information which could prove helpful.

I had a distinct advantage over the young men emerging from the sewers in as much as I could identify all of them, indeed, I knew most of their names, whereas it was extremely doubtful if any of them would have recognised me in my female identity, even in broad daylight. Alex and Hedwig had been insistent that they should accompany me to make sure that all went well and we arrived at the appropriate 'exit hole' a short time before I expected any activity. We were very tense and quiet, from time to time squeezing hands reassuringly, constantly scanning the neighbourhood for unwelcome intruders who might scupper the operation. It all sounds very melodramatic, but in reality, we were just amateurs, expecting the worst and crediting our efforts with more importance than they deserved, when, in fact, it was very debatable whether or not anybody other than the respective participants in the ensuing exchanges was aware that anything out of the ordinary was taking place.

Some twenty to twenty-five minutes had elapsed before a furtive figure emerged from the drain we had been intent on observing. He moved only a short distance to the narrow passage, which I knew so well; to be joined minutes later by a shadowy figure carrying two holdalls, which he handed over. They did not waste time, exchanging only a few words before the second person disappeared into the maze of alleyways and the first person, whom I had identified as Moishe, headed back to the sewers, the weight of the holdalls dragging his shoulders down to such an extent that it was unnecessary for him to take any other precautions to conceal his stature.

I stood up and as casually as possible, walked over towards the doubled-up figure and in whispered tones called out, "Moishe. Is that you?

He froze, staring round guiltily and furtively, unsure from which direction the voice had originated. In retrospect, it was quite amusing, like watching a cornered rat, but at the time, it was, for me, the decisive moment on which the fate of my future plans depended. "Who is that?" he challenged, standing like a rabbit caught in the headlights of a car. "It's OK, I replied. You don't know me but I know all of your friends and I want to help. There's not much I can do at the moment, but I've brought you some food to take back with you. It's not much, but I can get more and it won't cost you any more than it costs me, not like the prices you all pay to the bastards who are milking you dry in the market".

He stood for a moment, deep in thought, weighing-up the situation. Finally, he asked, "What have you got and why should you help us?"

"I'm on your side", I said in Yiddish, "Even though I'm a gentile. It hurts me deeply to see what has been done to you and all my dear friends. Please accept that I only want to be of assistance to you in any way that I can and that I am prepared to risk everything to help, whether it is carrying messages, obtaining food or anything else, I should be honoured to place my services at your disposal". He stood, uncertainly, mulling over what I had said, the weight of decision heavy upon his young shoulders, I felt great compassion for him in his unexpected predicament, but remained silent, awaiting his decision rather than arouse his suspicions by appearing too persuasive. To break the impasse, I handed over a bag full of food which, even in the dim light, he could identify and which represented more food than his family had seen in a long time. Finally, his shoulders lifted and I knew he had made a decision.

"O.K., he said, I'll talk to my friends and see if we can work something out". He had regained his composure and now wished to appear very assertive, in control, and with his desire to give the impression of importance he adopted a haughtier, 'member of the hierarchy' stance. Despite the seriousness of the moment, I wanted to laugh, but managed to keep a straight face and waited for his next instructions.

"We'll look out for you over the next few nights and advise you of our decision", he said, rather pompously.

"That's fine by me", I replied, and thinking ahead, I added,

"It will probably be Thursday before I can see you again; I'll bring you some more food and some cigarettes to be going on with and even if we are not here my friend will leave you some bread on the ledge behind that tumbled-down archway", I said, indicating the entrance to a severely bomb-damaged church.

He had the decency to thank me before he left, over laden with his two holdalls and the additional bag of food which I had provided.

Just before he was out of earshot, he suddenly turned and asked, "By the way, what's your name?"

He caught me off guard and just as I was about to say 'Janni', Hedwig clapped her hand over my mouth and whispered 'Lotti'

"Sorry, I can't hear you", Moishe said.

"Lotti, you know, short for Liselotte", I called.

"O.K., Lotti, thanks very much. See you soon", he replied and then vanished from sight.

"Wow, that was lucky; it was a good job you gagged me so promptly otherwise, I might have given the game away before we really got started", I said, holding Hedwig's hand. She said nothing, but just squeezed my fingers in acknowledgement.

After he had disappeared into the gloom, Alex emerged, apparently relieved that nothing had happened to cause any concern and we returned to the flat, happy with the night's work, content with the soft approach we had agreed to adopt, not rushing any fences.

Back in the flat, we talked for only a short time before having a bedtime drink and going to bed. Bed. For a long time, Alex and I had felt no need to pretend in front of Hedwig and Alex's impatience to get there was strained to breaking point when I insisted on taking a shower on the grounds that it was virtually impossible to have a decent wash in the ghetto. I told him that I could not possibly share his bed unless I felt absolutely perfect for him and he endeared himself to me forever by replying that it wouldn't matter to him how dirty I was, even if I was covered in cowshit, he would love me forever. It was a memorable night and the alarm clock had to exert its best stentorian efforts to rouse us from our deep, contented sleep.

"What an uncivilised hour to go to work", I complained to a bleary eyed Alex who was hopping about on one foot, trying to pull his trousers on. He deliberately made a pantomime of it and contrived to fall onto the bed where he grabbed hold of me, tousled my hair and said, "I've got to dash. Will you be here when I get back?"

"I'm not sure", I replied and seeing the immediate look of disappointment on his face, hastily I added, "It is a bit difficult, particularly without my papers. Until I retrieve them I face exposure every time I pass through the gates. Don't worry though, I shan't take any unnecessary risks but I'll be back very soon". Before he could say anything else, I continued, "By the way, I'll leave you some money and if you could buy some food to either give to Moishe or leave it on the ledge, I would be very grateful. I'll leave you enough for several nights and a note for the boys saying that they must leave you some money to enable you to continue with their supplies". He accepted the situation, finished dressing, gave me a brief cuddle and a peck on the forehead and headed to the kitchen. I heard him pottering about in there and some ten minutes or so later, the sound of the front door closing quietly behind him.

I moved over to his side of the bed and almost immediately went back to sleep.

It was just like old times, with Hedwig waking me, cup of tea in hand, ruffling my hair with the other. We chatted, as we had done on so many occasions before and then she said that she must go to work and that I should let myself out. She also asked if I still had my key to which I replied in the affirmative and, after instructing me to let myself in at any time, she gave me a brief kiss on the cheek and left. I got up, washed and dressed, applied my make-up and picked up my shopping bag from which I removed the small items of silverware, which I had brought from 'home' and put them under the bed. Next, I made the bed, took my cup to the kitchen, washed and dried it, put on my jacket and went on a scaled down shopping trip for items, ostensibly to barter in the ghetto market. An hour or so later, I strolled towards the ghetto, once again hanging back to wait for a larger crowd. It looked like being a long wait and to have been seen loitering would have drawn attention, so I went to a nearby cafe for a hot drink and observed the gates from there. Eventually, my patience was rewarded and I quickly finished my tea and joined the throng passing into the ghetto. Once again, we were not challenged and, still not wishing to attract too much attention, I made a point of looking at the goods on offer before, hidden from the sight of the gates by the intervening stalls, I slipped into the buildings and eventually, by a circuitous route, got back to our lowly rooms.

In my relief in getting back unscathed I had totally forgotten that both Rachel and Rebecca would be there and although Rachel had seen me on one memorable occasion, dressed in all my female glory, poor Rebecca, who had not seen me in my 'other existence', stood, mouth agape, totally transfixed by the sight that confronted her.

By contrast, Rachel's expression was one of both relief that I had come to no harm and deep concern about where I had been and what I had been doing.

To break the awkward silence, I put my bag down, walked over to them, put an arm around each and kissed them on the cheeks, and before they could ask, I retrieved my bag and displayed all the food purchased that morning together with a fresh loaf from Alex.

Rebecca regained some of her composure, not all by any means. Although her brothers and I had often been impressed and amused by her repertoire of swear words, she had never, at least to my knowledge, sworn in front of her parents.

On this occasion, without pausing to think, she almost screamed at me, "Shit! Shit! Shit! You stupid, bloody bastard. What the bloody hell have you been doing?" She stood, trembling with rage, eyes blazing and her mother and I could only look on in astonishment at this uncharacteristic outburst.

Personally, I was at a loss how to reply and leaving aside the dangerous way in which I had left and returned to the ghetto which, at this point, I had no intention of disclosing, it seemed better, if a little cowardly, to let Rachel do the explaining.

I turned to her imploringly and said,

"Mum, will you please explain everything to Becca, how it was that we were able to eat reasonably well before we came to this God-forsaken place and how, up until the time they barred me from the tunnels we still managed to eat well and Dad always had a few cigarettes."

Before she could answer, I played on sympathy by saying,

"Look, I've been up all night and I really am too tired for all this". At least part of it was true! She nodded, told Becca to calm down and said that I should go and rest. It was only later that it occurred to me that neither had thanked me for the food!

I took as long as possible to wash and change to allow time for Becca to calm down and digest her mother's explanation.

Finally, when it seemed pointless to delay the inevitable, I took a deep breath and, as casually as possible, joined the others in that portion of our rooms which was set aside by day for eating, sitting and talking.

As I entered, Becca looked me up and down and said, "That's better!" and noticing my sheepish expression, she stood up and said, "Oh, come here you little devil".

I complied and she wrapped her arms around me and apologised for her earlier behaviour. My sigh of relief was quite audible and they both laughed. The tension had melted and the first thing that Rachel did was to thank me for getting the food and cigarettes. They wanted to know how I had managed to get out of the ghetto and back again unscathed to which I replied, "The less you know the better", but, and they were not to get upset, I would be doing it again as often as possible in the foreseeable future.

When Julius, Aaron and Isaac returned home, it was all the reward I needed just to watch their faces, particularly as, after the best meal he had enjoyed in months, Julius sat back and revelled in the luxury of a decent quality cigarette. It was, in all probability, the point at which Rebecca forgave me for all the concern that I had caused. She sat beside me, as on so many previous occasions, holding my hand, joining in the general conversation and deftly fielding any awkward questions from Aaron and Isaac. Despite all the adversity, they were a truly wonderful, loving family; they made time to discuss each and everyone's individual problems, relegating their own concerns to the background whilst they gave their full attention to the difficulties that we were all experiencing. Very touchingly, Julius included me and my contributions by thanking the Creator for delivering me to them in their time of need, a sentiment which left me feeling extremely embarrassed when I considered what his beloved daughter and I had been doing on the landing just a couple of nights earlier!

Eventually, the talking stopped and we were all left very much to our own contemplations. Rebecca, as usual, and without raising any curiosity, broke the spell by saying, "Come Janni, lets have our evening walk".

It was a merciful relief.

Much as I valued their appreciation of my efforts, I could, in no way relate my actions to the intervention of their god, and putting me at the centre of their deliverance was causing me a great deal of embarrassment. On many such an occasion, I wished that I could summon up a mighty fart and let rip to break the solemnity of the moment.

This particular evening, my bowels failed to oblige and I had no other alternative than to follow Rebecca out of the stifling room to our favourite spot on the upper landing. We took up our usual posture, arms round each other's waists, leaning out over the windowsill. After some minutes of silence, just enjoying the close proximity, Becca turned to me and said, "I'm sorry about my reactions earlier. Everything welled up in me. It was a combination of anxiety for the danger to which you had exposed yourself on our behalf and the certain knowledge that you had spent the night in Alex's bed".

She took a deep breath and continued,

"O.K, don't look at me like that; I admit that I'm jealous. I know it sounds ungrateful because between you both, you are our benefactors and at heart, I know he's a truly lovely person who means almost everything to you, but, at this precise moment, I really hate him". It was my turn to emulate Rebecca and in my mind, I could only respond by using her expletives, "Shit! Shit! Shit!" to describe the overall ambience into which I had unwittingly allowed myself to be drawn. I remained quiet for so long that Rebecca obviously decided that some light relief should be injected to ease the tension caused by the revelation of her feelings.

"I suppose you'll let off a loud fart now to refute the challenge to your masculinity and skip over the intensity of the moment by performing some bizarre antics whilst you pollute the atmosphere. I know from observing my brothers that it is one bodily function in which you all seem to take inordinate pride and at which you all excel. God! You're all disgusting!"

I was both amazed and astonished by her appreciation, although that is perhaps an inappropriate choice of word, of the masculine preoccupation with flatulence. It is never, at least in male company, sufficient to break wind genteelly; it has to be performed with panache, elegance or gymnastic dexterity to achieve maximum impact and admiration.

With these thoughts going through my mind, it was impossible to keep a straight face and I pulled Becca round to face me and laughingly said, "I promise not to fart if you kiss me". For the moment, it seemed that her new, favourite word and her readiness to use it, would suffice in any situation.

"Oh shit", she said as she slid her arms around my neck and pressed her body against me, whispering between kisses, "Janni, I love you so much and I can't help it if I make a fool of myself". We kissed and cuddled and talked for a long time before returning to our rooms, which we had to convert from living quarters to sleeping quarters each and every night. Aaron and Isaac were already moving things around as we entered and very touchingly, they stopped what they were doing, came over to me, kissed me on both cheeks and almost in unison, they said. "Thanks for the food Janni, it was really marvellous and Dad allowed me one of the cigarettes", Aaron added.

"I didn't know you smoked or I'd have tried to get some more", I replied. "It was my first one, and in all honesty, it will probably be the last; they are awful and leave a foul taste in your mouth, added to which, when I tried to inhale, like Dad, I became very dizzy and nearly fell over. How the hell can anyone smoke a complete one, never mind twenty or so in a day?" Aaron asked. "Beats me", I answered.

It was very reassuring to see the boys more animated than they had been over the last few weeks, during which time they had been coming home exhausted, their eyes dead like those hopeless, helpless, unfortunate men, women and children who sat on the pavements or in the doorways, day and night, starving and without the energy to go indoors. Even had they been capable of doing so, they would not have had the strength to mount the stairs and they smelt so badly with their unwashed bodies in filthy clothes that people did not want them in the same room as themselves. More and more of them were dying and these poor, once proud folk were left to die, without dignity in their squalid bundles of rags, the skin drawn tightly over their malnourished bones so that they looked more like primitive, ape-like creatures than human beings.

Worse, was the indifference and callousness that others displayed where once they would have shown deep concern and offered assistance. Now, they could barely manage to feed themselves and to help others in their distress, whether such aid was offered by Jew or gentile was to invite a brutal thrashing at best, or to be shot out of hand at worst and left on the street with the other bodies. It appeared to be German policy to leave these corpses for as long as they dared to act as a deterrent to others. I say 'for as long as they dared', because if they had remained unburied for too long, the rats would have been attacking them and the Germans knew that if that were to happen on a large scale, it would not be long before we had an uncontrollable outbreak of typhus. Every so often, the self-important turncoats, who acted as a sort of civil police force within the ghetto and who had adopted the same brutal tactics as our persecutors, would assemble a work party to go round collecting corpses, place them on the wooden handcarts and march out of the ghetto, under guard, to 'bury' their charges in the adjoining Zydowski Cemetery. There was no formal service and most were just dumped into the open graves without the benefit of a coffin. These were quickly filled in and a simple wooden board bearing the names and dates hammered into the mound of earth. Some of the men on the work parties were very brave and defiant, fearlessly saying 'Kaddish', the Jewish prayer, recited in daily ritual in the synagogue and for the souls of close relatives or friends at a burial service. It was at these times that some of the more decent Germans showed what was left of their compassion by allowing such prayers to proceed without interruption. Unfortunately, these Germans were the exception rather than the rule.

70

CHAPTER TWENTY ONE

Early the next morning, I peered through the curtains to see if the market was being set up and was relieved to see that the stalls were already erected and being stocked with all manner of items. Bearing in mind how little we had been allowed to bring in with us, it was a constant source of wonder to me how these people managed to find the goods with which to stock their stalls. It was as if they had hidden, endless resources at their disposal and I suspected that quite a lot of the 'goods' were coming in via the sewer route from sympathisers and pockets of Jews still hiding undetected in various parts of the city. Also surprising, was the greed and avarice of the wealthier Jews who 'bought' or bartered items of food for the family treasures of others less fortunate than themselves, greatly increasing their own wealth without any hint of guilt or compassion. They were totally shameless and made me dislike them intensely.

Once the market was in full swing, I changed identities again, put some more household objects in my bag and, following the same procedure as on the previous occasion headed towards the gates. As we approached, there was a change of guard and two of them were inspecting the contents of the bags. They did not appear to be asking for identity papers and they were quiet busy paying more attention to the bags of those entering the ghetto than those leaving. In any event, it was too late for me to turn back, so I walked on, chatting animatedly to a couple of women who were bragging about their bargaining prowess and showing off their latest acquisitions.

We passed in front of the guards, opening our bags and jackets for inspection and the one inspecting my things gave me a very thorough visual examination and smiled, became quite talkative and kept me talking during his continued searches of the other people.

Previously, before we were confined to the ghetto, I quite enjoyed these exchanges with the soldiers, but this was altogether different and whilst I strove to be as calm as possible and smiled shyly in response to his flattery, I knew I would have to extricate myself fairly quickly from this dangerous situation.

I looked at my watch and said,

"It's been lovely talking to you but I must fly or I shall be late for an appointment". I started to walk away very determinedly but thought it better to soften my departure by turning after a few paces, waving to him with a smile and saying, "See you soon".

"O.K.", he called and gave a little wave of acknowledgement. I didn't look back again, just carried on walking without increasing my stride until I was well out of sight where I heaved a great sigh of relief and was surprised to find that I was shaking all over.

I let myself into Alex's flat and sat down to give my body time to recover. A hot cup of tea helped and the shaking finally subsided.

After sitting for a few more minutes, I got up, put my 'loot' under the bed with the other things and went out to do my shopping.

It was a tremendous relief to be out with the ordinary people going about their everyday business, acknowledging each other in a friendly manner, laughing and smiling, totally unthreatened. The tonic of this freedom dispelled the residue of my fear and by the time I got back to the flat I was surprised by the sudden realisation that, despite my uncomfortable encounter with the guard and my subsequent bout of the shakes, it had never crossed my mind that anyone had thought that I was anything other than a girl.

I was inordinately proud of myself and started humming to myself and performed a little pirouette as I let myself in.

Alex was already home and he stood up smiling as I entered the lounge so I put my bag down and continued my pirouette across the floor until, in the very girlish mood that had engulfed me, I wrapped my arms around his neck, balancing on one leg while I lifted the other as high as possible, thigh parallel to the ground and with heel and calf, pressed him tightly against me. He kissed me very passionately, came up for air and, holding me at arm's length he said, "Wow, that was nice, you randy little devil".

We both laughed and he walked backwards, holding my hands until he could feel the big armchair behind his legs. He sat down and I curled up on his knee. It was very comforting and we just sat holding each other in silence enjoying our close proximity and happiness. It seemed like ages but was probably no more than ten or twenty minutes when we where suddenly aware of Hedwig in the room, she was looking at us both with a wonderfully tender, indulgent smile on her lovely face.

"Oh, you're awake", she said. "You both looked so lovely and contented and yet so vulnerable in your sleep, I'm sorry I woke you."

We hadn't realised that sleep had overtaken us although it was hardly surprising since Alex had been up since three-thirty, had done a full shift at the bakery and I had spent a very disturbed night worrying about the developments in my relationship with Rebecca.

We grinned sheepishly and Alex lightened the moment by saying,

"It's just as well that you did, my legs have practically no feeling in them", and giving me a little squeeze he added, "Go on, get off. I'd no idea that within that slim body of yours lies a ton weight". "Don't be so uncomplimentary", I said in mock rebuke to which he responded by playfully smacking me on the bottom at which all three of us started to laugh as I skipped out of range. Hedwig was observing me, not in a critical way, but with a sense of bafflement and awe. Quite suddenly she said, "Come Janni, Dammit! I feel that I should really be calling you Lotti, come and help me in the kitchen." Once in the kitchen, she began opening tins and packets, assembling the ingredients of a meal occasionally indicating to me what I should do by way of help.

Quite abruptly, she stopped what she was doing and said,

"I've never seen you looking so beautiful as you do today and if I didn't know better, I'd say you are one of the loveliest girls I've ever seen; You have always looked entirely natural and convincing but today, there is an extra, indefinable something about you which makes it almost impossible to think of you as anything other than a very lovely girl. Do you know what it is?" she asked musingly. I knew what she meant, but did not have the explanation she wanted and to be honest, I was quite happy about how I felt and did not wish to question this strange, new elation.

I tried to appear thoughtful and in answer to her question I replied,

"Honestly, I don't know except that it is probably all down to Alex. I love him so much and it's as though his presence changes me physically and mentally... I just want to be whatever he wants me to be."

This at least was true and undoubtedly formed part of the reason for my transformation although I suspected that most of it was due to the additional confidence I had acquired after my encounter with the guard earlier that morning, even though the aftermath had left me feeling as limp as, and shaking like, a jelly.

Hedwig just looked at me rather wistfully and whispered. "Alex is so very lucky." We finished preparing the meal and finally returned to the living room where Alex was fast asleep in the chair. Hedwig woke him gently, telling him to go and splash some cold water on his face and come to the table.

"Sorry!" he exclaimed, rose and went to the bathroom.

During the meal we discussed the arrangements for the evening when we would once again intercept Moishe or one of his companions.

"You are going to stay the night aren't you?" Alex asked.

"Yes", I replied, "and all day tomorrow and tomorrow night as well if that's O.K. with you both" "Great, you can stay here forever as far as we are concerned, can't he Mum?" Alex enthused. "Of course you can Janni, but how can you stay so long, won't you be missed?" Hedwig responded. "I've been thinking about it and it would be more suspicious if I was seen to be going in and out of the ghetto too frequently. As it is, I watch the guard changes and try to leave during different shifts so that my comings and goings are not the cause for unwelcome attention. As it is, one of the guards is getting a bit too friendly and I want to ensure that he is never on duty at the important times." Both of them expressed real concern after I had described the events of that morning and Alex became quite agitated and reprimanded me furiously and hurtfully by saying, "I've warned you before about behaving like a wanton tart."

"Alex! That was nasty, cruel and totally uncalled for", Hedwig said in a raised voice as I put down my knife and fork and stood up with the intention of leaving the room. From the expression on my face, he must have realised how wounding his outburst had been and even though I knew him well enough to know that it was prompted by his love for me, a certain amount of jealousy and a great deal of worry over my safety, it had been said with such vehemence that he had reached deeply into my sensitivity and tears welled up in my eyes quite involuntarily. To cover my embarrassment, I used Rebecca's favourite word, "Shit, Oh shit!" I exclaimed, searching my tiny pockets for a handkerchief. Alex was suddenly all contrition, aghast at the reaction he had provoked, and he rushed over to me and said, "O hell, I didn't mean it. I'm so sorry, I'm so, so sorry". He held me closely, kissed my hair and my cheeks and then whispered, "Your tears taste nice and salty. Love you, really I do and I shouldn't have said what I did. I am truly sorry, please say you forgive me", he implored. I snivelled a bit and said, "O.K."

Slowly, everything returned to normal as we finished our meal and Hedwig broke out the apricot brandy which we thoroughly enjoyed particularly as she said we could have some more after we returned from our assignation.

True to his word, Alex had left some bread and groceries on the ledge as we had arranged and the first thing we did on arrival were to check to see if they had gone. They had been collected and there was a brief note of thanks and some money in an envelope strategically placed under a stone. Inwardly, I thanked God for the partial acceptance of what we were doing because over the next few days, I hoped to re-assert my right to use the sewers, which had become more pressing since my morning fright.

Moishe, this time accompanied by Solly, a youth of some eighteen or nineteen years, appeared out of the gloom and at first, Solly was hesitant to approach us until Moishe reassured him by saying, "It's O.K., it's Lotti."

I introduced Alex and told them that it was he who had left the food the previous night. Solly relaxed and shook hands with us both, which was quite solemn, and at the same time comical, because in my other identity, I had spoken to them both, indeed, I had shared trips through the sewers with them and it was all I could do to maintain a straight face. "We've brought you some more food and some cigarettes", I said, handing over the bag. "Oh, and by the way, thanks for the money", I added.

It had occurred to me that since I was familiar with the routes, I could enter the sewers at my leisure when none of the others was about and retrieve my documents without too much trouble but I had no idea if they maintained a watch on the inside or if they had perfected a system of securing the covers from the inside.

In the event, the solution was easier than I had anticipated.

It was Solly, who apparently was higher in the organisation than Moishe who, after only a few moments deliberation asked if we had access to all parts of the city and if so, would we be prepared to convey messages for them. He explained that it was difficult for them because all their 'business' had to be conducted at night and this, in turn, meant that others would have to emerge from hiding to make contact, a procedure which could spell the end if anyone was captured. It followed that if we, ordinary people going innocently about our everyday routines could carry messages without compromising the locations of the others, it would be to everyone's advantage.

It was now or never. I'd really got nothing to lose so I said, "Yes, alright, we'll do it, but only if you do something for me in return." "What would that be?" Solly asked suspiciously.

"Don't look so worried," I replied. "It's just that I used to play down there in the sewers unbeknown to my parents when I was a bit younger. I had a couple of secret places down there where I used to keep childish, personal things but they are extremely important to me now, firstly, because my identity papers are down there together with those of my brother and they are all that I have left of him since he and my parents were killed in the Blitzkrieg.

"It would be lovely to have them back again", I concluded with a hint of sadness in my tone and what I hoped was a look that would melt the most hardened heart.

They conferred in low tones for a moment before Moishe turned and said, "Sounds fair enough. Tell us where they are and we'll get them for you." I didn't want them prying into my papers, because had they seen the other identity papers, they would have instantly recognised Janni whom they knew was not my brother and was very much alive. So I walked towards the sewer and said, "Come on, it's only twenty or so yards inside and I'll be able to go straight to them. Even with my directions, you would be hard pushed to find them."

I didn't look back to wait for their approval, but just carried on and eventually, they fell in behind me. They removed the cover and Moishe went down first and shone a torch for me to follow I'd never descended an iron ladder in high heels and a skirt before and it was not easy. Moishe laughed and said, "Nice legs; are you sure you are going to be O.K. down here?" "No problem, it's just this ladder and my skirt is too tight. I'll be alright once I'm on the flat." Solly joined us after detailing Alex to keep a careful watch until we got back and the three of us went on to the first junction where I indicated that we should turn left, "Lend me your torch," I said to Moishe and when he handed it to me, I moved a further six or seven paces, found my loose brick, removed it and with great relief, retrieved my little bundle. I took it over to them and showed them my identity papers and some money and they seemed satisfied so I wrapped everything up again and said, "Thanks, both of you. That's a tremendous weight off my shoulders. Now I've got to climb that damned ladder and please Moishe, no shining the torch up my skirt!"

They both laughed and from then on, we all seemed to relax and it appeared that they had accepted me and liked me.

When we were back on the surface, I handed some more cigarettes to Solly, gave him a little peck on the cheek and said, "Thanks again, you deserve those."

I think he probably blushed, it was difficult to see in this light but he smiled, looking quite pleased.

Suddenly, and quite casually, I asked,

"Do you know Rebbeca Lipschitz and her mother?"

"We know them both. Rebecca is stunning isn't she?" Solly replied and added, "Why do you ask?" "The whole family are very dear friends of both Alex and myself, in fact they were our family doctors before the invasion and we've been terribly concerned about them. Are they all O.K?" I concluded. "Like the rest of us, surviving but just about", said Moishe.

"In that case, would you give them this", I asked and passed over the other bag, which Alex had been holding.

"You can check it, it's only food and cigarettes. If you give it to either Rebecca or her mother, they'll give you some money so that we can keep supplies coming. Just tell them that it's from Alex and Lotti." "I reckon we can do that for you, and before you ask, no, we won't keep any of it for ourselves. You can trust us and if you're good enough to provide for us and help with messages we'll make sure they get whatever you bring for them."

I thanked them again

"We have to go now. Shall we see you again tomorrow?" Solly asked. "Same arrangement, if were not here, we'll leave something for you and the Lipschitz family on the ledge, but in all probability, we'll be here ourselves", I promised. With that, they were gone and Alex and I walked backhand in hand to the flat. In bed that night, Alex was wonderful. He was in raptures about my 'tits' and the ensuing exploration of each other's bodies was one of the most remarkable, wonderful, inventive nights I have ever spent in my life. It was totally spontaneous and born out of love, the most gratifying and emotionally satisfying lovemaking I've ever experienced.

Because I now had an identity and the papers to prove it, I felt confident that I could come and go much as I pleased and because of the arrangement we had made with Moishe and Solly whereby I could get food to my 'family', I didn't feel any guilt about staying with Alex and Hedwig for quite a few days. We made our regular evening trips with food, and on the third night, we delivered our first messages. At that time we had very little knowledge of the existence of other ghettoes and we were not aware that our efforts and those of the others to whom we passed the messages were helping to establish contact with the inmates of an enormous ghetto in Lodz.

I think it is important at this juncture to point out that in my narrative, I've concentrated so far on events concerning myself, the Lipschitz family and Alex and his mother. In so doing I might have conveyed the impression that the 'ghetto' was quite a small place where everyone knew everyone else and that all activity was confined to one small street. Far from it. The ghetto was an area that had been designated by the occupying forces as the only place in the city that was fit for occupation by the Jews and other 'undesirables'. It was in broad terms a once proud residential and business area of something approaching five square kilometres combining shops, warehouses, houses and apartment blocks and a more run down area of inferior flats and housing. It comprised many streets, which had been walled off specifically for this purpose. We lived in a massive block off a street called Leszno.

There were many thousands of 'internees', the numbers increasing daily and until we spoke to the new arrivals, we had very little knowledge of the traumatic events which had befallen them and which explained their arrival in our midst. These new arrivals comprised not only Jews, but also Gypsies and homosexuals. Strange though it might seem, not then nor at any time since, did I identify myself with this latter group. It became known that the Germans had imported ethnic Germans from other occupied countries into Poland and had forcibly evicted Jews from their houses and businesses, handing them over at a moment's notice to the incoming 'Herrenvolk'. The Jews were then transported to established Ghettoes, swelling the population to bursting point and creating terrible problems in terms of accommodation and food supply. From later information we learned that, after first bleeding the population of the Lodz ghetto dry of virtually every material possession, they had set up small manufacturing units within the ghetto so that, in addition to providing slave labour, it achieved a certain amount of self-sufficiency. During my stay in the Warsaw Ghetto, this was not the case and the labour groups to which Julius, Aaron and Isaac had been assigned worked on the rebuilding and renovation of the best properties for occupation by the higher-ranking Germans, road and airfield repair gangs, in fact anything. The women worked in warehouses within the ghetto mostly on recycling work. Julius and Rachel had been very shrewd in as much as they had done their best to conceal their professions from the authorities and had stated their previous occupations in more humble terms since intellectuals and Jews with a highly respected profession were total anathema to the Nazi concept of their own racial superiority.

It is important to remember the circumstances which led to my predicament; I had no pre-knowledge of the build-up to the German expansion for 'Lebensraum', not a political thought in my head and I had no yardstick with which to make comparisons, nothing to prepare me for what was to come or to judge the behaviour patterns of one race against another. What education I had in these matters came from my two 'families' and initially, I had been led to believe that since the Germans were for the most part a very highly cultured race, courteous, well-mannered and renowned for their composers, poets, scientists and great thinkers it was inconceivable that their subsequent behaviour would be anything less than that of honourable soldiers, treating their conquests in accordance with a strict military code that was beyond reproach.

During the euphoria which followed the early successes on the Russian front, for the most part, the average soldier, regardless of rank in the Wehrmacht, adhered strictly to this code and although some could be surly and brusque, the majority were cautiously friendly in direct contrast to the members of the S.S. divisions whose conduct defied belief.

Following the reverses on the Eastern front with the loss of many lives, the beginning of the German retreat, the vast numbers of German soldiers taken prisoner and the barbaric, inhumane atrocities committed by the S.S. and the Einsatzgruppen (Units specially commissioned with the sole purpose of extermination), the whole of the German war machine, with a few notable exceptions, adopted the tactics of the S.S, and in so doing embarked on the most infamous programme of genocide the world has ever known.

In this account of my life, it would be impossible for me to recount in detail all the events which I witnessed, all the sad stories of other families, the gratuitous acts of terrifying violence carried out by one or more races or individuals against others and to try to describe adequately the unbelievable horrors which were perpetrated to satisfy the 'visions' of one totally unhinged dictator, but willingly carried out, often with incredible satisfaction, not only by thousands of his countrymen and women, but by those of the subjugated nations who actually volunteered for these barbarous tasks and, if subsequent reports are to be believed, accomplished them not only with great efficiency, but greater satisfaction. There must have been hundreds of books written about the Holocaust by many survivors, by politicians and many others who had never had the misfortune to be incarcerated in such a place, but had the advantage of having access to all sorts of classified documents and managed to write with such a sense of outrage and great detail that one could be excused for thinking that they were the ones who actually suffered the hardships even though these self-same politicians were the ones who procrastinated both during the war and after, when retribution was sought, whose vacillating and duplicity resulted in many thousands of the perpetrators going free, even though their names and current whereabouts were known to the relevant authorities.

But, I have allowed myself to get carried away. I'm sure you will understand. It is almost impossible to recount these events without expressing such abhorrence, such deep feelings and overwhelming sadness which will live with me forever together with the awful, recurrent question...WHY? I've jumped ahead and this was not my intention and in jumping ahead in the narrative, I've jumped back in time and must pause to regain my composure as the pictures, forever printed indelibly in my memory, spring to life once more and threaten to drag me along the familiar and frightening paths of utter desolation and despair.

CHAPTER TWENTY-TWO

After four wonderful days with Alex and Hedwig, I felt that I ought to return to the ghetto and make sure that my family were still there and in reasonable health.

I showered, washed my hair and pottered about until it was dry, put on my make-up and dressed in clean clothes.

I felt on top of the world.

It was a beautiful morning as I headed towards the shops and I enjoyed all the banter with the shopkeepers and customers and the whistles of approval from the soldiers. I'd timed my arrival at the gates to be there fifteen minutes before the guard change. On this occasion they inspected our bags and we all had to produce our papers. This was the test and I handed them over with some trepidation. The sergeant just looked at them, looked me up and down, folded them, handed them back and, with a wave of his hand, indicated that I could pass through. It was hard not to breathe an audible sigh of relief and I walked through at a steady, confident pace without looking back. Feigning interest, I prowled around the stalls until, well out of sight of the gates; I made my customary detour and arrived at our 'flat' somewhat out of breath, my shoulders aching from the weight of the two heavy bags.

There were a lot of stairs to climb and I remember thinking to myself "all this bedroom activity is sapping my strength".

No sooner had I entered the flat than Rebecca grabbed hold of me and gave me a huge hug and a kiss followed in like fashion by Rachel.

They both started to speak together, the words coming out in a rush, until, they stopped abruptly, looked at each other and started to laugh. I joined in and Becca, still laughing, said, "For goodness sake go and change out of that dress before some of the men see you and ravish you". I laughed, and as I went to do her bidding, I exaggerated the sway of my hips and bottom and called, "You're only jealous".

They grinned, made derisory sounds and threw cushions at me to speed me on my way. It was lovely to be with them again and I hadn't realised how much I had missed them, even if it had been only five nights.

As soon as I had cleaned off my make-up and changed, I joined them in the other room and sorted out my morning's shopping. Both of them were delighted that I had brought toilet paper and a good supply of sanitary towels for them. They said how thoughtful it was of me and that it must have been something of an ordeal for me to go and buy such items.

Moishe and Solly had been true to their word and had delivered everything that had been entrusted to them. Becca giggled when she recounted their stammering approach, giving a very passable impersonation of Moishe's somewhat surly, shifty demeanour. Rachel said that both boys were obviously smitten by her and were eager to do anything to please her. Rachel busied herself preparing vegetables and got a stew together from the meat, onions and other items I had managed to acquire that morning. Soon there was a savoury smell filling the small room and opened the windows to allow it to escape for fear of attracting unwelcome attention. Becca and I sat at the table as we often did, holding hands across its width, chatting inconsequentially, occasionally looking up at each other; A few times, when I looked up, Becca was examining my face and her dear eyes were so full of adoration, that, to avoid embarrassment, I would smile gently and she would give my hands an extra squeeze. My God, I thought, if she knew the extent of my lovemaking over the last few days, she would probably tear my hair out!

"We've all missed you so much, haven't we Mummy?" Rebecca said and when Rachel agreed, she added, "Mostly we were glad for you that you weren't here with us, but, and I hope this doesn't sound too selfish, you've been part of our lives for over three years now and we all love you, worry about you and hate it when you're not at home with us. I was going to say 'safe at home', but that would have been stupid in the circumstances, nobody is safe these days," she concluded, her voice almost dying to a whisper.

The fear that was always present had been banished during my stay with Alex, and Becca's words brought it all rushing back making me shudder involuntarily, feeling at once claustrophobic, angry with myself for allowing sentiment and love to bring me back here followed by a deep sense of shame at my uncharacteristic selfishness.

'Dear God', I thought, have I caught this 'every man for himself and to hell with the rest' attitude to life, which had so insidiously taken over the rational thinking of so many of the people we had known and admired.

Fortunately, Julius and the boys arrived and their faces lit up when they saw me. Aaron and Isaac rushed over, hugged me tightly in turn and kissed me on the cheeks. I was totally overwhelmed and my unworthy thoughts from a few moments earlier made me feel so wretched that I could not stifle the sudden sob, which escaped my lips nor hide the tears that coursed their way down my cheeks. To cover my misery and confusion I rushed over to Julius and gave him a big hug and murmured, "Oh, I do love you all and I have missed you so very much." Although I meant every word and tried to convince myself that my tears were tears of joy, which appeared to be what the family thought too, my temporary betrayal, even though it was only a mental thing, made me continue to snivel for quite a few moments longer and prompted Julius to hold me even tighter. He patted my back, stroked my hair, said nice, comforting, and complimentary things about me to which all the family added their agreement. My snivelling finally abated and Julius and the boys went to wash and change for 'dinner'. After dinner, we played cards for a while and as usual, Becca and I lost. Julius was enjoying one of the cigarettes I had brought for him and he was very pensive, as if something was troubling him.

After what seemed a very long time, he drew a deep breath and said,

"Janni, I have no right to ask you to do this for me and if you tell me that it is impossible, or too dangerous, I shall understand fully". He paused for a few moments and continued, "We have a small number of men on the work party who are quite ill; under normal circumstances there would not be a problem but these are not normal circumstances and they do not have access to the medications which are essential for their continued wellbeing. Without them, they will surely die. I have used up most of the medical supplies that we brought with us and, in any event, what little we have left I feel duty bound to keep for the family in case of emergency". I suddenly thought 'my syndrome must be infectious, everybody is thinking about self-preservation these days' and immediately felt relieved that my earlier thoughts no longer seemed so traitorous.

Julius broke in on my thoughts and asked,

"If I give you a list of requirements, would you try, through your contacts to obtain them for me?"

I nodded and said,

"I'll do my best, but won't I need prescriptions for some of them?" "I've thought about that and you are quite right but I happen to know that our former supplier is still very sympathetic towards us and for a princely sum he will be even more sympathetic," Julius added with a mixture of pity and sarcasm. The most important items are at the top of the list and the remainder, although desirable are not one hundred percent essential, they just extend the effects of some of the medications and make them easier to take".

He paused and then continued,

"No Janni, forget what I have just asked you to do, it's far too dangerous and I had no right to ask you to endanger yourself on behalf of people you don't even know."

Once again, my mind was in turmoil as his very real concern for the well being of others was in direct contrast to his earlier implications. However, I had already made up my mind that I would do what I could to help. I took his hands in mine and said,

"It's the least I can do Dad and I promise that I'll take lots of precautions. If I'm lucky enough to obtain these supplies, I'll have to send them in through Moishe and Solly. It would be far too dangerous to try to bring them in through the gate."

As soon as I said this, I realised that I had made a blunder because although Rachel and Rebecca knew of my dual identity and how I came and went from the ghetto, I was not sure whether Julius was aware, and positive that the boys knew nothing of my feminine alter ego and the risks I had been taking in this guise.

Julius squeezed my hands very tightly and I looked up to see him mouthing the word 'shush'. That answered the first of my thoughts and it seemed that the boys were too engrossed in what they were doing to have registered any significance in what I had said. The thought kept coming back to me that I would have to keep my wits about me in future because the next time I let something slip it might be in the wrong ear.

Julius handed me a bulging, leather wallet, which contained a very large sum of money and said, "I'll have to leave the haggling in your capable hands Janni and I'm sure you will get the best possible deal for us. But please Janni, don't take any unnecessary chances and if you feel that there is even the slightest threat, you will immediately abandon the project, even if it means losing money." I was pleased both by his confidence in my ability to carry out financial negotiations and his very touching concern for my safety.

I stood up and as I walked to my 'bedroom' to put the wallet with my clothes, I said, "Don't worry too much about me Dad, I have a lot of tricks up my sleeve and I promise you all that I shall be ultra careful."

It was rather smoky in the other room and Rebecca and I left, hand in hand, for our customary spot on the upper landing where nobody else bothered us. We opened the window and breathed deeply of the warm night air.

There was a flat area outside the window extending to some two metres and then a raised parapet with copingstones on top. I climbed out of the window and stood upright on the flat area. To my right, the flat area continued for about five metres where it met the vertical end wall of an adjoining building which rose another story above ours. To the left, where our roof finished, the flat area opened out to cover the remainder of the building, forming a square of approximately eight by eight metres. In the centre of this, was a shed-like structure with a door and at various points over the flat roof were poles with washing lines strung between them. We had no idea until now that these facilities had existed and Becca, who had joined me on the rooftop, went over to inspect the shed. She tried the door and after a couple of sharp tugs, it opened rather noisily. Inside, although it was very dim at this time of the evening, we could make out more clotheslines. It was apparent that this 'drying room' was for use during inclement weather. To one side of the room, steps led down to another door, which obviously provided access from the landing below. We tried this door and not only found it locked but sufficient cobwebs intact on the door and frame to indicate that it had not been opened for some considerable time.

Becca put her arm through mine and said,

"This will be our place. We don't have to tell the others about it. It will be our secret. We can bring up one or two blankets and a pillow and make it very, very cosy." It didn't take too much imagination to guess what she had in mind since it would have been virtually impossible to continue her 'lessons' on the landing! Considering the past five days, I was glad that we didn't have immediate access to blankets and pillows but happy enough to consider their use in the future.

We stood there, no doubt both our imaginations running riot at the prospects our discovery had opened up and, as if in anticipation of things to come, Becca wrapped herself round me in the most provocative way and I had to use all my powers of persuasion and self-control to persuade her that it would be much nicer, if we cleaned the place out and made it a cosier, more fitting place for our love trysts, particularly as I wanted her 'first time' to be something really wonderful, to be treasured, not a sordid fumble on a dusty old floor.

"Oh Janni, you think things out so beautifully; you're so considerate and I love you. You're absolutely right of course. It's just that when I'm with you, I become so impatient. In my fantasies about you and me, we don't have any clothes on at all and it would be beautiful if we could make the place secure so that we couldn't be interrupted and I could really live-out my fantasy." All the time she was talking, her hands had been all over me, down the back of my trousers, moving urgently round to the front and I must admit, arousing me in no small way. I had to reassert myself and gently stop these exciting ministrations.

"Stop it Becca", I said with as much authority as I could muster," We don't want anyone to discover us here before we can use it."

"Okay, Okay," she said with an air of resignation. "It's just that I wanted to hold it again and do it for you. I know you liked it and I loved doing it. Won't you let me?" she implored. I was tempted to give in to her wishes and I knew that in my state of high arousal it would not have taken very long to accomplish. But I also knew from experience that one thing led to another and it would not have been long before all my best intentions had gone out of the window together with Becca's virginity. Probably in a cloud of dust!

I grasped her hands and gently but firmly moved them away and walked purposefully towards the door. She followed and we closed the door behind us and returned to the window. After climbing back inside, I turned to Becca to help her down from the sill and said, "You must stop doing that, I had great difficulty negotiating that climb with a rigid willy". As she started to giggle I added, "We shouldn't have too much of a problem with that in the future!" With that, she let herself fall towards me, put her arms round my neck to halt her fall, gave me a long passionate kiss and said, "I can hardly wait."

We stayed chatting and holding hands, laughing from time to time until Aaron called to us that drinks were ready.

Back downstairs with the family we once again went over my methods for contacting Julius' supplier and what amounts Julius thought I should reasonably expect to pay for each of the listed items. I was thinking all the time that I must re-establish trust with Moishe and Solly since, sooner or later, even though I timed things to coincide with guard changes, the frequency of my comings and goings would be noticed, with disastrous consequences, not just for me, but the whole family. I slept fitfully, wondering in which identity to contact the supplier and finally decided to approach him first in one identity to establish contact and to arrange a further meeting, then, to observe his premises in my other identity at the appointed time to see whether or not he had informed anyone of our proposed transaction. It was as well to be cautious because Julius' ex -friend may well have had a change of loyalties by this time and any form of betrayal would stand him in good stead with the Germans.

Morning came all too soon and I awoke feeling stale, tired and totally un-refreshed. A cold wash and a hot drink worked wonders and as soon as Julius and the boys had reported for work, I set about my transformation yet again but without the customary feeling of exhilaration. In fact, I felt doubt and twinges of anxiety bordering on fear creeping into my thoughts and I had to shake myself, thinking that if I continued to let these thoughts disturb me, it would reflect in my behaviour and perhaps make me appear furtive. The last thing I wanted to do.

I cheered myself up with the thought that I would soon be seeing dear Alex so it would be worthwhile.

CHAPTER TWENTY-THREE

My initial worries fell away. I had gone through the check point virtually unchallenged, the guards smiled a lot and were quite chatty with the younger, prettier girls and I realised that in many ways, this damned prettiness of which I was quite proud could well be my undoing since some of the guards had given me a fairly thorough, appreciative, lustful inspection on quite a few occasions and might well look out for me either during their shifts or later in the town during their off-duty periods.

The thought also occurred to me that I should not be seen too often with Alex since, if anything did happen to me, he and Hedwig would be under immediate investigation and the consequences could be terrible. It was a very sobering thought. It was too early to go to the flat and I didn't want Alex to see me in an agitated state. I didn't want him to know that I was beginning to get more than a little uneasy. He would stop me from doing what I had to do and I owed it to Julius, who had been so kind to me, to do my best for him and his friends.

I found the street where the supplier conducted his business and located his premises. It was a wholesale chemist's establishment and the building was in a good state of repair, unlike so much of Warsaw which had been virtually flattened; the rebuilding as such had been very slow and limited during the last two years or so.

I didn't stop but carried on walking, noting any and every possible escape route should flight become necessary and I looked for a suitable place in which to hide a change of clothes and with it, my identity. I found a reasonably well-concealed spot and resolved to place a set of alternative clothing in it as soon as possible.

It was time to go to the flat and to my relief, it was a relatively short walk, taking just over ten minutes. Alex was already there and, as I let myself in, he came over to greet me in his usual way with a big hug and kiss. While he was making coffee, or at least a poor substitute for it, I told him of the latest developments, the precautions I intended to take and that the final delivery would be undertaken by Moishe and Solly.

Alex expressed his concern but, knowing that argument was futile, he agreed on the understanding that on both my visits, he too would be nearby both as observer and aide in the event of complications. We agreed that we would go over that afternoon, with me in my male clothes and stash an alternative outfit for me on the way over.

After I had changed and packed the other clothes in a stout bag, we had a sandwich, another drink and left the flat, hearts pounding.

We walked as normally as possible, something I was finding difficult to do since I had become used to walking like a girl and it took some time to re-adjust to the male gait. Once we had hidden my things, it was only a short distance through some abandoned buildings to our destination. Alex found a place from which he could observe unobtrusively and, after a quick squeeze of hands, I took a deep breath and headed for the chemist's.

A rather pale, slightly hunch-backed man of about forty came over to the reception counter and asked if he could help me. I knew from Julius' description that this was not the proprietor and when I asked to see him, I was told that he was very busy and that he never saw anyone without an appointment. I took the envelope from my pocket which Julius had hand-written and which contained my introduction, handed it to the assistant and said I would wait for a reply and that it was very urgent. I could see that he was going to be one of those typical 'job's worth' people who just had to show his authority and with as much severity and impatience as I could muster, I said, "Please take that to your employer immediately. I'm sure that he will be extremely angry if he finds that you have kept him waiting over such an urgent matter; come along, quickly now." His face reddened and I thought he would explode but at that instant, his boss came into reception and seizing the opportunity, I said to the assistant, "Will you give it to him or shall I?"

The proprietor looked up, first at me, then in a questioning way towards his assistant who spoke very quietly to his boss as he handed him the envelope. He opened it, took the letter out and glanced first at the signature. He folded the letter, walked over and lifted the flap on the counter and said, "Come this way please".

Once in his inner sanctum he said,

"I'm so relieved to hear that Dr Lipschitz and his family are still safe and well and you may convey my warmest regards to them, but from now on, we shall not use names, I don't want to know yours and I'm pleased that you have not used mine. Now, down to business. I shall not be able to supply all of the requirements at such short notice and it may take a few days to get them all together but at least I can provide the most urgent items and fortunately, they won't take up much space and are easy to transport. Those you can take with you now and in a moment, we'll go to the stores and get them together. No one else should know about this and I'll think of a way to cover the depleted stock so that no questions will be asked. Come." He motioned me through another door and as we went through he picked up a medium sized bag, which he proceeded to fill with items from the list, ticking them off as he went.

Finally, he said,

"That's all I can do for now and I've been thinking, it might be better if you didn't come here again. Is there somewhere you consider safe where we could meet?"

I thought hard for a moment and asked him if he called into any of the bars for a drink on his way home and on receiving a positive reply I suggested that it might be a good idea if he went there for a drink two nights hence, taking the other items in a bag with him and that when I left today, I would take several empty bags with me which I could fill with anything. Then, at a prearranged signal from me, he would go to the toilet and exchange his bag for one that I would have placed there moments previously. He would take this and leave then I would collect the substitute bag and depart. In the event that one of us was unable to attend, we would repeat the process for the next two nights, or I would telephone his office to make other arrangements. We confirmed the time of the operation and then, when it came down to the matter of money, I was agreeably surprised when he said that he would never take advantage of anyone, let alone and old and valued friend who happened to find himself in such terrible circumstances. The outcome was that he charged me only what he had paid for them plus a very small mark-up.

This was very reassuring and as he escorted me to the door, he handed me my bag and said, "It was very good of you to call, I do appreciate it and please give my warmest regards to your family". He smiled as he shook my hand and I was convinced that his performance, although mainly for the benefit of his assistant, was nevertheless very genuine.

I left the offices and headed down one of the secluded passages between the deserted buildings and after a few minutes, Alex emerged from hiding and fell in beside me, a very relieved expression on his face.

"You were so long in there that I was becoming really worried about you. Anything suspicious happen?" he queried.

"No, it all went much better than expected", I replied and gave him a blow-by-blow account of the meeting.

"I don't much like the sound of his assistant and since I don't really trust anyone, I'd like to keep an eye on the place for a while to see if there are any unusual comings and goings", Alex said. Everything had seemed so normal and unthreatening to me that I thought Alex's precautions unnecessary but he always gave great consideration to my safety and I loved and respected him for it.

So, we hid my parcel with my change of clothing and returned to a good observation point from which we watched the front and side exits of the office and warehouse. An hour passed without any activity except for two civilians who entered the office and came out after ten minutes clutching bags similar to my own. Alex said, "Come on Baby", I was both amused and pleased when he called me that. "My fears were groundless, but you can never be too sure. I don't know about you, but I'm starving," he concluded. We collected my bag and parcel and hurried home where Hedwig greeted each of us with a huge smile and kiss. I liked her very, very much.

While Hedwig prepared the meal, Alex and I drank some plum vodka then I played the piano and indulged in some outrageous mimicry, which had Alex in stitches and prompted him to bring his Mother in to watch. At one stage, they both danced with grotesquely exaggerated actions while managing to maintain expressions of such solemnity, that they looked like cats on a litter tray. We were all laughing quite madly by the end of this performance and it was only the sound of a pan boiling over which brought us back to our senses and sent Hedwig rushing to the tiny kitchen shouting "Oh shit! Oh shit!"

The good-natured banter and sense of fun continued throughout the meal and we livened up our poor excuse for coffee with some apricot brandy.

Alex cleared the table and I washed and dried the dishes, then went to change into my other outfit.

"Why are you changing darling?" Hedwig asked.

"I've got to take something very urgent to Moishe and Solly", I replied. "Is it really that urgent? Alex goes to see them or to collect messages every night and has taken a few messages for them. Can't it wait until tomorrow? You have only been here a short while and you're off again already," she concluded.

I was surprised that Alex had not mentioned his errands or meetings to me, but then we hadn't really had much time for talking and I said, "Yes Hedwig. I really do have to do this tonight. It is very urgent and I wouldn't do it except that quite a lot of people are depending on me. Anyway, it won't take more than a few moments and when I come back, we can have another drink or two and play some more music." I paused and ended, "Is that O.K?" "Sounds fine except for the part where you said a drink or two," and with mock severity she continued. "You're becoming far too fond of alcohol and in any event, it's not good for your love life!" she added with a wicked grin and a giggle.

Alex and I went to meet the boys and on the way over he told me that he had gone over every night without fail to wait for the boys or to see if they had left any messages in our secret spot. He had also taken some messages to other people on their behalf and had explained my absence by saying that I was away on some urgent business and as it happened, the production of the medicines this evening would cover it nicely.

It was a lovely, warm evening and we strolled arm in arm or hand in hand to our meeting point and, so that our disappearance into the tumble-down buildings didn't arouse any curiosity on the part of others who were out enjoying the evening air, we stopped every so often for a brief kiss before Alex took hold of my hand and firmly pulled me into the ruins, eliciting indulgent smiles from passers-by. Once out of sight, we headed quickly to our destination and only moments later, Moishe and Solly appeared.

"Hi Alex, Hi Lotti", they greeted us and after we had returned their greeting, Solly said, "It's great to see you again Lotti. Where have you been these last few nights? We've missed you."

I handed over the parcel to Moishe and said,

"Didn't Alex tell you, I had to go out of town and arrange to get these medicines for Dr Lipschitz? Apparently, some of the people on his work party are becoming quite ill and he asked if we could get some supplies for him.

"There are more to come, but I'm not sure how soon I can get them. As usual, if I'm not here, Alex will bring them and take messages or we'll leave them in the usual place for you."

I'd almost forgotten the food and I handed over the other bag saying,

"Oh, and by the way, there are two smaller bags in here, one for you and one for Mrs Lipschitz. They are both the same", I said and as I passed them over, I added, "Just a minute, we've brought some cigarettes for you both and some for Dr. Lipschitz and you'll find some more in the parcels."

They thanked us profusely, both of them shaking Alex by the hand whilst briefly touching their cheeks to his and then, to my amusement, holding me by the shoulders and kissing me on both cheeks. I pushed Solly away, because he had a distinct tendency to linger and with a cautionary tone I said, "Before, you go, I know any warning is probably unnecessary, but be very, very careful that no one sees you handing over the medicines to the doctor; their discovery could bring all sorts of problems for all of us."

"No problem", they chorused, "We'll be ultra cautious. Don't worry about a thing", and Solly continued, "Thanks again for everything, we'll bring some money for you tomorrow and another couple of messages if that's O.K.?"

We both nodded and left quickly before Solly could use our leaving as an excuse to get his hands on me yet again!

We hadn't gone many paces before Alex burst out,

"That bloody Solly, he thinks you fancy him ever since you gave him that first peck on the cheek.

Christ, if he hangs onto you again, I'll knock his bloody head off". He was quite petulant and as he always did when he suffered pangs of jealousy, he tried to make me feel that it was, in part, my fault. I didn't like this but I was not going to enter into an argument over it by defending my non-existent complicity. I took his arm and placed it around my waist and slid my own around his and said, "You're so protective of me that I feel completely safe from anybody when you're with me; it's a lovely comforting feeling and I love you for it."

This seemed to mollify him and I could feel the tension go out of his body, and his pace, which had been rather furious, slowed down. He pulled me closer to him and said, "Sorry, I haven't had much sleep lately and I'm becoming a little bit crotchety. While you're here, if you wouldn't mind shopping in the afternoons so that I can grab a couple of hours I'd be very grateful." I felt terrible. How could I have been so thoughtless? He'd been up since half-past three this morning, then been to the warehouse with me, then out to meet Solly and Moishe. He must have been shattered. I stopped him in his tracks, turned him towards me, put my arms around his neck and said, "Oh darling, I'm so sorry, I've been very selfish and stupid. The trouble is, my brain goes to pieces when I'm with you. Come on; let's get home and into bed. In future, I'll make sure that you aren't disturbed until after four o'clock. Is that O.K?"

He hugged me tight, said "Smashing, let's run, and by the way, I liked it when you called me darling." With that, he took hold of my hand and started to run then with a look of consternation which turned into a cheeky grin, he said, "Oops, forgot about the tight skirt and the high heels, still, I'll have them off you in no time at all!" I grinned back and said, "You can put any naughty ideas out of your head. You have got to get some sleep."

"We'll see", he replied as we trotted hand in hand to the flat.

We stayed up only long enough to have a final drink and when Hedwig offered me a glass of vodka, I grinned at her as sexily as possible and said, "No thank you, not tonight!" She almost fell over with laughter, caught hold of me as though to steady herself and said, "Go on you two, off you go then". As I was about to pull away she whispered, "Don't be so damned smug and blatant. You make me feel quite randy and envious." She kissed me lightly on the lips and as I turned to go, she gave me a gentle, playful smack on the bottom. Dear Alex looked on with a tired smile and great affection for us both and I draped my arm around his shoulder as we walked to the bedroom.

It had turned very warm and humid and I thought we might get a thunderstorm. After a couple of minutes and by mutual consent, we pushed the covers to the bottom of the bed and lay there naked, side by side.

Alex got hold of my arm that was nearest to him and put it around his neck as he rolled towards me. He laid his head on my shoulder, cheek on my breast. With his hand, he cupped my other breast and with a sigh of contentment, fell asleep. I felt such a great wave of tenderness come over me and it was now my turn to feel very protective towards him. I was very happy and held him as closely as I dared without disturbing him but eventually, the weight of Alex's head was making my arm go numb and pins and needles made it imperative to extract it. As carefully and gently as I could, I lifted his hand from my breast then, moved my body away from him and withdrew my arm very gingerly from beneath his neck. He hardly made a sound, just a muffled sigh and then turned onto his other side, drew his knees up slightly and placed his hands between them in a sort of foetal crouch. After some minutes, I pulled the bedclothes back over us and fell asleep. The insistent clamour of the alarm clock woke us and Alex turned it off very quickly. It was only three a.m. and I thought that in his tired state of the previous night, he had not set it properly. I was mistaken; he had known precisely what he was doing and his ulterior motive soon became very clear. He turned towards me, slipping his arm beneath my neck and around my shoulder and pulled me towards him. I loved the closeness of his body and as soon as our stomachs touched, the fingers of his free hand began describing gentle circular movements between my shoulder blades, creeping ever lower until he held my bottom very tightly, pulling us even closer together. He kissed me briefly and then grinned at me saying

"Good morning Janni Baby, do you still love me?"

By way of an answer, I pushed him away gently, ran my hand down his stomach, grasped his erect penis and said.

"Good morning to the both of you! Of course I love you.... and your little friend."

He giggled and said, "Don't be so disparaging. I'm quite proud of it and it always does what it's told." There followed half an hour of sheer indulgence during which he told me that I was completely wanton and that he approved totally.

The time passed too quickly and it was suddenly all a mad rush for him to get washed and dressed ready for work. While he was doing this, I went to the kitchen to make tea and toast. We only had a few minutes together before he left and I finished my breakfast still in a happy, languorous frame of mind, reliving the excitement of the last half hour. Eventually, I went to the bathroom, cleaned my teeth, had an all over wash, put on a light-weight dressing gown and went to sit in the lounge. It was still only four o'clock and I was wide-awake. Another cup of tea seemed like a good idea and after returning from the kitchen with my steaming mug, I settled down to work out a secure plan for my forthcoming meeting with the chemist. The deliberations, assessing alternative strategies and potential escape routes, occupied more time than I had realised and I was still deep in thought when Hedwig emerged from her bedroom, hair tousled, still sleepy and moving trance-like towards the bathroom.

Suddenly, she became aware of my presence and in an involuntary movement, pulled her robe tighter.

"Good morning. Did you sleep well?" I asked.

"So so", she said and slowly changed direction towards me. I had been sitting cross-legged and she lifted the upper leg off and sat down on my knee, put her arm round my neck and laid her head on my shoulder.

She smelt of sleep and warmth and a lovely muskiness. It was a very pleasurable experience.

She started, almost as though she had nodded off again and said,

"I must get dressed. Be a good girl and make me some tea and toast while I'm getting ready."

As she stood up to go, she stopped suddenly and said,

"Oh Janni darling, I am sorry, I didn't mean to say that, but that's really how I think of you these days."

She looked so crestfallen, so remorseful that I answered instinctively,

"It's O.K., honestly. I'm happier this way and I don't have to pretend otherwise with you."

Strangely enough, only the night before, I'd still been amazed at her ready acceptance of Alex and I openly sleeping together and her sexy banter about it.

The tea and toast didn't take long to prepare and Hedwig joined me at the table for the few minutes we had remaining before she left for work.

I broke the companionable silence by saying,

"I'll do my shopping this afternoon so that Alex can have a few hours undisturbed sleep. I'd no idea that he had been doing so much."

"He's a very good, conscientious boy, but I do get worried about him and I'm glad that you are here with him," Hedwig replied and before I could say anything, she continued, "He does love you very much. He mopes around when you are not here and this business with Moishe and Solly makes him feel close to you, even though you are not there in person. I just don't want him to take any silly chances because I love him very much too and he's all I've got. Please Janni, promise me that neither of you will do anything really dangerous or stupid. Promise me please."

I took her hands and said,

"I love you both too much to allow anything like that to happen and although all the precautions I'm taking may seem excessive, I'm trying to cover every eventuality. I promise you that if there is even the slightest hint of possible danger, we will abandon what we are doing and do nothing stupid."

She squeezed my hands in response and said,

"Thanks for that reassurance darling, I feel much better about it now." She kissed me goodbye and couldn't resist a provocative wiggle of her bottom, accompanied by her lovely, impish grin as she closed the door.

Still in my dressing gown, I whiled away the morning playing the piano and my happy frame of mind was reflected in the way I played. I cannot remember ever playing better than I did that morning. Finally, I went and showered then dressed and left to do the shopping.

CHAPTER TWENTY-FOUR

It was a glorious day and I'd put on a light blouse, a flared skirt (no stockings,) high heels and a sling bag. I swung along without a care in the world and smiled happily at the soldiers who whistled and called out. It was all very good natured until I was spotted by one of the off-duty guards, one I thought particularly creepy, who, upon recognising me, came over, fell into step beside me and began to make a thorough nuisance of himself, trying to take my arm and making very suggestive remarks. I told him a number of times to leave me alone, but he became more persistent, first putting his arm around my waist and then stroking my bottom. With that, I lost my temper, turned round and slapped him really hard across the face.

His first reaction was shock which very quickly turned to extreme anger, especially as his colleagues had started to laugh and catcall.

"You bloody little bitch, I'll teach you a fucking lesson", he cried and grabbed hold of my shoulder as he raised his fist to punch me.

"Oh shit!" I thought as I prepared to duck and then to kick him in the balls. To my great relief, neither manoeuvre was necessary since a tall young officer who shouted, "Stop that at once soldier, had grabbed his raised arm mid-way on its path towards me. What are you, some kind of animal? Stand to attention when I'm talking to you."

The officer turned to me and said,

"I'm extremely sorry about this young lady. I hope you haven't been harmed?" I assured him that I was not hurt, only frightened and he turned to the soldier, obtained details of his name and unit then called an N.C.O. (Non Commissioned Officer) over, telling him to escort the man back to his barracks and to place him on a charge.

Having accomplished this duty, he apologised again very stiffly and formally, with a courteous little bow and a sharp click of his heels.

"We are not all the same ", he said and then continued, "By way of reparation, would you allow me to buy you a cup of coffee?"

I was about to refuse when I thought it would be very churlish to do so especially as he had saved me from a beating and I would have had a very hard time explaining a black eye and swollen face to Alex. In the circumstances, I thought it would be all right to accept.

"Thank you Herr Obersturmfhrer (Lieutenant) that would be very nice and thank you for rescuing me", I said.

He was a perfect gentleman. He moved to the outside of the pavement, said, "Pardon me", took hold of my hand and tucked it under his arm.

It all happened so quickly that I didn't have time to protest.

He guided me firmly in the direction of an up-market restaurant where he was greeted like an old friend and all the staff were very deferential. Unusually, since he was German, they all seemed to like him.

Once we were firmly installed in our alcove, he asked,

"What do I call you? My name is Gunther and I'm very pleased to make your acquaintance." For a moment or two, I was caught off balance. This German was such a perfect gentleman and he was so correct in everything he did. He held my chair for me, remained standing until I was comfortable and was generally very solicitous. His total command of the situation was made evident simply by him saying to the waiter, "The young lady has just had a very unpleasant experience and I think a couple of measures of your best brandy would be appropriate."

He turned to me with a charming smile and said,

"Please forgive me, I hope you drink brandy?"

I'd recovered my composure and before replying, I took time to study him. He seemed very nice, very correct and determined to create a good impression. I responded in kind and said, "This is very kind of you and yes, I like brandy. Oh, in answer to your question, my name is Lotti." Initially, I'd thought of giving a different name but I thought that if he had to give evidence against the soldier who was going to assault me, the soldier may well have said that he had seen me before and knew my name from the regular checks that they made. In the circumstances, this could have proved to be a great mistake.

We drank our brandies slowly and he ordered coffee and two more brandies. The coffee, when it arrived was very much better than that which they served to the general public and I must confess to enjoying the attention Gunther was bestowing upon me. Don't misunderstand me, I didn't fancy him, but enjoyed the civilised company and being treated with such deference and courtesy. He was obviously from a very good home, well educated and able to engage me in conversation without once mentioning the war and how it had disrupted so many peoples lives. In fact, he was thoroughly charming and I found him excellent company.

Quite suddenly, he said,

"I'm sorry, but I have to go. I'm on duty in half an hour and much as I would like to prolong this enjoyable occasion, I'll be in serious trouble if I'm late."

He called the waiter over, settled the bill and as he stood up he said,

"This has been very pleasant, but I wish we had met under more auspicious circumstances". He smiled and continued, "Perhaps I should be grateful to that horrible soldier for bringing this meeting about. I'd very much like to meet you again. Is that possible?"

This was totally unexpected and for a moment I was quite at a loss because apart from the wolf whistles and randy comments of the soldiers, I'd never been seriously propositioned before and what had happened between Alex and me, Hedwig and me and Becca and me didn't fall into the same category. After a split second's hesitation I replied, "Gunther, you have been very kind to me and I'm very flattered that you wish to see me again, but I already have a boyfriend whom I happen to love very much. Please don't be offended if I decline but it just is not possible." "I do understand, but you can't blame me for trying. You're a very beautiful young girl and your boyfriend is very lucky."

Ever the gentleman, he bowed, took my hand and brushed his lips over it, clicked his heels and said, "It has been a great pleasure and my only hope is that you do not ignore me if our paths should cross in the future."

I almost felt sorry for him, he was so earnest. I assured him that I could never be so rude as to ignore someone who had come so gallantly to my rescue and bade him farewell as he marched away, cutting quite a dashing figure in his immaculate uniform.

I lingered on, finishing my coffee and brandy and then, on a whim, I ordered another, making it last while I tried to come to grips with my conflicting thoughts and impressions of the 'enemy'. I reached no conclusions except that I was very mixed up and questioned my innocence and naivety. It was very disturbing to realise how unworldly and vulnerable I was and I felt an overwhelming desire to run home to Alex and feel the comfort of his arms around me. I thought, "Alex, how right you are when you call me Baby." Until this moment I'd thought of myself as being quite sophisticated and capable of handling anything and everything fate threw my way.

Now, I had serious doubts. In a chastened and subdued mood, I shopped aimlessly and when I finally arrived home and started to empty my bag, I was surprised to discover that I'd purchased some totally useless items and worse, I couldn't even remember buying them. Fortunately, none of them was expensive or large. There was nowhere to hide them so it occurred to me to have a bit of fun and I placed various items in cupboards where they stood out like a sore thumb against the usual contents. Amongst the items I had purchased were two small teddy bears. Some insight told me that I had been seeking comfort in childhood without the responsibilities and worries of adulthood when I bought them. Brushing such deep thoughts aside, I placed one on Hedwig's bed and then went to 'our' bedroom to put one on Alex's pillow. He was still fast asleep, so relaxed and handsome and I was tempted to bend over and kiss him gently. I resisted the impulse, put the little bear on the pillow within inches of his face and crept out again. For the next twenty minutes or so, I busied myself peeling potatoes and preparing vegetables. I was drying my hands as Hedwig arrived, came straight over to me said, "Hi darling" and kissed me on both cheeks. She spotted the pans of prepared vegetables, gave me a big hug and exclaimed, "Oh, that's wonderful. You're so very thoughtful and I can have a bit of a rest before I need to do anything else."

"When you have time, you must teach me how to cook some of the easier meals and I can have them ready for when you come home", I volunteered.

"That's a nice thought ", she said as she put the kettle on to make some tea. As she turned away, almost as an afterthought, she asked, "Bye the bye Janni, have you been drinking?"

I hadn't thought to clean my teeth when I'd returned from town and counting back, I realised that I'd consumed three double brandies fairly quickly and the smell on my breath must have been quite powerful.

"I felt a bit queasy for a moment or two, it was probably the closeness and humidity, so I had a coffee and a brandy and that seemed to work O.K," I fibbed.

"It must have been one hell of a large brandy, because your eyes are very bright, you smell like a distillery and you 're a little bit squiffy," she said, her eyes full of laughter and indulgence, and then, thoughtful as ever, she got out the plum brandy, poured two glasses and said, "I don't want Alex to know you've been drinking alone in town, he'll get very mad with you. So take a small sip of this and I do mean small and leave it there for him to see when he wakes up." I loved her conspiratorial attitude and the fact that she was protecting me from a fight with Alex. I just gave her a long, lingering hug, which was broken up by the sound of laughter from the bedroom. The laughter continued and Alex came into the living room in his dressing gown, clutching the little teddy bear to his cheek.

"You, I suppose", he said and gave me a mighty cuddle with the little bear pressed between our cheeks. Hedwig was laughing and wanted to see the bear. Alex handed it to her and she gave it a playful cuddle and said, "What a lovely thing to do. You are so sweet Janni."

Alex chimed in, "I woke up and there was this furry little thing on the pillow staring into my face. It made me smile immediately and I love it, thanks baby."

Hedwig went to change out of her work clothes and we were in the middle of some serious kissing when peals of laughter came from her bedroom. Her door opened only a fraction and she pushed the other little bear round the door and in a muffled voice, said, "Hey you two, what have you done with my girlfriend? No hanky-panky with her or I'll scratch you to death."

We all had a fit of the giggles and Hedwig came out to join us. Using her bear like a puppet, she made a couple of amorous advances to Alex's bear and I thought I ought to put a stop to this before everything became too suggestive.

I turned to Alex and said,

"Why don't you get dressed, you look too damned provocative like that."

He smiled his lazy smile, blew me a kiss and replied,

"Sorry, in all the excitement and hilarity, I'd forgotten."

With that he went to the bathroom and I went to help Hedwig in the kitchen.

"Just how much did you have to drink Janni?" she asked with an indulgent smile.

I shrugged my shoulders and said, "Not a lot, why do you ask?"

"Because I think you are more than slightly tiddly; Look what I found in the cupboard", she said, handing me a box of birdseed.

I started to laugh thinking, 'wait till she opens some of the other cupboards' and still laughing I said, "I think you must be right. I don't remember buying that. It isn't as if we have got a bird!" "It's O.K., you can buy whatever you like, but seriously, promise me you won't go drinking on your own again. The thought of it frightens me to death." she said, suddenly very earnestly. "Promise", I said.

We had been keeping our voices down so that Alex couldn't overhear us and I had just finished making my promise to Hedwig when Alex emerged from the bathroom, all fresh and smiling. He picked up a glass and saying, "You two are way ahead of me, at least Janni is", he poured himself a large measure of apricot brandy. We sat down to our meal, during the course of which, I told them that until I was absolutely sure that it was one hundred percent safe, I had no intention of collecting the remainder of the medical supplies. Instead, Alex and I would go out as boyfriend and girlfriend and have a coffee in the bar just as ordinary couples do in the evenings and we would observe the comings and goings. When the chemist arrived, we would stay for five or ten minutes then leave, and, doing our usual 'young couple in love routine', we would endeavour to keep the bar under observation until the chemist had left. After my experience earlier of just how badly the German soldiers could behave, I didn't fancy the idea of being arrested and questioned by them; so I would be lying if I said that fear didn't play a part in the elaborate precautions.

Fortunately, Hedwig and Alex though it a splendid idea and Hedwig in particular was visibly relieved. It was still warm and Alex donned a lightweight jacket with pleats in the back (it must have been the English in me coming to the fore quite subconsciously because I remember thinking that it was one of the most popular yet unstylish items of clothing I had ever seen...I never said as much to Alex!). For the girls, it was easier, a cardigan to carry over one's arm and a pair of cotton gloves. Thus attired, we strolled along, holding hands and arrived at the bar some twenty minutes before the chemist arrived.

When he finally entered, he was carrying a bag under his arm. He stopped in the doorway as if adjusting his eyes to the dimmer lighting and briefly scanned the room before sitting at a seat in a corner from which he could observe all present. He called the waiter over, ordered a coffee and lit a cigarette. Two other people entered and I felt a slight chill as I recognised them as the two men whom Alex and I had seen going into the front office of the warehouse just after I had left. Alex spoke to me in Polish asking, "Do you see who I see?" and after I'd confirmed this, he said, "I think we had better go." We called the waiter and paid our bill and then, Alex told me a very rude joke to make me laugh, put his arm around my waist and still giggling, we left the bar as unhurriedly as we dared. We stopped and had a bit of a kiss and cuddle several times whilst we covered a distance of about seventy metres, taking it in turns to keep our eyes open (not very satisfactory!!) and look back over the other's shoulder.

We spotted movement here and there and we nearly came to grief at one point when, still carrying our young lover's act to extremes, we turned into a bombed out building. There were two German soldiers in there and they grabbed hold of us, told us to be on our way and indicated the direction in which we should go, away from the bar. We apologised and almost ran away. A car was parked on the next corner. A driver and a corporal sat in the front and, in the rear, sitting beside an officer, was the hunch-backed assistant from the chemist's. We walked by on the other side of the road, still holding hands and we deliberately stopped for another steamy kiss as if we had not noticed anything untoward. After we were out of sight, we breathed a sigh of relief and, much as we wanted to get home safe and sound, we didn't increase our pace lest we attracted attention to ourselves. All the time, we wanted to look round to see if anyone was following but resisted the temptation. Instead, just a few minutes from home I dragged Alex into a deep doorway and holding each other tightly, we waited to see if anyone came past or followed us in.

To our great relief, nothing of the sort happened and a few minutes later, we were in the sanctuary of the flat. From our expressions, Hedwig could tell that all had not gone well and we told her, with all the details, what had transpired.

"My God Janni, you must be psychic. Did you have a premonition or something or were you just being ultra cautious?" she said, eyes still wide.

"A bit of both, I didn't like the look of that hunchback fellow from the start. Not because of his handicap, but he just seemed too shifty and his manner didn't exactly invite trust," I replied. "What will you do now?" Hedwig asked.

"Nothing. Forget it, it's too bloody dangerous", I responded and then excused myself for swearing. They both laughed and Hedwig said she would have been surprised if I hadn't sworn in even more colourful language and added that she could think of a few choice words of her own to describe the hunchback. We all had a warm drink and thought about the brandy but decided against it since we still had to meet Moishe and Solly to pass on the bad news. Hedwig did not want us to go out again but it wasn't far and would only take about twenty minutes in all.

Alex and I left the flat and headed to our usual spot. There seemed to be far more soldiers about than usual and we decided that it was too risky to keep the appointment. We turned off our usual route with the intention of circling back home and were promptly confronted by a large body of soldiers in the charge of an officer. With growing horror, I recognised Gunther and in exactly the same moment, he spotted me. He marched over, clicked his heels and gave his stiff little bow, more a formal nod, looked Alex up and down and nodded to him, then, to my great relief, without showing any sign of recognition, he said, "Good evening Frulein, good evening Sir, this is not a good time to be out on the streets. There is an operation going on and we wouldn't want you to become involved and place yourselves in danger. Please return to your homes and stay indoors for the rest of the evening". He paused and then, pointing in the direction from which we had just come, he continued, "If you go in that direction, you should be well clear of any possible trouble." We thanked him and Alex asked him if the operation was likely to go on all night since he had to come this way to be at work at four in the morning.

"It should be over well before then", Gunther replied and then he asked, "Do you have a special pass for that purpose?"

Alex nodded and said, "Yes sir and I'm very careful about carrying it with me during my journeys to and from work."

"That will be alright then," Gunther said, and with a smile he added, "Rather you than me having to go to work at such a Godforsaken hour."

With that, he gave us a partial salute and said,

"Goodnight Frulein, Goodnight Sir, now please, hurry home."

We didn't need a second bidding and we hurried back home, hardly daring to speak, but the same thought was in both our minds. The soldiers were so close to our intended destination that we were convinced that they must have discovered the sewer exit and were waiting to see who came out and who they met. We decided not to tell Hedwig of this second setback in the one night, she would have forbidden any future involvement and to be honest, I was beginning to have my doubts about the advisability of carrying on.

CHAPTER TWENTY-FIVE

Hedwig was relieved to see us back so soon and without asking us, she poured drinks, put on a record and got out the cards.

We played a few hands, danced occasionally and I played some songs so everyone could join in. As usual, Hedwig let Alex and I use the bathroom first to clean our teeth, and then to have a quick wash before we went to bed. Sometimes she stayed up later than us doing some washing, ironing, sewing and darning and the results of these labours were always neatly folded on the table in the morning.

In bed, Alex's hands were all over me and he said,

"You're beautiful all over, but particularly your bum and tum, they're fantastic. Do you know, I wish the bed was longer and wider, then, I could put you across the top and use your tummy as a pillow, or, if the bed was long enough, you could be at the top of the bed, face down with your legs apart and I could snuggle up in between them and use your bum as a pillow, I'd love to go to sleep like that", he concluded. "That could prove very dangerous. I might fart in my sleep and damage your eardrums", I joked.

Alex laughed and said, "You're far to nice to do anything like that."

"And what am I supposed to be doing while you're using my body as your bedding?" I enquired.

"Just lie back and think nice thoughts about me", Alex replied with a chuckle.

Taking a leaf out of Rebecca's book, I said,

"You smug, self-centred bastard."

Alex went into hoots of laughter, cuddled me like mad and we embarked on a truly marathon session, finishing up soaked in perspiration, sliding all over each other and, after our gymnastics had subsided, the cooler night air blowing through the window over our moist bodies made us shiver and we dried ourselves quickly, pulled up the bedclothes and fell into a contented sleep, all our earlier cares completely banished from our minds. After Alex had gone to work I slept on until well after nine. Hedwig slept late also since she didn't have to work that day. I was already washed and dressed when she put in an appearance. As she went to the bathroom, I made tea and toast, she kissed my cheek briefly and said, "Thank you darling", as she joined me at the table.

She noticed that I was in my 'girly' clothes and remarked,

"If you're going to dress like that all the time you are here, I'll have to call you Lotti, otherwise, it's going to be very confusing."

After a few seconds of silence, during which she'd obviously been thinking carefully, she asked, "Are you dressing like that purely for Alex's benefit, because you prefer it, or for some other reason?" "All three", I answered and continued, "That bloody hunchback will have given my description to the authorities and I was pretty well known in some of the shopping areas; let's face it, as a boy, I was a little bit different and therefore easy to describe. If by any chance they are looking for me I'm better off by far dressed like this." "I hadn't thought of that", Hedwig said and went on, "We'll shop together today and we'll listen to all the gossip and try to find out what went on last night and whether or not they caught anyone." "Good idea, but let's not ask any questions until we hear others talking about it first", I cautioned. "You're getting wiser every day darling", Hedwig said admiringly as she gave my hand a squeeze. "Come on then, let's wash up these few things and go and look at the big, bad world." We walked arm in arm in the warm summer sunshine and we really enjoyed each other's company. We were often laughing as we made disparaging remarks about other people, their choice of clothes, the way they walked, hairstyles, in fact, everything came in for a barrage of good-natured bitchiness with both of us trying to outdo the other with our caustic comments.

We were in a great mood by the time we had finished our shopping and although there had been plenty of comments and wild guesses about the events of the previous evening, nobody knew anything for certain. We felt sure that if anyone had been apprehended, someone, somewhere would have known about it and since no one had been shot or hung yet this morning as an example to the rest of the population, it was a pretty sure bet that no one had been caught.

Hedwig suggested that we have a coffee and before I could stop her, headed for the bar in which I had spent part of the previous afternoon.

The barman smiled and said, "Good afternoon ladies. What would you like?"

"Coffee for me please and what about you Lotti?" Hedwig enquired.

"Same for me please", I agreed.

"O.K., two coffees", the barman said and as he was turning away, he smiled and queried, "No brandy today then, Frulein?"

"No, thank you" I replied rather sternly and I heard Hedwig say "Oops!"

I muttered, "Cheeky bastard" and Hedwig giggled, saying, "Be sure your sins will find you out!" We laughed together and just when I thought that things could not get worse, a shadow fell over the table and we looked up to see Gunther standing there, going through his usual correct, stiffly formal greeting. "Good afternoon Frulein Lotti, I hope you got home safely last night", he inquired. This had two very embarrassing effects; Hedwig's eyebrows shot up so quickly, they almost disappeared out of sight and her expression was such that I almost peed myself with laughter while struggling to maintain a straight face. Secondly, Gunther's enquiry had produced a lot of knowing looks amongst the bar staff and customers who had concluded that I had spent part of the night with him and was probably sleeping with him. I introduced him saying, "Gunther, this is Hedwig, my dearest friend, Hedwig, this is Gunther, the gentleman who came to my rescue yesterday." I saw no reason to say how many times!

If anybody knew anything about the outcome of the previous night's action, it would be Gunther so I said, "Would you care to join us for a coffee or a brandy, it's the least I can do by way of thanks." He was obviously very pleased at the invitation and as he sat down, he called to the waiter, "Coffee and a large brandy please," and then, turning to us he said, "Please, I insist, allow me to get these and would you both care for a refill of coffee and a brandy?" He wanted to make the meeting last and looked from one to the other of us, very appealingly and with a nice smile.

Under the table, I gave Hedwig a nudge with my knee and before she could respond, I replied for both of us saying, "Thank you Gunther, that would be very nice", then turned to Hedwig, and added "Wouldn't it dear?" Hedwig had recovered her composure and she kicked me hard on the shin while maintaining a lovely smile. She turned her smile on Gunther who appeared suitably devastated by it as she said, "Thank you Gunther, that would be delightful".

The waiter brought us fresh cups and tidied the table; after he had left, Gunther said, "This really is a great privilege, I must be sitting with the two loveliest girls in Warsaw."

Hedwig inclined her head and said,

"You're very gallant sir" and to my surprise, she added, "You're a pretty good-looking chap yourself. By the way, are you married?" before she continued, "All the best one's are!"

I could see that Hedwig had got the devil in her and she continued to kick me under the table when, with mock severity, eyebrows raised, she said, "I hope you haven't been taking liberties with dear Lotti. She's only very young you know." Gunther's face was a picture of shocked indignation and I felt so sorry for him that I sprang to his rescue. "It's alright, she's only joking," turning to Hedwig, I said, "Don't be so beastly to the poor man, he's been a perfect gentleman."

To Gunther I added in a conspiratorial tone,

"She is right, I am quite young and she is very protective which is a pain in the bum from time to time."

We all laughed, tensions eased and we fell into easy conversation.

After a while, I ventured,

"What time did you get finished last night, Gunther?"

"Probably about the same time as your boyfriend was going to work", he replied.

As nonchalantly as possible I said,

"It all seemed very exciting, but, and I do hope you'll forgive me, there is still a marked antagonism towards the occupying forces and you could cut the 'us against them' attitude with a knife. You must be aware of it all the time and it's hardly surprising that most people would be very relieved if whoever it was you were out to catch, evaded you successfully. It must be very difficult for you in such a hostile environment", I concluded. "You are very understanding Frulein Lotti", he answered and continued, "Believe me, Lotti, I take no pleasure in persecuting civilians over petty misdemeanours. I am first and foremost a soldier, ready to fight anything that an opposing army can muster against us and that is what we envisaged when we committed ourselves to the armed forces to do our patriotic duty."

He paused for a moment, a little self-conscious because he sounded a bit pompous, and then followed on, "In our eagerness to serve our country, we looked no further than the conquests, we didn't foresee that the occupation and underground resistance would tie us up in constant strife, nor that such stringent measures of example would have to be carried out as a form of deterrent." He leaned forward lowering his voice to a whisper, then with great sadness in his voice, he added, "I find this part of my duties most abhorrent, not at all what I committed myself to do and I hate being tarred with the same brush as some of my fellow officers and soldiers who take great, sadistic satisfaction in that particular aspect of their job."

Still whispering, and very conspiratorially he carried on,

"If it's any consolation to you, our mission last night was a complete failure. We caught no one and can only assume that the information we received was a deliberate attempt to make fools of us. Any retaliation on our part would only indicate that the perpetrators had scored a victory and for this reason there will be no reprisals." He called over his shoulder and without asking us, he ordered refills, took out a silver cigarette case and ever the gentleman, proffered it to Hedwig and myself. When we declined he asked, "Since neither of you smokes, would you be very offended if I indulge?" We both assured him that we would not be offended and he lit up with great enjoyment.

Hedwig looked pointedly at her watch and said,

"I'm sorry to be a killjoy, but we must get home. I have a family to look after and must start getting the meal ready and Lotti has promised to do a load of ironing for me. I've enjoyed your company immensely and it's been a lovely afternoon. Oh, and thank you for being so considerate in looking after Lotti and her boyfriend last night."

The latter part of her little speech was delivered in louder tones so that the staff and customers could hear. It was a lovely gesture to salvage my tarnished reputation.

Gunther stood up, moved our chairs for us, shook our hands, did his heel-clicking and mini-bowing routine and watched us with the adoration of a devoted puppy as we headed out onto the street.

Moments later, Hedwig said,

"God, I should have had a pee before we left, but I didn't want to leave you on your own with him, he couldn't keep his eyes off you."

I had a fit of the giggles as Hedwig clutched her shopping in front of her and did a very funny, cross-legged simulation of having reached bursting point.

I hadn't thought of it until she mentioned it then I too was desperate to pee. By mutual consent, we agreed to go in one of the damaged buildings. One keeping lookout while the other performed.

When it was my turn, Hedwig said she had never seen anything so incongruous as an apparently beautiful young girl hiking up her skirt and peeing against a wall. I made a mental note not to do it again while so attired. It struck me that we were both a bit tiddly, me for the second time in two days. As if I had placed the thought into her head, Hedwig looked at me in a strange way and in a mildly accusing tone she said, "You were drinking with Gunther yesterday afternoon weren't you?" I'd only lied by omission before, or been economical with the truth to prevent her from worrying. Now, I did not want her to think my deception was purely because I had been drinking with a German officer. It was time for explanations.

After my 'confession', I concluded by imploring her not to tell Alex, in fact that had been my only reason for not telling either of them in the first place.

We must have created a strange impression on passers by as Hedwig put her bag down, enfolded me in her arms and kissed me on the cheek saying, "You poor darling, you must have been terrified. How fortunate that Gunther turned up when he did." I snivelled a bit and said, "Come on, we've had a long day and Alex will be wondering where we have got to. Oh, you promise not to tell Alex, he'd probably give me the beating I almost got at the hands of that soldier." "I wouldn't dare tell him. You're right, he'd go stark raving mad. He loves you to the point of distraction and love like that is a very powerful emotion."

CHAPTER TWENTY-SIX

We rang the bell to let Alex know we were on our way up and he met us halfway, gave us both a kiss and, having relieved us of our bags, led the way back to the flat.

He looked and sounded a bit miffed and when I asked what the problem was, he said, "You two have all the fun, you've both been drinking again and here am I sitting at home worrying about you and all the time you're getting pissed."

"Don't exaggerate so Alex. We've had to cover a lot of ground to do our shopping today since Janni daren't show himself as Janni any more. It was hot and sticky and the bags were heavy and all you were doing was sleeping. We deserved our couple of drinks. But, if drinking offends you that much, we'll pour all ours down the drain and we'll all refrain from now on. Would that please you more?" Hedwig queried somewhat aggressively. Alex looked suitably abashed and mumbled an apology.

Hedwig put an arm around my shoulder and said, "You looked particularly lovely today, Janni, er Lotti. Oh shit, I don't know what to call you. You've caught the sun so much these last few weeks and your long brown legs were the envy of everyone. Honestly, if I hadn't known otherwise I'd have bet that you were a girl. All your actions and mannerisms are so completely natural, your voice too, you talk exactly the way you look."

I suppose I felt a little uncomfortable at these compliments and was stuck for words when Alex, still a little truculent, said, "And you still sound like a bloody girl."

Whether it was the drink that made me react the way I did, the fact that I had, on two separate occasions within the last twenty-four hours, been treated with great courtesy and had enjoyed, for me, really sophisticated conversation, or whether it was the constant stress catching up, I don't know. It could have been the constant changing of personality, having to revert to being Janni when I went home, because of the boys and Julius. My dalliance with Rebecca may also have had something to do with it too. In any event, I lost my composure completely and shouted, "What the bloody hell do you want me to be? You tell me you love me the way I am and you say the same when I'm just plain Janni. I'm so confused all the time. Sometimes, I think that what we are doing is not quite right and that therefore I must be very weird and that means that you must be bloody weird too." I paused to get my breath and collect my thoughts then carried on, "And your mother, she not only lets us sleep together, knowing full well what we are doing, without batting a bloody eyelid, but she openly encourages us. Christ, I don't know where the bloody hell I'm up to."

I think that by this time I had given up any pretence of concealing my tears and as the pair of them gaped at me, open-mouthed in astonishment at my outburst, I stormed off to the bedroom where I flung myself onto the bed and lay there feeling very miserable and sorry for myself. Even in my misery, I thought, "Hell, I'm even behaving like a stupid, petulant little girl."

It didn't bring me any comfort. Quite the contrary, I began to realise the enormity of my outburst, how unkind I had been to Hedwig who had always been so kind, considerate and loving to me and dear Alex must have been wondering what the hell had hit him. In turn, I felt uncomfortable then deeply embarrassed, then remorseful, particularly as I had never behaved in this way before and didn't know how to redeem the situation.

As I lay there, I could hear muted voices from the other room, after some ten minutes or so, there was a gentle knock on the door and Hedwig asked, "May we come in please, darling?"

"O.K," I snivelled.

They entered and closed the door behind them and it was at once apparent that I had made everybody quite miserable since they both had tear-streaked faces. I was not feeling very proud of myself. They sat on the bed; one on either side of me and both of them took one of my hands in both of theirs. Hedwig let go with one of her hands, reached over and began to stroke my head very gently saying, "Poor, poor Janni, we love you so much and you always seem so happy and cheerful, you always lift our spirits when we're feeling low, and all the time you've been suffering this inner turmoil and we never noticed." She kissed my forehead and said, "I'm so sorry darling please forgive us."

I sat up, gave her a big weepy cuddle and said,

"I'm sorry too. I spoke without thinking and I shouldn't have said what I did, it was unforgivable. All the strain of leading this double life, together with the scares of the last few days suddenly seemed to overwhelm me. Sometimes when I'm out, or going through the check point I'm terrified that I might be stopped and searched."

Feeling a little better and with my sense of humour returning, I continued,

"In all probability they would think I was trying to hide something other than my genitals and when they couldn't find anything on a boy other than a fairly impressive pair of tits, they'd shoot me just for being a bloody freak." Alex hugged me, rocking back and forth saying, "Oh baby, poor darling baby, I'm sorry too, but you must know that I love you however you are."

We held each other very tightly while our collective snivelling subsided and to lighten the mood I said, "Come on, let's drink some of that nice Tokay, have something to eat and play silly-buggers." There was relief in laughter and after one final, communal hug, we got up and went back to the other room, where Hedwig and I tried to race each other for the bathroom to freshen up our faces. She won and Alex was so attentive, either holding my hand or with his arm around my waist as we went to the kitchen and took the wine from the icebox. He uncorked it, passed three glasses to me and, with arms around each other's waists, we returned to the living room. We put the wine and glasses on the table and instinctively wrapped ourselves round each other and indulged in some very tender, making-up type kissing. We were quite oblivious to the fact that Hedwig had returned until she said, "Break it up you two, I'm feeling left out and I'm dying for a drink. Be a darling Alex and pour for us." Normality returned and we seemed to relax a little too much, opening another bottle of wine and settling for a simple salad with lots of fresh bread for our main meal of the day.

We carried on drinking, dancing, singing and generally acting like happy idiots and by midnight we'd not only finished the wine, but made substantial inroads into the apricot brandy. It was the first time that I had been completely drunk and though, for the most part it was quite enjoyable, the aftermath was disastrous. When I went to lie down both bed and ceiling were swirling round in opposite directions and every so often I would have to sit up to halt the motion, only to fall back again and suddenly feel the urgent desire to vomit coming over me. I reeled to the bathroom on several occasions and emptied my stomach so thoroughly that, despite continuous retching, there was nothing left to bring up and finally, in a cold sweat, I fell asleep on the toilet floor. I was unaware of most of this and it was only in the morning (Thank God it was Saturday and Alex didn't have to go to work) that Hedwig told me Alex had spent a great part of the early hours holding me in his arms, bathing my face, and finally carrying me to bed. Apparently I never stirred during these ministrations, neither when he picked me up and carried me nor when they both undressed me and tucked me into bed. I still felt unwell when I awoke and it took several cups of coffee before I could face a couple of rounds of toast.

Soon after that I began to improve and uttered the legendary words, "I'm not going to do that again!" We all spent a busy morning doing household chores and a load of washing and then, after a light lunch, the three of us strolled in the park, lay on the grass and generally enjoyed the lovely weather. Over the previous weeks, the sun had bleached my hair and it was now a mix of the original brown with blonde streaks, which both Alex and

Hedwig thought looked fabulous, and with which I have to admit to being greatly pleased. A decision had been made that Alex and I would go and leave a message for Moishe and Solly and only wait around to see if they turned up after a lengthy surveillance period to ensure that there were no hidden dangers. Our evening stroll was the usual hand in hand, imitating the young lovers routine, during which, we scanned every nook and cranny for any signs of unusual activity and having satisfied ourselves that all was quiet, we made our way to the hiding place where we retrieved two notes and some money. The first note with the money was to the effect that there was too much activity in the neighbourhood that particular night and they had beaten a hasty retreat to the sewers and the second, more worryingly was to advise us that they would be lying low for a few days because there had been a substantial build-up in the numbers of S.S. in the town over the last few days and people were becoming more and more wary of any covert activity. They cautioned us to be extra careful and finished with; "Rebecca and the rest of the Lipschitz family send their love to you both."

Alex took my hand and we walked home deep in thought. I'd hoped to see the boys because it was imperative to re-establish my credibility with them as Janni. Going in and out of the ghetto via the main gate was becoming too much of a strain and I was feeling more and more nervous on each occasion. It was necessary for me to do at least two more trips to my family and I'd hoped to be able to do these by way of the sewers. As it was, I would have to risk the main gate and all its hazards at least once more. Additional dangers were posed by the 'Ghetto Police', which was made up of Jews in the pay of the Germans, specially selected to perform unpleasant tasks against their own kind in return for favours and the promise of leniency. They wore uniforms and had become very officious, copying their masters and looking for approval by administering savage beatings with heavy sticks upon the inmates.

They lived within the ghetto and although there were many thousands of us crammed into those dreadful quarters, they were forever watchful and for scant reward, ready to betray anyone to improve their standing with the S.S. guards.

I didn't say much about this to Alex, because he would not have let me out of his sight, in fact, he would probably have locked me in my room as a virtual prisoner if he knew of my fears. As usual, Hedwig was relieved at our return and was full of praise for Moishe and Solly for being so sensible. We settled down to a relaxed evening, talking and listening to background music. Mercifully, we abstained from drink. I was still remembering my total incapacitation of the previous night and as far as I was concerned, I never wanted to see alcohol again!

Alex had to work this Sunday so it meant an early night and after all the excitement of the last few days, it was a good thing.

We said goodnight to Hedwig and climbed into bed.

Alex was all gentle tenderness, whispering comforting words, taking my breath away with his deft touches and strokes and showering compliments on me. He liked me to curl up against his body, my back against his chest while he wrapped his arms around me and nuzzled the nape of my neck and shoulder. In this position, I always felt very safe and comfortable, like a small animal being protected by a parent. We fell asleep in total contentment.

CHAPTER TWENTY-SEVEN

Alex went to work and I climbed back into bed where I alternated my time between cat-napping and serious thought. I would have to tackle Moishe and Solly as Janni once I had returned to the ghetto. It would be a difficult confrontation and I would probably need Rebecca's help.

Thoughts of Rebecca disturbed me. I had always loved her very much, but more as an older sister and although I had allowed myself to get carried away on a couple of occasions, I had to admit to myself that I was much happier in my current role and that it was only the desperate circumstances in which we had found ourselves, with Rebecca being cut off from a social life with her own contemporaries in which she would have undoubtedly found a more suitable and worthy young man, that had convinced her that her love for me was anything other than that of brother and sister. I tried very hard to convince myself that this was so but felt it would prove more difficult to convince Rebecca. I couldn't bear the thought of hurting her in any way and knew instinctively that if it appeared that my rejection of her was going to have this sort of effect, then I should capitulate and succumb yet again to her undoubted charms.

Eventually, without having reached any positive conclusions or deciding upon any plan of action, I got up, showered and dressed and made a pot of tea.

Hedwig joined me and we sat for a long time discussing various options. It was during this talk that we finally decided that once I had paid my next two visits to my 'family', I would come back here and not take any more chances. Hedwig tried exceedingly hard to persuade me to give up now, never to go back there, she almost begged me, telling me that I would be much safer with her and Alex, a fact of which I was becoming more increasingly aware.

It was very difficult to ignore her common sense approach to the situation and I was defying all logic by insisting that it was something I had to do and that if I didn't, and for some reason I never saw them again, the feelings of guilt and abandonment would haunt me forever.

Hedwig knew how much I loved and respected all of my adoptive family and with great reluctance, agreed that I should go to see them so that we could say our goodbyes in a proper way. We had become sombre. I was saddened by the thought of never seeing the family again and knew that the farewells would be a very sad and tearful experience.

Hedwig gave me a brief cuddle and said,

"I'll go and get washed and dressed and we'll go for a walk. It will be lovely in the park at this hour." With that, she headed for the bathroom and I spent the next twenty minutes playing some cheerful music in a bid to raise my spirits.

It seemed to work for Hedwig because she came out of the bathroom humming along with the music and her happy smile lifted me out of my depression.

The sun was very warm and the park was extremely popular. If it hadn't been for the uniforms bringing constant reminders of subjugation, it could have been a beautiful summer's day in any park in the world. There was the sound of children's voices as they played happily together; couples young and old were ambling along, arm in arm or holding hands, others were just sprawled on the grass; a few dogs chased around after sticks and balls or had playful fights and mad chases with other dogs. It was all so very natural and peaceful that it seemed inconceivable that only twenty minutes walk away, there were bodies in the streets, of which numbers were increasing very rapidly as more and more people were being shot on the slightest pretext and others were dying of starvation and untended illness. It was particularly distressing to see the number of skeletal children's bodies amongst the lifeless, rag-doll figures which littered the pavements and gutters and even more distressing to observe the callousness with which people ignored or even stepped over these poor, contorted little bodies without the slightest show of pity or compassion and not even a backward glance. The Germans were strange people; on the one hand, they were committing terrible, unforgivable atrocities and at the same time, trying to create an air of absolute normality. One of their creative ideas had been to have a regimental band play in the park and once again I was struck by the strangeness of the German mind. It was as if they desperately needed to show that they were, in reality, jolly nice chaps and that we shouldn't think too badly of them just because they had a penchant for murdering helpless people in a very random and arbitrary fashion. They played a selection of music so beautifully and with such feeling that you could almost be forgiven for believing them, even if the music was punctuated from time to time with the distant sound of solitary shots or short bursts of sub-machine-gun fire.

Like many others in the park that day, Hedwig and I stayed and listened to the music, drank water from the drinking fountains, sat on the grass enjoying the diversion and, to our surprise, clapping at the end of each piece of music.

I thought, "How easy it would be to take the sensible path which Hedwig implored me to follow. No more covert assignations; no stupid risks; no having to change identities and personalities and never having to leave Alex again. Never mind, it'll only be a few more days."

We stayed a long time in the park taking advantage of the beautiful sunshine and in no particular hurry to return home since Alex would be able to sleep better in our absence.

Eventually, we made our way homeward; just as many others were doing as teatime approached. On our way, we passed many German officers, accompanied by their wives or girlfriends. Quite a number of wives had taken up residence in the city and in so doing, had acquired some of the best residences including their furnishings, which often numbered priceless paintings and artefacts amongst the contents. Most items of real value had already been shipped to Germany, but many more turned up from time to time when temporary hiding places were discovered. These new discoveries would later be sent to Germany as the troops withdrew in the retreat from the advancing Russians.

We were caught slightly off-guard when a voice from behind said,

"Good afternoon ladies", and we turned to see Gunther and a fellow officer a few paces behind us. As we turned at the sound of his voice, they came to a halt and Gunther performed his familiar routine of clicking his heels and touching the peak of his cap.

"May I introduce my colleague?" he enquired and without waiting for a reply, he continued "Untersturmfhrer Werner Knolle, Frulein Lotti und Frulein Hedwig, I'm sorry, I'm not sure whether that should be 'Frau' Hedwig", he concluded with a charming smile.

Hedwig and I acknowledged the introduction and Werner went through the same stiff, formal routine, which always characterised Gunther's greetings and departures and we were hard-pressed to conceal our desire to burst out laughing. It was all too serious.

Under lowered lashes, I gave Werner a thorough inspection while, in response to Gunther's question about her marital status, Hedwig explained to Gunther that she was a widow.

Werner was about twenty one or two, quite tall and athletic looking. He had brown hair and brown eyes and the recent sunshine had tanned his face and hands. I got the impression that this was another extremely well educated young man from a good family and he had about him an air of easy assurance which only comes from inborn confidence and a long history of being brought up with, and being comfortable with, the finer things in life. He was very easy to get along with, his conversation was witty and his eyes sparkled along with his wit. In next to no time, we were laughing and joking like old friends and I could see a look of concern spreading slowly but surely over Gunther's face when, after one wild burst of laughter, I held on to Werner's arm for a second to steady myself and Werner, seizing the opportunity, took hold of my hand, tucked it under his arm and started towards the park exit. Gunther had no alternative but to offer his arm to Hedwig who took it with a mischievous smile and they both fell in beside us.

It was almost as if Hedwig and I were telepathic. In a way, both of us were enjoying this diversion but at the same time we wanted to get away from them so that we could give vent to our feelings and have a good laugh together.

When we reached the park gates, Hedwig stopped, came over to me, took my arm and with an air that brooked no argument, said, "It has been a great pleasure meeting you again, Gunther, and equally pleasant to meet your comrade but we really must get home now. We are late already; I have to feed my son and Lotti has to get ready to meet her boyfriend. They have a hot date tonight!" she concluded in a conspiratorial manner, which imparted tacit innuendo, and, as intended, drew indulgent, wistful smiles from the two young officers.

They looked quite crestfallen and I couldn't help feeling sorry for them since it was apparent that they had imagined themselves to have made a conquest, that the rest of their evening was going to be spent in our company and as far as Werner was concerned, there was no doubt in my mind about his intentions. Ever the perfect gentlemen, they accepted this disappointing blow to their plans with equanimity and after the mildest protestations, reluctantly agreed to let us go on the promise that should we all be fortunate enough to meet again, they would be permitted to treat us to a meal and maybe, just maybe, take us dancing. Hedwig and I took our departure and once we were out of sight, we could contain ourselves no longer and virtually fell about with laughter as we commenced to do poker-faced impressions of the officers, with much heel-clicking, bowing and for good measure, a couple of Zieg Heils, whilst pulling our fringes to one side, holding fingers under our noses and stretching our right arms out to the front. As one, whilst continuing our impressions of Adolf, we fell in step side by side and gave a fairly good rendition of the 'goose-step' accompanied by the first verse of the Horst Wessel Lied.

In the near distance we spotted more soldiers and abruptly stopped our capers, suddenly aware of the enormity of our joint indiscretion and the consequences our actions could provoke. Although subdued, we couldn't help smiling and giggling from time to time and as we walked happily homeward, Hedwig surprised me by saying,

"War is such a dreadful thing. Here we are, behaving like a couple of idiots yet in ordinary times, we could both like those two young men."

While I was digesting this, she turned to me and continued,

"Be honest, they were very good company weren't they and that Werner was a bit special wasn't he?" I remained silent for a while as though I was mulling over her question and choosing to answer very carefully simply because she was, after all, Alex's mother. The truth was that I had also found Werner extremely attractive and the same thought had crossed my mind "Pity there's a war on!" but I was not about to admit this to Hedwig and in any event, if Werner once discovered that I was not what I purported to be I sensed that his anger at such humiliation would have known no bounds whereas by contrast, I felt that Gunther, the duller of the two would have been very sympathetic.

Eventually I answered,

"Yes, I suppose they are both quite nice in their own way but let's face it, not only are they Germans, they're also bloody S.S. and I wouldn't trust them within a kilometre's distance." I had concluded my answer with a certain amount of venom and I was surprised to realise that my anger was not so much directed at Gunther and Werner but at myself. I was feeling guilty and angry with myself for being attracted to Werner, which amounted to a betrayal of my feelings for Alex. I was suddenly aware of the restrictions imposed upon me by the prevailing circumstances during the past three years and my limited knowledge of relationships. Furthermore, my attraction to members of the same sex was now beyond question and all the suppressed feelings of doubt and confusion resurfaced to make me feel insecure and wretched. I am sure that Hedwig had an uncanny insight into my predicament because, without hesitation or comment, she linked her arm with mine and said, "Let's get home. I'm dying for a cup of tea and a pee and Alex will be worrying about us." In mentioning Alex, whether unwittingly or not, she gave my arm a very motherly, understanding squeeze. I felt like shit!

At home, Alex had prepared a salad and was busying himself in making the table look attractive. As usual, he greeted us both with a hug and kiss then, holding me at arm's length but addressing both of us, he said, "My word, you really have caught the sun, both of you", and looking directly at me, he added, "I don't think I've ever seen you looking so beautiful."

Simultaneously, I was overwhelmed with joy, love for Alex and gut-wrenching guilt and before I could stop it, a tear trickled down my face. To hide my confusion, I pulled Alex towards me, put my arms around his neck and said, "You say such nice things to me and I love you very much". I kissed him very passionately and as he responded, all other negative thoughts went out of my head. I had overcome my temporary insanity and was happy, even ecstatic just to be with my dear Alex.

We spent a relatively relaxed evening and later, Alex and I visited our 'post-box' to see if there were any messages from Moishe and Solly. No messages, in fact the last message that we had left for them was still there and from this, we deduced that security must have tightened up considerably within the ghetto or that they were giving plenty of time for things to settle down before resuming their activities. I think we both felt a sort of relief that they hadn't turned up and we were far more relaxed as we walked home, not needing to put on an act for the benefit of any observers since our conduct that evening was entirely automatic and purely for the benefit of ourselves.

In bed that night, Alex was full of concern, pleading with me not to risk it when I told him of my intention to visit my 'family' because there were very important things which had to be attended to. He hadn't persuaded me to change my mind and it was an angry and tearful Alex who left for work that morning. It had been the longest time we had ever spent together and it would come as a blow to both of us to be separated, even for at most a couple of days. Not only that, although Hedwig's flat was not large, it was comfortable, had running hot and cold water, there was plenty to eat and we didn't have to share any facilities with anyone else. It would be quite a sobering experience going back to the ghetto. Before leaving for work, Hedwig begged me to be very careful and not to even think about going through the checkpoint if there was even the slightest hint of anything amiss.

I reassured her and gave her a farewell kiss feeling far less confident than I had led her to believe.

CHAPTER TWENTY-EIGHT

I did my usual shopping rounds and when I could put it off no longer, I headed towards the ghetto, every step increasing my anxiety and making me ultra cautious. I had never been away for so long and in the meantime, I had lost track of the guard changes. For this reason, I devoted more time to observation than was normal for me and finally, after satisfying myself that there was no one on duty whom I recognised as a potentially dangerous threat, I gathered up my courage, put on my brightest smile and headed to the barrier. A guard said, "Good morning Frulein. It's another beautiful day."

I smiled and said,

"Good morning. Yes, isn't it? We've been really lucky with the weather lately."

He nodded and said,

"Indeed we have. I'll be glad when I've finished this shift so that I can make the most of it."

"How much longer before you finish?" I asked, feeling much more confident now and wanting to find out what time the next change of guard would take place.

"Just over an hour to go. I've been on duty since seven," he replied.

"Well at least you have plenty of the day left. Make the most of it. I hope you enjoy yourself," I enthused as I started to walk away and gave him a wave of my hand as I left. I didn't turn but could feel his eyes following me as I headed to the stalls, giving the impression that I hadn't a care in the world.

After much prowling about through the stalls ostensibly seeking out bargains, I made my way to the flat and attracted some curious looks from several of the inmates on my way. Despite all the dangers of this awful place and notwithstanding my misgivings of the previous days and nights, I felt a sense of relief and the joyous, loving greeting from Rachel and Rebecca made my 'homecoming' incredibly heart-warming.

As I cuddled them in turn, Rachel said,

"Oh Janni darling, we thought we would never see you again. We thought you had gone for good and although we were very happy for you, we knew that we would miss you dreadfully." The effect of this little speech, the very real depth of their feelings for me had quite an emotional effect and as the tears trickled down my face, they reacted in similar fashion and we stood, arms around each other, waiting to regain our composure.

With steaming cups of tea, we sat at the little table and they expressed their gratitude for the food I had brought, especially as stocks had been running low since Moishe and Solly had been unable to keep their nightly rendezvous.

I brought them up to date on everything that had happened since I'd been away and they were both in stitches when I described, with graphic impersonations, the incidents involving Gunther and Werner. They praised my caution in my dealings with the chemist and listened with awe, hanging onto every word as I related my altercation with the soldier who was going to punch me and how Gunther had acted so gallantly. I told it all in a light-hearted way as if there was never anything much to worry about except the one occasion of the near beating. It didn't fool them for one moment and Rachel said, "My God Janni, you've taken some enormous risks and at times, you must have been terrified." "Now and again," I acknowledged and continued, "But I didn't do it all alone. Alex and Hedwig helped on every occasion and were always there for back-up."

"I do so wish I could thank them personally," Rachel said somewhat wistfully. "They have turned out to be really staunch friends, doing so much for us and we never got the chance to meet Hedwig," she concluded. "Mum, Becca, I can't go through the barrier again, I am becoming more and more frightened on every occasion," I started, and as soon as I had their full attention I continued, "Can you imagine what would happen if they took me in for a strip search? Can you foresee the inevitable outcome of that? It doesn't bear thinking about." "Oh Janni, you must think very badly of us to allow you to take such risks, but in all honesty, that possibility and the probable consequences had never occurred to us. It's too awful to contemplate," Rebecca said in subdued tones.

I thought for a moment or two and said,

"I've a suggestion to make and it involves Moishe and Solly. It's imperative that I be allowed to use the sewers again and in order to do this, I have to regain their trust. So, it might be a good idea if Becca went and brought them both here and I'll confront them just as I am as Lotti. Obviously they'll have to make their way here without being seen, particularly by the ghetto police who would wonder why two such fit young men were not on a work party.

After giving them a few moments for this to sink in, I asked,

"Do you think you could manage that alright, Becca?"

"I'm sure I can and it does seem like a very good idea," Becca replied. Before I could add anything further, she got up from the table saying, "I'll go now, tell them there's someone here I'd like them to meet and that they should make their way over here as soon as they possibly can."

She smoothed her dress and left the small flat.

Rachel took my hands in hers and said,

"It must seem very stupid of me not to have given your physical differences any serious consideration when thinking about the dangers you have been facing, but honestly darling, you look so beautiful I never thought for one moment that anyone would question your identity nor did it occur to me that you might be searched." She paused for a moment and caught me off-guard by asking, "Just how pronounced are your physical changes now?" and with a smile she continued, "Have you got padding in there or is it all you?"

We both laughed. I had forgotten that although Hedwig had often seen me near naked since none of us had any inhibitions in her flat, Rachel had not seen me in that state since we moved into the ghetto. This was more due to the presence of the two boys whom I did not wish to see my unusual, developing figure. "You had better have a look while no one else is around"; I said and undid my blouse, removed it and unfastened my bra. As I turned to face her, Rachel's eyes opened really wide in amazement. My breasts were not overlarge but firm and nicely proportioned, what some men would refer to as a nice handful! I swung this way and that and as light-heartedly and impishly as possible, I said, "Not a bad pair of tits are they?"

Rachel held me at arms length examining me; her face broke into a grin and she agreed, "A very impressive pair of tits indeed!"

We were giggling as I put my bra and blouse back on and before she could ask any awkward, searching questions I said.

"And before you ask, they don't worry me. I love my body the way it is, even if I am a bit of a freak. I'm totally happy with it but I do accept that it may cause problems for other people. One thing is for sure though, it is much easier to conceal my masculinity than it is to conceal my femininity, and my figure is somewhat hard to conceal in boy's clothes."

"You are right, any girl would be envious of your figure and looks and you must go through absolute hell every time you change your identity." Rachel ventured.

"Mum, I've lived as a girl outside ever since the chemist's affair because I was too well known as Janni in most of the shops and markets and a few enquiries would have been all it took to learn my shopping habits. I'd have been picked up in no time," I said and added, "The boys will have to know about this and the reasons for me dressing the way I do, without going into too much physical detail." Rachel pondered for a moment before replying, "Yes, that's probably a good idea, but prepare yourself for some of Aaron's stinging witticisms."

We both smiled, knowing that I was going to be the brunt of some good-humoured josh-ing and Rachel suddenly asked,

"How do Hedwig and Alex react to your present form of dress? I know that it was her who helped you with your original plans when it was for the sole purpose of acquiring extra shopping, but all that's changed now hasn't it?" I thought carefully before replying and came to the conclusion that there was already too much deception in my life and what was more, I loved and trusted these people who had always been completely open and hon-est with me. I took a deep breath and answered, "You would have to see it to believe it. Hedwig and I are just like sisters and everybody treats us that way. As for Alex, everybody thinks he is my boyfriend, and Mum, I know that you've suspected this for quite some time, it's true, he is my boyfriend and I love him very much."

I'd finished my explanation in something of a rush and now I waited with baited breath for the reaction to my confession.

Rachel held my hands again and looking straight into my eyes with great compassion she said, "Thank you for being so honest darling. I'm not shocked or angry. It would have been a miracle if this hadn't happened. When you first came to us all that time ago, I recognised then that there was a distinct possibility, no, probability that you would have to confront these issues and I tried to explain it to you at the time, but you were very young and at that time, I don't suppose any such thoughts had ever entered your head. In the meantime of course, you have been so busy looking after us that, until now, we have never had an opportunity to discuss it." She paused and then added, "I don't think it would be wise to tell the boys about this aspect of your life. There is no knowing what their reaction might be. I may or may not tell Julius although, like me, I'm sure he has suspected for some time. Just one thing darling, as long as you are happy, that's all that matters. After all, you weren't responsible for creating your own body and, given the alternatives, it's your right and nobody else's to choose to live in the way in which you are happiest, most comfort-able and feel more natural." "Thanks Mum," I responded and made a mental note to con-trol my impulse to blubber when anyone was so kind and understanding. To regain my composure, I got up from the table, took a bottle of plum vodka out of my bag and to a sur-prised Rachel I said, "Come on, let's have a drink to celebrate my birthday. I know it isn't my real birthday, I still haven't a clue about that, but it feels like one and I don't want to drink on my own."

Rachel's response was quite unexpected, she got two glasses, looked at them, swapped them for larger one's and advanced towards me with a huge grin, saying, "Goodness gra-cious Lotti, how quickly you've grown up. Sex and alcohol, whatever next. I suppose you smoke as well?"

I was surprised at being addressed as Lotti, but pleased at the same time because it indi-cated her total acceptance of me as I was. She took the bottle from my hand and poured two fairly stiff measures, raised her glass and clinked it against mine saying, "Happy birth-day darling, may you always look as beautiful as you do today." She leant over and gave me a big kiss and added, "This is the only birthday party I've been to where the birthday girl brought all the presents." We were still laughing and hadn't heard Rebecca return. I was just answering Rachel's earlier question, saying, "No, I don't smoke and I suppose you could say that out of sex, alcohol and smoking, two out of three is good or one out of three isn't bad!" The very open matter of fact way in which I said it made Rachel laugh even louder and we were both unprepared for the sudden voice saying, "My God, what on earth have you two been discussing? It sounded quite outrageous."

Rachel carried on laughing and said,

"Oh you know how funny and impish Janni can be. I only asked him if he had started smoking and you heard what his reply was. Cheeky little devil," she added, giving me a happy grin. Then to Rebecca she said, "Fetch yourself a glass, we're celebrating Janni's birthday and before you ask, no, we don't know the date, but it's about time he had a party anyway."

Rebecca joined us at the table, sipped her drink, coughed and said, "This is amazing!" Suddenly, there was a knock at the door; I'd forgotten the immediate sense of panic any unexpected knocks brought and there was a hushed silence until a voice said, "Are you there Rebecca, it's me, Moishe."

We heaved a collective sigh of relief and Becca went to open the door.

Both the boys were there and Becca invited them in.

Suddenly, they spotted me and their faces broke into huge smiles; they almost ran across the room, pulled me out of my chair and gave me all-enveloping hugs and kisses on the cheek saying, "Lotti, what on earth are you doing here? Don't you know this a very dangerous place? You must be out of your mind."

Now that the moment had arrived, I suddenly lost my nerve. It was all going to be so embarrassing. These two boys who thought on numerous occasions that they were hugging and kissing a girl were about to find out that all was not as it seemed! I didn't know where to start. I couldn't take my clothes off to prove anything without flashing my willy around and I could hardly do that anyway in the presence of Rachel and Rebecca although I thought that Rebecca might find it very amusing. To make matters worse, we had been so engrossed that we hadn't noticed the passing of time. The flat door opened and Julius came in followed immediately by Aaron and Isaac. They stopped, taking in the scene, Rachel, Rebecca and another girl sitting at the table with glasses of plum vodka in front of them and two very personable looking young men standing beside me. Julius sized up the situation very quickly. I'm not sure whether or not he knew that, as yet, I had not revealed my identity to Moishe and Solly, but he walked straight over to me, drew me to my feet, hugged me and said, "Janni, how lovely to have you back with us. We've missed you terribly and thought you had gone for good." He turned and said, "Hello Moishe, Solly. Did you bring Janni back with you?" Both boys were speechless and Aaron and Isaac just stood there with their mouths agape staring at me as if I was something from another planet.

Aaron was the first to recover and he said,

"We always said our little brother was far too beautiful to be a boy and the ease with which he can assume his other role has made life a lot easier for all of us, including you and your families", he said as he addressed Moishe and Solly. He put his arm around me and said, "It must be a great disappointment to you both because he really does look very fanciable doesn't he? Even though we're used to seeing him like this, he's excelled himself today."

Turning to me he said,

"I'll bet you've been enjoying your deception, you've got half the German army trying to date you, you brazen little hussy."

His eye spotted the bottle and glasses and playing along in the role, I fluttered my eyelashes at him and said, "Be a darling Aaron and fetch some more glasses, it's my birthday party today. Well one day's as good as any other isn't it?"

He grinned, brought glasses and poured for everyone, raised his glass and said,

"Happy Birthday Janni, it's great to have you back." He squeezed my shoulder and gave me a kiss on the cheek.

He kept a protective arm round me for quite a long time!

I opened a packet of cigarettes and asked,

"Mum, is it alright if everyone smokes in here?"

"Just this once as it's a special occasion," she replied and added, "So long as you don't make a habit of it." Only Rachel, Becca, Isaac and myself refrained and I was amused to note that Aaron had overcome his professed intention never to smoke again after his first disastrous attempt.

We finished the bottle fairly quickly between the eight of us and I'd had to recount all my recent adventures for the benefit of them all.

At the end of my account, Moishe said,"

"So it was you they were looking for that night was it?"

"I'm not really sure. It could just have been coincidence. In honesty, I think I was too small a fish to warrant such a large-scale operation. There must have been something else going on at the same time," I responded. "Nevertheless, it must have been pretty scary. We took one look and bolted back down the sewer," Solly said, and to my surprise, he added, "You're very brave and resourceful Lotti er Janni." The poor boy blushed and then laughed saying, "Hell, you had us fooled completely, didn't he Moishe?"

It was the moment Moishe had been waiting for; he looked at Solly quite disdainfully and with an air of nonchalance he boasted,

"I had my doubts all along, but you fell for Lotti hook, line and sinker. You were totally besotted."

Solly took this in good part and with a huge grin he announced to everyone,

"You can always tell when he's lying, he rubs the end of his nose to see if it's grown any bigger and you can tell from the size of it that he rubs it a lot."

We all laughed and I thought that whilst we were all in this happy, playful mood, it would be the best time to request that I should be allowed to use the sewers again.

To my relief, they agreed whole-heartedly.

I hastened to point out that I would be dressed as I was now and hoped that this would not embarrass them. "Hell no, you're the one who should be embarrassed, after all, we've seen your knickers when you were climbing up and down the steel ladder. Not a pretty sight!" Solly said in response. Everyone laughed again, but poor Isaac had not said a word the whole time and still followed me everywhere with his eyes. I walked over to him, put an arm round him and said, "There are lots of nice salad things in my bag Izzy, come and help me to prepare everything so that Mum and Dad can have some time together, O.K?"

"Oh yes, sure Janni, just let's get rid of Solly and Moishe first," he said and with that, he assumed an air of authority, took the smaller bag which I had indicated to him was for the boys, walked over to them and said, "Great that you came over and that you'll allow Janni to use the sewers again. Sorry we can't invite you to stay, but Janni has brought this for you."

He handed the bag to Solly, who with great panache, walked over to me put his arms round me, gave me a peck on the cheek and announced to everyone, "We always used to say our thanks and goodbyes this way and I can't think of any good reason to change a nice habit. Can you, Moishe?"

"No, it's fine with me," he said as he followed Solly's example and then added,

"Thanks for everything Janni. Come over whenever you want to; you know what times we go out." They headed for the door, thanked Rachel and Julius for their hospitality, shook hands with Aaron and Isaac and lingered over their farewells to Rebecca. Solly, with his happy-go-lucky manner couldn't resist a final comment, "Pity you're not a real girl Janni, you really do look super, but then nothing is for real these days is it?" I threw a cushion at him and the pair of them bolted, still laughing, out of the flat. Izzy and I washed the salad things and Becca came to help us. Finally, we laid the table and set out the food. I opened a bottle of wine, poured and waited for Julius to give everything a blessing and to give thanks. It was strange and never ceased to amaze me how quickly one could switch from solemnity to laughter, jocularity and good-natured ribaldry.

Aaron started off by asking me whether or not I used the ladies loo and in answer to his own question said that obviously I'd have attracted more attention walking into a gents in the guise of a woman. He pondered for a moment and then asked, "It must have been very confusing for you Janni. How did you remember what to do all the time to remain convincing?"

"Simple", I said, "You look at what you're wearing and decide whether you have to do it standing up or sitting down. Even you should be able to work that out Aaron dear." Then I told them about me peeing on the bombsite, standing up and wearing a dress, which they all thought hilarious, particularly as I had given a very theatrical impression of the scene.

When the laughing had subsided, I turned to Julius and said,

"Incidentally Dad, everyone else was completely fooled, but you spotted me instantly when you came in. How did you know it was me?"

"Mum and Rebecca had told me of the risks you had been taking on our behalf and how through this dual identity idea, you had managed to secure the supply of food and things so successfully. I've known since before we came to the ghetto, but Mum thought it best that as far as you were concerned, it was a secret between the both of you. It was very easy for me to put two and two together but I must admit that if I hadn't had any prior knowledge, it would have taken me far longer to work out who you were. Oh, and while we're on the subject, well done Aaron on picking up so quickly, your reaction, despite what must have been a startling revelation does you great credit. I'm very proud of you."

"Me too!" I echoed and reached over to squeeze Aaron's hand.

He smiled squeezed my hand in response, and to everyone he said,

"He's really lovely our Little Janni, whatever would we have done without him?" He raised his glass and said, "A toast. Birthday or not, boy or girl. "To Janni!" We all love you very much." They all raised their glasses and echoed Aaron's toast. I felt the familiar, uncontrollable urge to snivel, but covered it by saying, "I hope you don't mind, but I'm really very warm and I have to get some fresh air. Are you coming with me Becca?"

She got up; we excused ourselves and went to the upper landing, opened the window and enjoyed the night air. We talked a lot and Becca told me of how she had cleaned our 'Den' and made it comfortable. By mutual agreement, we decided not to spend any time there that night as it was already getting late and in any event, I thought it would be a bit odd getting involved in anything of a passionate nature attired the way I was! Eventually, we rejoined the others and all sat around the table, reluctant to break up this happy re-union. Julius said,

"Janni, it's good that you can use the sewers again because they're putting an end to the short term market concession and you would never be able to get in or out that way again. They only allowed it in the first place to get as much of value out of us as they possibly could. It seems the result was to cause arguments amongst the families regarding the split of valuables and treasures they acquired and the regional commander has put a stop to it ostensibly for this reason." He paused for a while and then continued, "Indeed, it was in direct contravention of their original orders that no one was to give food or sustenance to a Jew and as you know, on the numerous occasions when people have been caught passing food through holes or gratings at the bottom of the walls, they have been shot or hung instantly. Likewise, any Jew caught outside the ghetto without the expressed permission of the authorities will be shot on sight. Several small children have climbed over the walls at night in search of food for themselves and their families and the poor little souls have met a dreadful fate."

I expressed my pity and concern and knowing that what I was about to say would not cause offence, I said, "Dad, it's O.K. for me on the outside, really it is. I have genuine documents and I'm not strictly Jewish and provided I'm not seen to be doing anything subversive, carrying anything illegal or acting in any way suspiciously, there is hardly any likelihood that I would be stopped. In any event, I have numerous bolt holes to go to and I can change my appearance very quickly so don't worry yourselves too much about me."

"It's not just that", Aaron said and went on, "You won't have had time to notice, but in the short time that you've been away, thousands and thousands of people have been taken away and there are so many empty apartments now that you could virtually take your pick.

The worst part of it is that the Germans made us form a committee whose responsibility is to hand over so many thousand people per day for transportation. The bastards have put the burden firmly upon our shoulders. How bloody sadistic can you get?"

I must have appeared amazed by these revelations and before I could make any suitable comment, Aaron continued,

"Honestly Janni, I'm not joking. I'll bet the numbers here have been more than halved. They have been taking them away at the rate of five or six thousand per week and now, that has more than doubled. You wouldn't have noticed since, very wisely, you kept out of sight for most of the time since we've been here. Now, we could move into a larger apartment any time we wanted to, have a bath in any one of hundreds of quite sumptuous apartments, without having to ask permission. They've cleared out the far end round Sliska Panska and Grzybowska and the other end all around Nowolipki and Pawia. They march nearly all of them out to the sidings through the Zamenhofa gate and they are going at it non-stop. I can't see us being left alone for much longer."

"There has to be something we can do", I said and looked at them all for some inspiration.

Rachel stood up and paced a tiny area saying,

"Darling, we have given it a lot of thought and there are friends who would shelter us if only we could get to them undetected. It will take a lot of organisation and much as I hate this part, we are going to have to ask you to put yourself at risk again and act as go-between."

"Oh Mum, I'll do whatever I have to. Just tell me where to go, who to see in fact everything that is necessary and if it's humanly possible, I'll do it", I promised.

"I don't think we're going to have much time, but even so, we must not rush things without careful planning," Julius said and went on, "Initially, you will have to make contact with our friends and then, to establish you're bona fides, you will have to take one of the boys or Rebecca with you through the sewers. Once there, whoever goes with you will remain there and the rest of us will follow during the next couple of nights. In the meantime, we will take provisions down to the sewers and await your return there." "That makes sense and I can always get food to you from the other end at specific times when you can open up for me," I enthused.

"We must act quickly and I hope that you will not feel pressured if I ask you to go out tomorrow," Julius said with reluctance.

When I nodded approval he continued,

"Before we came here, you may recall that I disposed of many of the bulky, valuable items from the old home. Some things of great value I managed to get out of the country before the invasion and apart from keeping a reasonable sum of money, I purchased quite a number of precious stones because they not only retain their value, but they appreciate and are a viable currency anywhere in the world. You will take some of these and some money because bribes may be necessary. Apart from these, there will be a similar number of stones and some money for you to hide at Alex's flat so that if anything should happen to us, you will be well provided for." I wanted to protest that this was unnecessary but Julius told me to be quiet and surprised me further by saying, "Janni, we have agreed everything between us and our decision has been made. Whether we get out of here or not, whether we are transported or not, whether any of us survives or not is in the hands of God. All that we can do is make provision so that if any of us is lucky enough to survive, he, she or we will not be destitute. To this end, I have made a will. Each of you, and that includes you Janni, will receive a copy, duly witnessed and it is quite simple.

However many of the six of us now present in this room may survive, whether it be all, only some, or just one, everything in my possession, everything in my name abroad and the properties to which I hold title will be sold and the proceeds divided equally between the survivors and if there is only one survivor, he or she will inherit everything. There is to be no argument in this matter."

I was speechless and the grave tone of Julius's voice brought the vivid feeling of impending doom, fear so palpable that I was almost sick and a dreadful feeling of cloying claustrophobia. I wanted to run away from this place as fast as I could. Knowing the perils this loving family would face on the outside saddled me with a terrible responsibility and by the same token, if I hadn't tried to help them and they were taken away, I would never be able to forgive myself. Thinking about this filled me with misgivings. Apart from Rebecca, they all looked so very Jewish, Rachel could possibly get away with it, just, but the men stood very little chance of passing themselves off as gentiles and I didn't know enough about hair dying to venture any ideas on the matter. It would all have to wait until I initiated contact and then I hoped that we would receive some constructive suggestions and instructions.

It was a great responsibility being placed on my young shoulders and although my first instinct was to ask Hedwig and Alex for their help, I discarded the thought immediately. If they were caught helping Jews to escape, no matter how small the part they played, they would be executed on the spot, without trial. We all went to bed but I couldn't sleep. My mind was in turmoil, filled with all sorts of hopes but resigned to the agonising truth that the possibilities of success were very, very slim. Julius and the boys were sleeping soundly, but they had all done a hard day's work. One of them was snoring lightly and it became more and more irritating and far from sleep inducing. Eventually, I gave up, climbed out of bed and hunted around in the gloom for my gown and slippers. My boy's clothes were in the other room and I didn't want to disturb anyone so I crept out of the flat, putting the lock on the catch and went to the upper landing.

I opened the window and gazed out over the sleeping city. It was so calm and peaceful with just the normal sounds you would expect from any city anywhere in the world. It was almost impossible to believe that during the day at least one, possibly two hundred people would have died from the combination of summary executions and starvation and that tomorrow would bring a repetition of the same thing. I was about to climb out of the window onto the roof with the intention of visiting our 'Den' to see what changes Rebecca had made when I was aware of quiet footsteps climbing the stairs towards me. Aaron, still in his nightshirt, appeared in the half-light. He walked over to me saying, "Hello little brother, couldn't you sleep?" He put an arm round my shoulder and said, "I couldn't sleep properly either and Izzy's snoring was driving me mad." "I was thinking of all the things I have to do, what can go wrong, what are the best options, are there any additional precautions I should take. You know, all that sort of thing." I replied He pulled me close against him and said, "I'm so sorry Janni, we've saddled you with so much. It really is far too much for you to undertake and Dad should never have asked you, he's virtually asked you to take responsibility for our lives. Janni, none of us will blame you if you refuse and none of us will love you less than we do now." I was very touched by Aaron's brotherly concern. He still had his arm round my shoulder so I put my arm round his waist and said, "You are so thoughtful Ari, but honestly, the thought never crossed my mind to refuse. It isn't a case of me paying you all back for looking after me these last few years it's more because I love you all so much and couldn't bear the thought of anything happening to any of you. It will be alright, you'll see." "You are a wonderful, beautiful little brother Janni. We don't deserve you." Aaron responded, turned towards me, put his free arm around me and kissed the top of my head.

Suddenly, quite firmly, he pushed me away from him, reached over to the windowsill where he had placed his cigarettes and matches, asked if I minded and lit up a cigarette. He leant on the sill and blew smoke into the night air. It was as if he had suddenly drawn a curtain round himself and I couldn't understand his sudden loss of warmth.

I moved really close to him and with one hand I lifted his arm and placed it back round my shoulder and put my other arm round his waist, pressing him against me.

"Whatever is the matter Ari?" I asked.

"It's you Janni, you are very disturbing", he replied and carried on, "I've only seen you on and off for a few minutes at a time over the last few months but I've never ever seen you like you were today, you looked incredible. When I was holding you just now, I was thinking how nice you smell, how lovely and soft you feel and then, to my surprise, I could feel breasts against me. Christ Janni! I didn't know! Suddenly I began to feel excited, aroused and thinking unworthy thoughts. That was why I pushed you away so sharply." He paused for a moment before asking, "Whatever must you think of me? I'm really quite embarrassed." "Oh Shit!" I thought, "As if I haven't got enough complications in my life right now. I can do without this." I wondered what it was about me that had this effect on people of either sex and whether it was something that I would always have to expect and learn to live with.

I was quiet for some time thinking that our family had remained too insular, too aloof from the other ghetto families who seemed to mix more, had love affairs, got engaged and even married. Perhaps if Aaron and Rebecca had fitted in with the others I would not be the object of their repressed sexual frustrations and urges. My long silence was unsettling Aaron and I strove to answer in the least hurtful way so I said, "Ari, don't worry about it. It's nothing new, I seem to have that effect on people and I can't help it. Why should I think any less of you? After all, I have a boyfriend, Alex, and I sleep with him, what's more, I love him very much. You probably knew that anyway."

It was Aaron's turn to remain silent for some time before finally saying,

"You seem to be able to take all this in your stride and I'm grateful to you for being so understanding. Feelings which appear natural to you came as a great surprise to me and even if I had known about you and Alex, which I did not, it still would not have made me feel less ashamed and embarrassed."

I smacked him lightly on the bottom and said,

"Don't worry, I'll put my boy's clothes on in future and keep temptation out of your way!" He laughed, sounding relieved and said, "Bloody good idea too," removing his arm from my shoulder at the same time.

We stared out into the night, side by side and Aaron lit another cigarette. He passed it to me and I took a tentative puff. I couldn't understand how anyone could like the awful taste. My face must have said it all because Ari grinned at me and said, "It only tastes awful because you're not doing it properly; you're supposed to inhale, like this." He demonstrated the process somewhat elaborately, opening his mouth so that I could see the smoke disappearing down his throat then ostentatiously closing his mouth and exhaling the smoke through his nose. He passed the cigarette back to me and said, "Now, you try it."

I put the cigarette in my mouth drew deeply on it, then, as I had been instructed, opened my mouth and drew the smoke down into my lungs. Immediately I began coughing and spluttering and my head began to spin just as it did when I'd got drunk and I reeled against Ari who caught hold of me, steadied me and jokingly said, "There. That wasn't too bad was it?"

"You rotten bastard", I said. " That was horrible. How could you let me do that?" He was all contrition and said, "Sorry Janni, that was stupid of me." He ruffled my hair and looked at me imploringly as he said, "Forgive me?"

I said O.K. and suggested that we ought to go back down and try to get some sleep, as he had to go to work again in the morning.

Reluctantly, he agreed and we returned to the apartment, climbed into our respective beds and thankfully, Ari fell asleep within minutes.

CHAPTER TWENTY-NINE

The next morning after breakfast when they had all left to do their various jobs, I dressed in my boy's clothes for the first time in what seemed like weeks but was in fact only a few days. So much seemed to have happened in those few days that it seemed more like months than weeks or days. I walked about the flat finding my boy's shoes strange at first and the trousers very uncomfortable. I had been going to put a light jumper on but this was too revealing, even without a bra, and I finished up wearing a loose shirt and one of Ari's jackets which was really too big for me but did an excellent job of concealment. The only problem was that it was another warm day and the excess clothing was making me perspire.

I decided that my call on Moishe and Solly would be a short one.

Travelling across the ghetto to their dwelling was a laborious process. Ghetto police were very much in evidence and would seize upon any opportunity to stop and search whoever happened to incur their displeasure. I was not violent by nature, but on many occasions, I wished upon them the worst, most painful form of death. They were despicable. An affront to every code of decency, desirous only of protecting their own skins no matter what the cost to others, even those who had been their closest friends so long as they believed that such betrayals would save their miserable skins. Cowardice never knew such perfidy.

After my tortuous, roundabout route, I eventually caught up with the boys.

"My, you look different today!" they greeted me

I acknowledged their greeting with a grin and accepted the barrage of innuendo and badinage with all the aplomb that I could muster but was unnerved by the overt, detailed examination they were carrying out over every inch of my body.

I felt really uncomfortable and eventually, I said,

"For God's sake you two. It's only the clothing that's different. Underneath I'm Janni, a boy. Whatever you may or may not think, I only do what I do to make life easier in avoiding patrols and possible awkward confrontations with the Germans."

"Bollocks!" Solly said, and continued, "You and Alex have definitely got more than a friendly relationship. He is so protective of you and he would beat the hell out of us if we dared to touch you, but let's leave it at that shall we?"

"O.K." I acquiesced, knowing that in so doing, it was a tacit admission of my loving relationship with Alex.

I prepared for more joshing, but thankfully, it did not materialise.

Moishe broke the silence by saying,

"We had a look out last night and everything seemed to be safe. There were no patrols in the vicinity and I think it will be alright to resume operations."

Moishe made it sound as if we had all been involved in some monumental conspiracy, when, in reality all we had done was to convey a few messages and traffic in some contraband goods. Still, it made him feel important and more significantly, even in the pursuit of these menial chores, it had made him very wary, acutely observant and extremely safety conscious. I must add that, at the time, I had no way of knowing that the two boys had transported countless rifles, pistols and ammunition through the sewers and on many occasions they had taken appalling risks, dodging from building to building, laden with weapons. They were a very reliable part of the underground movement and had counterparts on the outside comprising Jewish and non-Jewish patriots. They were prepared to shoot their way out of trouble as a last resort but hoped that it would not prove necessary because the death of any one member of the occupying forces brought instant reprisals when a hundred people would be chosen at random and executed immediately.

I told them what it was that I had to do and that it was essential that I went out that night. We arranged to meet at eight, go through the sewers, do a quick recce and if everything was safe, I would go to Alex's and, from there, try to establish contact with the people whose names Julius had given me. Arriving back at our apartment, I was surprised to find Becca, sitting on the stairs. Her face lit up as I climbed the stairs towards her and she rushed forward to envelope me in her arms. "What are you doing home so early?" I asked.

"I've missed you so much and you'll be gone again tonight so I made out that it was that time of the month and I needed to go home," Rebecca replied and added mischievously, "It isn't really though!" She took my hand and started towards the upper landing, leaving me in no doubt about the way she hoped we would spend the afternoon.

By way of delaying tactics but without appearing to be lacking in enthusiasm I said, "Why don't we go and have a look in some of the empty apartments and see if we can find a few things to make our den more comfortable? Apparently there is any amount of good stuff abandoned in them." "Good idea, but let's not be too long," she replied a little impatiently. At one end of our building, there was a walled-in courtyard and a walled passage leading from this into Plac Mirowski; the end of this passage had been bricked up. The other end of the building ended against the outer wall of the ghetto but had the advantage of being connected to the neighbouring area of the ghetto by means of an enclosed structure, which bridged the wall between the two compounds. This second area had been almost completely cleared and we would be able to go through the buildings and emerge in Walicow virtually unseen.

On our way, the few people we encountered paid us scant heed and upon arrival at our destination, we roamed from apartment to apartment unchallenged. It was a very sobering experience to see all the evidence of other people's lives abandoned in the forced, hasty exodus. Finally, we entered a truly beautiful apartment, sumptuously decorated and furnished. It had hardly been touched. A Bechstein boudoir grand piano had pride of place in one room and the number of music stands and the piles of sheet music were evidence that whoever had lived here, they were very musical and it must have been heart-wrenching to leave such a superb, valuable instrument behind. I was sorely tempted to sit down and play it but reluctantly abandoned the idea in the interests of safety.

Rebecca had been silent for some time and as I looked round the room, wondering where she had gone, her voice from another room called, "Janni, come and have a look in here."

I entered a luxuriously furnished bedroom. The carpets, curtains and bed covers were all in place and hardly anything had been touched. Rebecca was stretched out on the bed looking extremely provocative. She said, "Close and lock the door then come over here." It was more of an order than a request, even though it was delivered in very soft, alluring tones.

There was no point in trying to find excuses and in any event, they would not have sounded very convincing so I did as requested, locking both the outer door and the bedroom door. The windows were large and the sun had been blazing into the bedroom all day. We dare not open the windows lest we attracted attention. As a result of the heat and the close proximity of our bodies once I had joined Becca on the bed, it wasn't long before we had removed our outer garments, followed in rapid succession by the rest of our clothes. Becca was truly beautiful and my mind went back to the time, so long ago, when the pair of us had stood, naked in the kitchen. She hadn't changed as far as I could remember and this knowledge made me very self-conscious. Now, we were about the same height but my figure had changed so much. Apart from my masculine appendage, we were almost identical although my breasts were marginally smaller than Becca's. I manoeuvred myself into strange positions in order to conceal them, but Becca was having none of it.

"Don't be silly Janni," she said. "Don't try to hide them, they're beautiful and I want to feel them against me." I remember thinking that she had obviously gone to extremes in her fantasies, which helped me to lose any inhibitions, and we enfolded each other in one of the most exciting embraces I can ever remember. "My God! Your skin is incredible Janni. I've never felt anything like it," Becca murmured. We kissed, lightly at first and then with ever increasing passion, and all the time our hands were exploring the other's body. I kissed her all over her body, running my tongue round and round her nipples. She did the same to me. I progressed lower down her body, kissing her tummy, groin and inner thighs. She did the same to me. I licked all round her 'naughty bits' and she did the same to me. Eventually, I turned her on her tummy and massaged her bottom, parting her legs, raising her midriff slightly off the bed, parted the cheeks of her bottom and licked from her vagina to her anus, probing occasionally into the deepest recesses. She was panting and squirming so vigorously that it was difficult to maintain contact, so finally, I turned her onto her back and continued the ministrations with my tongue until she was panting and shuddering in increasingly violent spasms before subsiding into a series of decreasing shudders accompanied by low moans. I moved to her side, my stomach towards her right side, raising her right leg, I moved into such a position that I enveloped her left leg between both of mine, like scissors and placed her raised right leg over my right thigh. We now formed a cross, meeting at the genitals.

From her own secretions and the ministrations of my tongue, she was very moist and slippery and I eased myself inside her, wondering what to expect since this was only my second encounter with a woman and my first with a virgin.

All went well and soon we were engaged in a wonderful rhythm. I began to stroke her breasts and play with her nipples, then ran my right hand down to her mound where I massaged the very sensitive area in the manner Hedwig had taught me, occasionally, arching my back so that I could lick her right breast and suck her nipple, finally, sliding my left hand beneath her wonderful bottom, I moistened a finger in the secretions from her vagina, inserted my finger in her bottom and co-ordinated the in-out movements with the other activity. My intention was to stimulate as many areas as possible simultaneously and it was a major triumph of imagination and contortion to do four things at once. Becca was moaning so loudly that I half expected to hear guards banging on the door at any moment wondering who was being murdered! She started moving quicker and quicker in time with me, her breathing taking the form of short, irregular panting. Her hand gripped my hair so tightly my eyes were watering and her left hand circled round and round my right breast, tweaking my nipple, then cupping and squeezing as she erupted into such loud moaning, almost screaming, that I had to quiet her. We exploded together in a wonderful shuddering finale and as the tremors finally subsided, we lay, still coupled, waiting for our breathing to return to normal. Meanwhile, I continued stroking Becca's wonderful body and kissed her very gently on the eyelids, forehead and tip of the nose, anywhere but the mouth for fear of arousing her again. I was shattered!

She propped herself up on one elbow, looked me directly in the eyes and said, "That was incredible, wonderful. I still can't believe it. All my friends who've done it said that the first time was painful and very disappointing. I'd love to be able to tell them about this, but they've all gone. Janni darling, you're wonderful."

I felt inordinately proud of myself and the adoring expression on Becca's face was a delight to behold. In an attempt to lighten the atmosphere, I said, "Just wait for lesson number three!"

"It could never be better than that," she replied.

We cuddled some more and finally, I suggested that we should explore the bathroom, clean ourselves up and go home before the others returned.

We found everything we needed in the beautifully appointed bathroom and eventually, washed and dressed, we prepared to leave.

Becca leaned towards me, put an arm round my neck, kissed me very warmly, softly and lingeringly and said, "I could take to this life, what about you Janni?"

"Indeed I could, " I answered and meant it but a sudden thought occurred to me and I asked, "I hadn't thought about it until this moment, but what if you become pregnant?"

"I don't think there is any chance of that happening. My period is due tomorrow or the day after so it should be O.K." she replied.

The significance of this escaped me since I had no knowledge of the important role menstrual cycles played in the business of conception. Nevertheless I felt both relieved and reassured by her answer. We did a quick tidying operation and left the flat hand in hand and made our way home. We had become so carried away in our love-making that it took some time to return to reality and reassert our natural caution when moving about in this infernal hole.

We had obviously become as callous and indifferent to the fate of others as most of the remaining inmates had, since our attitude was happy, almost carefree, still suffused with the body-tingling afterglow of our sexual gymnastics and we raced each other up the stairs to our flat. I let Becca win the race and when she arrived at the door, she stopped, only slightly out of breath and leant against the door in the most provocative way, pulled me towards her and slid her hands up inside my shirtfront. She held both my breasts in her hands, rubbing her thumbs gently over the nipples and kissed me in a series of short but intensely arousing brushes of her lips and murmured,

"I love your body Janni, it's so exciting and because of your feminine bits, it's like doing something really naughty, breaking a taboo. They say that forbidden fruit always tastes the best and now I know why!" "Then you'll know how it is between Alex and me", I said and regretted it immediately, as her eyes narrowed and from the expression on her face I could tell that she was examining mental images of Alex and myself engaged in the same activities we had indulged in just a short time beforehand and it was obvious that they did nothing to please her.

I put my arms around her and said

"Sorry Becca. That was thoughtless of me and I didn't mean to upset you or make you jealous in any way, particularly when we have just spent the most wonderful afternoon together and I do mean most wonderful. Honestly, it was the best ever."

I felt her relax against me and she looked up and said,

"Really? Honestly? Was it truly the best? You're not just saying that to please me are you?" "No Becca darling. It really was the best ever," I replied, hoping that this would put an end to any further questions.

She seemed happy with my response and we went into the flat, opened the windows and set about preparing the evening meal.

Rachel arrived home first, followed a quarter of an hour later by Julius and the boys.

They all washed and changed and came to sit at the table where we talked of the day's events omitting any reference on the part of Rebecca and myself to the way in which we had occupied our afternoon!

I told them that it was my intention to go out that night to begin the process of establishing contact with Julius's friends.

We ate our meal in relative silence, drinking only water with it and after clearing the table and washing up, I said that I had to change. There was no problem in changing clothes since I could manage this in the other room. The window in there was quite small and didn't provide sufficient light for me to apply my make-up properly. In the main room, I moved the table close to the window, propped a mirror against the wall and to a hushed silence and inquisitive, incredulous stares, deftly applied my make up, finishing with lipstick, blotted on a piece of toilet paper.

The silence was broken by Aaron and to my knowledge; I'd never heard him swear in front of his parents before but he said,

"Bloody hell Janni! Anyone would think that you've been doing that all your life. It's amazing, a dress, a pair of high heels, a few expert touches with the make-up and you are completely transformed. Obviously, we know it's you now, but you look so lovely, so dainty and feminine that it's hard to remember you how you normally are."

Playing the part, I did a little curtsy, kissed Aaron on the cheek and said,

"Thank you for those nice compliments dear brother and before you ask, no, I won't go out with you tomorrow night, my heart is promised to another."

Everybody laughed and Ari said, "Mean little minx," as he aimed a playful smack at my bottom, which I just managed to dodge.

Julius handed me a package which he told me contained two emeralds, eight diamonds and a large sum of money together with a list of the values of each of the stones in their numbered packets. In a second package there were five diamonds and two emeralds and some money for me. The third package contained even more of the same, which I was to keep safely for them until they were able to join me on the outside. I was astonished to say the least.

I pointed out to him that I still had a very substantial amount of money at Alex's, left over from the attempt to buy medicines.

"I should like you to give that to Hedwig and Alex for all the help they have given us over the years. I hope that one day we shall have the opportunity of thanking them personally," Julius responded and I was struck by the contrast between this wonderful, generous man and those of his race, who, even in these times of terrifying adversity, were still trying to make profit out of those less fortunate than themselves. I gave him a huge cuddle, cheek to cheek and finally kissed his forehead. If either he or any member of the family felt any embarrassment as a pretty transvestite kissed the father of the family, they didn't show it in any way.

I checked my bag to make sure I had all my papers, put the packages inside, slung it over my shoulder and picked up a light cardigan.

As I moved about the room I was very conscious of the fact that all eyes were upon me, particularly those of the boys who were both looking at me with a mixture of awe and admiration. "Before I go, I'll put the kettle on for you," I said, just to break the awkward silence. Aaron, the first to respond, said,

"It won't suit you, wear your beret!"

We all laughed, I threw a cushion at him, then went round giving them all my normal 'Goodbye' cuddle. To a chorus of pleas to be very careful and not to take any unnecessary chances, I left the flat and made my way to Solly's place.

CHAPTER THIRTY

The nights were drawing in and although it was still warm, it was getting darker much earlier. It was almost dark by the time Solly and I had collected Moishe as we headed to the 'escape' hole. Batteries were difficult to obtain and the boys and their accomplices had stashed candles at various strategic points along the route. As we reached each point, we would light a new candle, blow out the old one and leave it on the shelf. This conserved the supplies and everyone knew the locations of these caches. At least one member of the party would carry a spare candle in case, for some reason or another, the original candle was lost somewhere between stages. We arrived at the rendezvous without incident and moments after we emerged, Alex and two young men appeared out of the gloom carrying what appeared to be fairly heavy, canvas bags. They handed the bags over to Solly and Moishe and once relieved of his load, Alex put his arms round me, kissed me and said, "Hi darling, didn't expect to see you so soon."

Solly and Moishe exchanged 'I told you so' glances, their half smirks more imagined than discernable in the dim surroundings.

I'd never met the other two young men before and it was essential that they should know me only as 'Lotti.' I went over to Moishe and Solly, put an arm round each of their shoulders and whispered, "For God's sake remember that I'm Lotti out here. O.K?"

"Oh yes, of course," they replied

Very deliberately and ostentatiously, I kissed them both and as I said, "We'd better not hang around. See you tomorrow, or we'll leave a message as usual," Solly mumbled under his breath, "Bloody hell, you don't have to overdo it." Then playfully, with a huge grin, he squeezed my bottom. "I grinned back, said, "Cheeky bastard", and left arm in arm with Alex who introduced me, very briefly to his two friends before they disappeared amongst the ruined buildings.

"What was in those bags?" I asked.

"Rifles, pistols and ammunition," Alex replied.

"That was terribly dangerous Alex. I had no idea that you were actually helping to transport arms. You mustn't do it again. For God's sake, you would be shot instantly if you were caught. I promised your mother that I'd never get you involved in anything that posed a threat to your life and here you are, playing the most dangerous game of all."

"Don't go on so Janni," he replied and continued, "I'm not doing this just for you lot, I'm doing it for my dad.

Don't you think that I hate the bastards and want to see them all dead just as much as you do?"

I was suitably chastened and replied,

"I'm so sorry darling. In our misery, most of us tend to forget the sacrifice and gallantry of your father and his comrades and how they battled against the enormous superiority of the Germans. You have never said anything about it before and I've never broached the subject for fear of perpetuating the sadness that you and your mum must feel. Please forgive me, I've been thoughtless and very selfish", I concluded. He stopped and held me close and said,

"It's O.K. Janni. Of course I forgive you. I never say much about it for fear of upsetting mum but we both miss him terribly. He was wonderful, great fun, always giving me encouragement in whatever I happened to be doing and he would spend hours with us, making us laugh, telling us wonderful stories and he and mum would regale me with hilarious tales of their time on the stage. Dad was like you and mum; he could do the most amazing impressions, capturing mannerisms as well as voices and once he and mum got together in some of their reminiscences we would be rolling about laughing. Our little flat was nearly always full of his friends from the band with their wives and there was never a dull moment. I loved him very, very much and I shall miss him for the rest of my life."

We walked home in silence, arms round each other's waists.

As always, Hedwig expressed her delight at my arrival and the three of us sat at the little table, holding hands for quite some time whilst I told them what it was I had to accomplish.

Since I could move about the city with a fair degree of confidence, I was not too worried at the thought of travelling to the outskirts, especially as the trams were running, bicycles were very much in evidence and apart from the occasional roadside check, which now held no fears for me as my papers had withstood careful scrutiny on numerous occasions, there appeared to be no immediate problem in travelling to the initial contact. Nevertheless, I was relieved and grateful when both Hedwig and Alex insisted that either one or both of them should accompany me, saying that it was imperative to carry out a surveillance of the premises and the immediate vicinity of the flat before attempting to establish contact. This made good sense and despite my earlier decision not to involve them, I agreed without hesitation.

I turned to Hedwig and asked,

"May we have some vodka please?"

"Why not!" she replied and went to fetch the bottle and three glasses. Meanwhile, I went to the bedroom and opened the draw in the chest of drawers, which Alex had made available to me. From it, I took a folded jumper and from the folds, removed the fat leather wallet, which Julius had given to me.

I returned to the table as Hedwig was pouring the drinks. As I sat down, I opened my sling bag and took out the three packages.

I told them about the contents of the larger package and the purpose for which they were to be used. Next, I handed over to Hedwig the fat wallet, bulging with high denomination notes, and told her that this was the only way in which Julius and his family could express their gratitude for all help and support she and Alex had provided during the last three years.

They were absolutely flabbergasted, speechless, struggling to come to terms with the fact that I had just handed them what amounted to a small fortune.

Finally, Hedwig spluttered,

"Janni, I just don't know what to say. I've never seen so much money in all my life." Alex added, "And I was always taught that the Jews were bloody mean and would never give anything away. It just goes to show how wrong you can be!"

We sipped our vodka and I opened the smaller package.

Their eyes almost shot out of their sockets as I revealed yet more notes of large denomination, five large diamonds and two large emeralds. Each of us lifted and inspected the stones in turn. I knew nothing of their respective values but Hedwig said that each of the emeralds was well over three carats and the diamonds only slightly smaller at about three carats each. She did not profess to be an expert in these matters but said that as far as she could tell, there were no imperfections in any of the stones. Flawless, she said and a wonderful colour. I explained that these were for my future and that they would be lodged with Hedwig for safekeeping but that if I should be killed, then they would be my legacy to them. If, on the other hand, I was caught and transported to one of the camps, they were to wait for at least five years after the end of the war and if I had not established contact by then, they were to assume that I was dead and they could use them as they saw fit. The same conditions would apply to the contents of the two larger packages or what remained of them after I had completed negotiations with Julius's friends. Similarly, if we were transported before any monies or gemstones had changed hands, Hedwig would keep the contents on behalf of the Lipschitz family or me for the same period and if they had not been claimed by that time, they would become her property.

"I'm totally overwhelmed Janni. It's just incredible that someone whom I have never even met would entrust such a fortune to me. I can understand it as far as you are concerned, because we are like a second family to you and of course because of Alex. But the others, I'm amazed, humbled by their trust and lost for words. One thing is certain. If I'd ever doubted how much they all love you, those doubts have been more than dispelled now." I too had been very humbled by their love and trust especially as I was no relation, not of the same faith, only sixteen and a half or seventeen by Rachel's calculations, sleeping with a Polish boy, dressing like a girl and virtually free to run off without as much as a good-bye if I felt so inclined. It took time for all this to sink in and I was very close to tears at the realisation of the full magnitude of their trust. I could never betray their faith in me. We packaged everything up again and Hedwig put them away somewhere safe. Alex must have realised what I was feeling and without saying a word, he squeezed my hands, leant over the table and kissed my eyelids. I nearly did cry then!

Fortunately, Hedwig returned, replenished the glasses and we sipped our drinks in silence until I got up from the table, sat at the piano and played a selection of music from memory. Soon, they were singing along and our earlier, sombre mood was replaced with one of unforced good cheer, helped along by more vodka.

Hedwig finished her drink, inspected the small quantity left in the bottle, giggled and said, "I was about to say we'll have to take it easy on the drink, we can't afford to go on drinking the way we have been, but with all the money Dr Lipschitz gave us, we don't have to worry any more," and as an afterthought she added, "Even at the pace you two drink, we'll never run out again!" Alex and I hooted with laughter, grabbed her, an arm each round her waist and a hand under each knee, lifted her off her feet and did a couple of quick circuits of the room before dumping her unceremoniously on the settee. In fits of laughter, she responded by grabbing the pair of us round our necks and pulling us onto the settee with her, one on each side.

She cuddled and kissed us both, telling us how much she loved and asking us

"Wouldn't it be nice now to go to the bar on the corner and have a couple more drinks. Then we could come back, have a late supper, Janni could play some more or we could play records and dance and then go to bed. Hands up all those in favour!"

"Sounds great," Alex responded and got up to go to the bathroom.

"A lovely idea," I said and added, "So long as we don't go to the bar Gunther and Werner frequent. I couldn't cope with difficult explanations and possible tantrums tonight. Could you?" "Hell no, it would spoil what has been a very memorable evening", Hedwig replied.

We walked the hundred and fifty metres to the corner, Alex in the middle and Hedwig and I linking our arms in his. Hedwig was very lively and before we reached the bar, she had us all performing a simple chorus-line routine with lots of high kicks and we were in very good spirits as we entered the bar. By contrast, the patrons were very quiet, almost surly, even to the point of appearing resentful at our lively intrusion.

Alex ordered three large plum or damson vodkas and asked the barman if it would be all right for me to play the piano.

After much protestation, the proprietor, mollified by Alex's invitation to join us in large vodka, reluctantly agreed.

"I can't guarantee that it's in tune, mind," he said.

"Never mind, I'll try to miss out the bad notes," I replied and sat down to play.

It was a lovely old upright grand, very solid and with a splendid, if somewhat 'honky-tonk' resonance. Fortunately, with the exception of a couple of notes right at the top of the range, it was near enough in tune. In all probability it was pitched well down from what it should have been, but being the quality piano that it was, the tension on the strings had lessened uniformly. The overall sound was quite pleasing. I played popular Polish music, some classics and then some songs from well-known shows. The formerly surly clientele were now tapping their feet and when Hedwig began to sing whilst gyrating rather provocatively, their bodies began to move in time with the music. Smiles broke out on their stern faces and eventually, they joined in the choruses.

It seemed to be good for trade. More and more drinks were being ordered and Hedwig obliged some of the sillier old farts by dancing with them.

I declined any more alcohol and settled for coffee. If I was to continue playing, I needed a clear head and it was beginning to get a little fuzzy round the edges!

Four German NCOs came in smiling and I turned to them, saying,

"Guten Abend meine liebe Herren. Wunschen Sie das ich irgendwas speziell spielen sollte?

This was a very polite way of asking if they wished me to play something for them. Any requests. They joined in wholeheartedly. I played the numbers that I knew, apologising if I didn't know others but promising that if they sang them, I should do my best to accompany them. Suddenly, Alex drew our attention to the lateness of the hour, pointing out that he had to be up early even if we didn't.

Reluctantly, we prepared to leave and were only allowed to do so after the proprietor had secured our promise to come again. Everyone was very nice to us, saying how much they had enjoyed themselves and the German boys could not have been more enthusiastic in echoing these sentiments and were extremely courteous in their farewells, asking us if we had far to go and offering to escort us home. We assured them that it was only a matter of minutes away and we should manage O.K. The fresh air was very welcome and I was glad that I hadn't drunk as much as the others since they were a little unsteady and seemed to find plenty of excuses to dissolve into fits of the giggles. Once in the flat, none of us could be bothered with making a proper supper, so we just had some sandwiches and a hot drink. Neither did we play any music nor dance as we had planned but we were all agreed that it had been a fun evening.

We went to bed and dear Alex just cuddled up to me and immediately fell asleep. I followed suit seconds later, feeling very content and happy.

After what seemed like only a few minutes sleep, the alarm clock was ringing insistently and after a Herculean effort, Alex dragged himself from the depths of sleep, shut off the alarm and said, "Christ! Is it that time already?"

"'Fraid so," I replied drowsily.

He turned towards me, snuggled up and said,

"Damn it. I really want to stay here with you, but if I stay any longer I'll go back to sleep again."

He climbed out of bed, switched on the light, picked up his clothes and headed to the bathroom. I got up, put on a dressing gown and went to make tea and toast in the kitchen. Moments later, Hedwig emerged from her bedroom and said,

"I know it's early, but that toast smells wonderful and I'm suddenly very hungry. Do some for me too would you darling?"

She plonked herself down at the table and propped her chin in her hands, looking very sleepy but still managing to look very beautiful. She was extra special. At times, she was full of vigorous energy, at others, she had about her, an ethereal quality, which lent the impression that she floated rather than walked, and her faraway expression led one to believe that she was in the open countryside, surrounded by all things beautiful. It was always a delight to see her in this mood and I was always careful never to break the spell. How lucky I was to have two such wonderful families.

"What have you got planned for today?" Hedwig asked.

"Just a bit of shopping first. Oh and I need a new bra. Will you come with me?" I answered and when she nodded her agreement, I continued, "If you feel up to it, we'll cross the river, I hate those bridges with their check points, and head for the park with the lakes. If possible, I want to establish a meeting place not too far from here so that we don't have to spend more time on the streets at night than is absolutely necessary. Then, we can take a tram out to Julius's contact and give the place the once over. I hope I'm not asking too much of you." "As soon as Alex has gone, we'd better try to get some more sleep, then I'll be ready for anything." She replied.

Alex joined us at the table looking all scrubbed and glowing with health. He ate his toast, gulped his tea down and said,

"Must go or I'll be late." He gave us both a peck on the cheek and said,

"See you later and don't go mad with all that money you two." He closed the door quickly before we could throw anything at him.

Hedwig was still smiling as she said, "He means it you know."

"I know he does. I'm sure he thinks we are completely irresponsible and bound to land ourselves in trouble," I replied and as an afterthought, I added, "Mind you, I suppose we have given him a few grounds for concern." I stood up, bowed and clicked my heels and in a fair approximation of Gunther's voice I said, "How lovely to see you again Fräulein Hedwig, may I feel your tits?"

Hedwig had been sipping her drink and she blew hot tea all over the table and laughed uncontrollably. Finally, still chuckling she said, "You are so funny Janni. It's a pity we weren't on the stage together; you would have been a sensation. Come and give me a cuddle and then we'll try to get some sleep."

We stood cuddling. She felt warm and soft and I could feel every contour of her body against mine. She smelt so nice and I could feel my willy starting to misbehave itself. Firmly, I disengaged myself from her embrace and with a wan smile, she said, "It's O.K., we promised each other didn't we!"

I thought to myself that I had already cheated on Alex with Rebecca, but this was different. It had seemed all right when we first did it but that was a long time ago, before my love for Alex had become so intense and as far as my dalliance with Becca was concerned, it was a different life, unconnected with either Alex or Hedwig. We went to our separate bedrooms and even though I had been convinced that I felt far too wide awake to sleep, once back in bed I fell asleep in seconds.

CHAPTER THIRTY-ONE

Sounds of movement from the living room roused me. I got up, pulled on my gown and opened the door. Hedwig was already dressed, had made a lunchtime snack for Alex which she had covered and added a little note telling him that there was soup on the stove ready for heating, that we were going out shopping and would see him later. She was so efficient. Whatever she did, she seemed to accomplish with the minimum of effort.

"Come on sleepy head. Get your skates on," she greeted me.

"What time is it and how long have you been up?" I enquired.

"It's ten-thirty and I've been up since half past nine," she replied.

"May I have a cup of tea before we go please?" I begged, my mouth felt very dry!

"Go and get ready and I'll make one for you," She responded.

I did as she bade me and it was a great relief to clean my teeth, wash and begin to feel normal. I dressed, put on my make up and drank my tea in three deep draughts. I felt as though I could drink two more mugs, but Hedwig was impatient to go so I picked up my bag and cardigan and we left the flat. Hedwig suggested that we should cross the river and do our checks first; otherwise we would be lugging our shopping all over the place.

I agreed and we crossed the Wista unchallenged and headed out to the suburbs. Our destination was closer than we had anticipated and fifteen or twenty minutes walking at an easy pace had brought us to the correct area. It took only a few more minutes to locate the street we sought which turned out to be quite narrow, unremarkable and almost devoid of activity.

There was nowhere from which we could observe the contact's house without drawing attention to ourselves so there was nothing for it but to amble, arm in arm along the road, on the opposite side and take in as much of the surroundings as we could. We passed the house, crossed the road and walked to the end where we turned right then right again and walked along, inspecting the backs of the houses.

Again, we saw nothing to arouse suspicions.

There were some public gardens nearby and we sat there for half an hour before retracing our steps, examining the backs of the houses, then, staying on the same side of the road, we strolled casually past the contact's house. He had the downstairs flat, his name was over the doorbell.

Hedwig said, "What do you think. Shall we risk it?"

"Seems O.K. Let's give it a try," I replied and immediately began to feel the familiar tingling sensation, a mixture of excitement and apprehension, which I always experienced on such occasions. Hedwig rang the bell.

At first, we thought there was no one at home, but a movement of the curtains revealed that we had been given a pretty thorough inspection before the occupant finally responded to our impatient ringing. I established his identity and introduced myself as a friend of Dr Lipschitz but did not give a name or mention Hedwig's.

He looked up and down the street then invited us inside where I handed him the brief note from Julius, which was to establish my bona fides.

He appeared satisfied so I wasted no time in telling him what it was we wanted to accomplish and asking if he was prepared to offer assistance.

"It is becoming more and more difficult to arrange these things. We can only provide hiding for a limited number of people at any one place and we are constantly looking for new sympathisers who are prepared to take risks, and as you are no doubt aware, they do not do this cheaply," He ventured. I assured him that I had sufficient funds available for this purpose but that time was of the essence since the deportations had increased to alarming proportions and that we had no way of knowing how soon it would be the turn of the

Lipschitz family.

After a great deal of thought, he said,

"Unfortunately, it can't be arranged over night, these things have to be meticulously planned to ensure the safety of all concerned and it will take some time. However, I'll make a start and if you meet me in Pcaski Park at noon tomorrow, near the zoo gates, I may have some news for you."

I thanked him and agreed to meet as arranged. He added a word of caution, saying,

"When you come to the park tomorrow, do not approach me directly, just walk past without showing any sign of recognition then leave the park, walk towards the Gdansk bridge and if all is clear I'll catch up with you. It pays to be ultra cautious and I suggest that you stop a couple of times to look at the river, and have a good look round. When you see me, make sure there is no one following me and if I should walk straight past you without acknowledging you, you'll know that it's not safe to proceed. It all sounds very 'cloak and dagger', but we've all learned that you can never be too careful."

We confirmed the arrangements, thanked him again and left his flat.

"That didn't go too badly did it?" Hedwig commented.

"I'm not so sure. Did you notice that he'd left the door to the other room ajar? I'm almost certain that there was someone in there, listening to every word and giving us a pretty thorough examination," I answered and continued, "I'll be very surprised if we don't find ourselves being followed before we've gone much further. Don't look round. Leave it for a while then we'll see what's what. Of course they're bound to take all necessary precautions, you can't blame them. On the other hand, we mustn't be too trusting either. If anyone does follow us, we'll lead them a merry old dance round the old town and finally lose them in the ruins. The only thing that would scupper the whole plan before it's even started would be a chance encounter with Gunther, Werner or both before we've shaken our tail. We would be regarded as 'being in the enemy camp' immediately. Come on, let's go shopping, I need that new bra, this one's too small now."

We deliberately re-crossed the river by one of the other bridges and although it made our trip longer, we were heading away from the area where we lived. Once over the river, I made a pretence of having something in my eye. We stopped and Hedwig went through the motions of removing the offending object with the corner of a handkerchief and used the opportunity to scan the length of the bridge, making a mental note of those persons crossing to the same side as ourselves.

"Only three. Two women and a man. They're not together." Hedwig said.

We took several turnings until we came within sight of the ghetto. At this point, I said to Hedwig that we should split up and meet at the bra shop, but we'd make a point of saying goodbye to each other before going our separate ways. I was on my own territory now and knew every inch of it, every nook and cranny. I could disappear from sight within seconds and observe anyone without them being aware of it. Hedwig and I hugged, said our farewells and she strode off towards the shops while I virtually vanished from sight after turning the corner. I took up my observation post and after a few moments, one of the women Hedwig had described arrived at the corner. She looked to the right and was mystified by my disappearance. Hedwig, on the other hand, was still visible. The woman hesitated for a moment, then, having made up her mind, set off in pursuit. The boot was now on the other foot. I could follow her without showing myself because I knew Hedwig's destination. Finally, I quickened my pace, almost running along one of the parallel streets and when we were about one hundred metres from the shop, I watched as Hedwig went by then as the woman appeared, I fell into step beside her and said, "Good afternoon again. It was you in the other room wasn't it?"

She was taken completely by surprise and before she could answer I said,

"You don't have to worry, we are doing nothing more sinister than going to do our shopping and to buy a new bra for me."

She had recovered from her shock discovery, smiled and said, "When did you know I was following you?"

"We expected to be followed, but we were not sure until we crossed the bridge, even then we weren't really sure until we went our separate ways and I did my vanishing act," I replied. "You are pretty good. I suppose you've had a lot of practise," she probed. "Quite a lot," I answered and added, "I've been dodging people for three years now and it's almost second nature."

"What about your friend?" she asked.

"Oh, she's my boyfriend's mum and she only came with me because two women together, chatting animatedly look less suspect than a single person wandering around aimlessly. I would trust her and her son with my life and both of them often accompany me on some of my little jaunts, going on ahead to see if there is any unusual activity, or following behind at a discreet distance to make sure I'm not being followed." The woman appeared satisfied and she was in no doubt that I could lose her within seconds any time I chose and as Hedwig had long since disappeared from sight, she realised the futility of keeping up the pursuit. She confirmed it by offering her hand and saying,

"You'll do! I'd better get back. My friend will do his best, but he can only do so much and he already takes some pretty risky chances. I hope we can help your friends in time but at the moment, we can't promise. Keep the appointment tomorrow and try to be on time, it's not good to hang around and my friend will not wait more than ten minutes."

I promised to comply with these instructions and she turned and walked off in the direction from which we had come. I watched her until she was out of sight, immediately turned off the street and approached the shop by a roundabout route. Inside the shop, I examined some garments near the door and kept watch for a few minutes before going to the upper floor to meet Hedwig.

I told her what had transpired as we went into one of the cubicles with a selection of bras. Dear Hedwig could hardly contain herself when this very severe looking woman came in to offer advice and help with the fitting and when the assistant remarked that I had a wonderful figure, I thought Hedwig would pee herself. I looked at Hedwig with an attempt at a hard stare. It didn't work. Instead, I just grinned and said, "Hedwig, be a dear and see if you can find me some knickers. You have such wonderful tastes in that department!"

She bolted from the cubicle and headed straight for the loo.

I bought two bras and Hedwig had found some knickers, which she said she would pay for. We left the shop, did the remainder of our shopping and since we didn't want to go home too early for fear of waking Alex, we stopped off at the corner bar near the flat. By contrast to the previous evening, it was almost empty and we sat, making our coffee last as long as possible. Hedwig was still highly amused by the episode in the shop and confessed that when I asked her to go and look for some knickers, she'd had a mental image of the po-faced woman assisting me into my new briefs, trying not to be too taken aback by the sudden appearance of a penis.

We both laughed, looked at each other enquiringly and ordered a couple of apricot brandies.

It would have been all too easy to carry on. Good company has that effect and we loved each other very much.

Common sense prevailed and we made our way to the flat in a happy, reluctantly virtuous mood. Alex was already up when we got there and wanted to know what we had been doing in detail. Hedwig did the honours and told him everything, right down to the episode in the bra shop, even her imaginary scene with the assistant and it was only when she repeated my request to find me some knickers because she had such wonderful tastes in that department that she became aware of the double entendre. Alex guffawed, Hedwig

turned scarlet and said, "Janni! You're dreadful!" Then she started to laugh with us and added, "God, I hope old po-face was as slow on the uptake as me. If not, she'll probably think we were a pair of lesbians."

This good humour set the tone for the evening. On his way home from work, Alex had replenished the depleted alcohol stocks and we spent a pleasant hour before dinner playing cards and drinking modest amounts of plum vodka. I had written a note for Julius and left it at our secret 'post office' with the usual two parcels of food and on my return, we had our meal, played music, danced and just enjoyed sitting and chatting. It all seemed so incongruously normal.

There followed yet another wonderful night with Alex and even after all this time, we had lost none of our excitement. If anything, it seemed to get better every time. I slept for a long time after he had gone to work and I didn't even hear Hedwig leave.

Finally, I got up, washed and dressed, had a cup of tea and set about doing the family washing. I took it up to the roof and hung it out to dry.

Photography, sketches and paintings.

In doing the cartoons and sketches, Janni had only a pencil, pen, small paint brush, ruler and one bottle each of blue, black red and yellow inks. They were done on the backs of exercise books or manila covers or any scrapes of paper which 'Emil' obtained for him. It was 'Emil' too who provided the inks etc. Inmates were not allowed to take photographs or make any form of drawing and to be caught perpetrating either of these 'offences' meant almost certain death. For this reason, Janni had to memorise all the details and then draw or paint them (ink and wash) in the relative security of 'Emil's' quarters. When one compares his drawings with later photographs, it indicates what a truly remarkable memory Janni possessed.

'Emil' retained all these sketches, but some later ones which Janni did in coloured chalks did not fare so well because he had no means of 'fixing' the chalk and over the years they have become very smeared and almost indecipherable. A great pity because his artistic skills had improved considerably and these would have added greatly to his pictorial record.

'Emil' also retrieved Janni's bogus identity cards and these, together with all the sketches were returned to him in 1947.

The original clandestine photographs were taken in Birkenau by a young SS Officer and Janni obtained a set of prints from one of the officer's relatives. I believe the negatives were either sold to a journalist or handed over to the occupying forces.

The photos of the former guards at Bergen Belsen being made to load corpses onto carts and the British soldier bulldozing lifeless bodies into mass graves were taken by one of the soldiers who liberated that awful place.

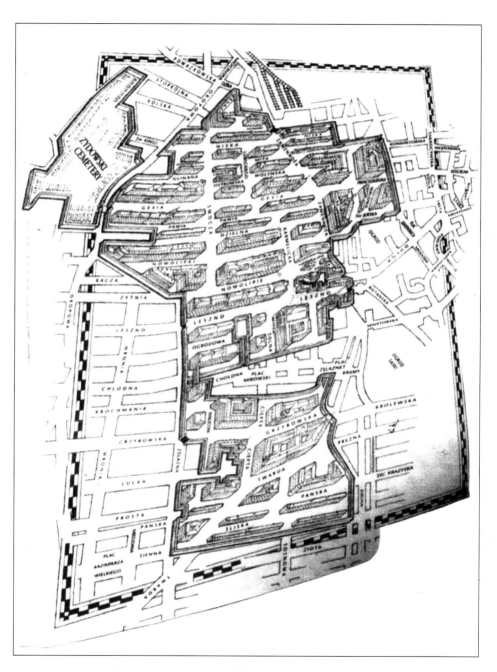

Map of the Warsaw Ghetto.

One of a series of bricked up sections which effectively sealed off the streets to form the Warsaw Ghetto.

A group, being cleared from their 'homes' in the Ghetto before being driven like animals to the station, crammed tightly into cattle trucks and transported to one of many death camps, principally Auswitz-Berkenau. At the end of the journey, almost certain death awaits 95% of them, more than half, within an hour of arrival at their destination.

A regular morning event in the Ghetto, (sometimes at random, up to 100 per day). Everyone was made to watch.

A war time aerial view of Birkenau. To the left of the picture, the long railway tracks and 'selection ramp' can be identified as the line dividing the male and female camps. The main gate is at the end of this line towards the bottom of the picture. Top centre is 'Kanada' compound and, to its left, crematoria II, III, IV & V. The SS Barracks and Administration Block where Janni worked is outside the main camp just off-centre at the bottom of the picture.

Looking towards the infamous main gate to Birkenau (Auschwitz II) from the direction of the 'Selection Ramp'. In this picture, the male camp is to the left of the ramp and the female camp to the right.

Arrival at Birkenau and being 'assisted' from the trucks. This 'assistance' usually took the form of helpful Kapos adminstering brutal beatings and SS Guards allowing their savage dogs to bite anything within reach.

"Leave your luggage where it is. This will be brought to you later!" The new arrivals are marched to the main 'selection' area. Here, they will first be formed into two columns; those fit to work to one side and those too old, too young, sick and mothers with small children to the other side. The latter group will all be reduced to piles of ashes within approximately one hour. The men and women in the remaining group will then be separated.

The first part of the 'selection' process. The group on the left of the picture have less than one hour of their lives left. The officer to the right of the picture is Doctor Josef Mengele, known as the 'The Angel of Death'.

The old and infirm take their last walk, believing that they are going to take a shower. They are going straight to the Gas Chamber.

The empty platform with the piles of 'luggage' and personal possessions left in heaps. These items will be taken to the 'Kanada' compound where they will be sorted prior to shipment to Germany. In the meantime, another train has arrived on the neighbouring track and awaits the completion of this clearance operation before disgorging its terrified 'passengers'. Between mid May and early July, 1944, 147 trains, transporting over 425,000 Hungarian Jews arrived at Birkenau. Nearly all of these were gassed upon arrival, reputedly at the rate of 12,000 plus per day.

Elderly Jews about to be escorted to the gas chambers.

The banks of ovens in Crematorium II.

Dentures removed from the victims after gassing.

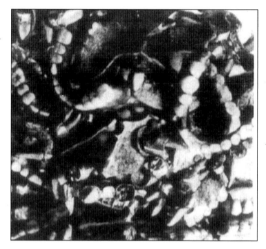

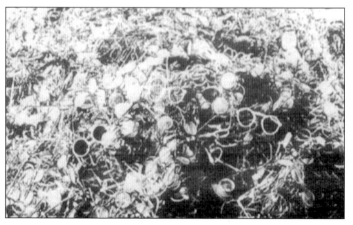

Spectacles from the victims.

The bodies of Russian prisoners of war, who had been worked to death or brutally murdered, being cremated in large pits prior to the completion of Krematoria II, III, IV & V.

Staring out to unattainable freedom.

The former guards at Bergen-Belsen being made to load bodies onto hand carts.

Either the first or the second of Janni's wash and ink paintings. He says of it, "My skills were very primitive, but so were my tools!"

A better example of his developing talent. The women's camp was still being extended at this time. The buildings in the painting are the original brick built 'blocks'. They were just starting to put in the 'stables', similar to those in the men's barrack and one of the chimney blocks for these later additions can be seen to the left of the picture.

Electrified fence and barbed wire enclosing a barrack area in Auschwitz I.

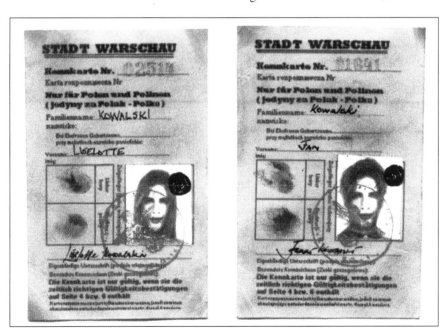

Janni's/Liselotte's bogus identity cards. These, together with a couple of Janni's 'treasured possessions' were recovered by 'Emil' and returned by him to Janni, together with all his sketches, in 1947.

Titled "Ascension Day" Crematoria II & III. The striped inmates sitting and standing within the compund are the next shift 'sondercommandos' (special units), who will work throughout the night collecting the corpses from the gas ovens below, putting them in the special lifts and bringing them up to the ovens. The night's total for the two banks of ovens could reach as many as 6000 for the proceeding 24 hours.

Appelle - Morning count. *"Who shall we hang today? How many?"*
Morning roll call where we would stand, sometimes for many, many hours regardless of the prevailing weather conditions until the guards got the count right. They were not very well educated and their numeracy skills left a lot to be desired. To keep warm, we used to rub the backs of the men in front of us. Some mornings, we would have to witness ritual hangings, carried out for the slightest misdemeanour, as an example. If only one 'offender' was to be hanged, they would use a special, portable, wooden gibbet.

HOME !!.

"Schlaf gut kinder. Nachts brauchen Sie kein angst zu haben". Der Totesengel kommt nur Morgens vorbei!"

"Sleep well children. At night you have nothing to fear. The Angel of Death (Doctor Mengele) only calls round in the mornings!"

The inside of a standard 'Block'. The brick structure to the left is a stove and chimney. This is repeated at the other end of the block and the two were connected with a brick tunnel. Heat was supposed to flow freely between the two when the fires were burning efficiently. To achieve this required more fuel than that with which we were provided so we were never able to prove or disprove the theory!

British army bulldozer pushing corpses towards mass graves.

Winter, so cold that even the guards and their dogs have not ventured out to leave any footprints in the virgin snow between the two electrified fences.

"Heute gibt es Schweinefleisch Suppe und Schinkenbrot. Juden dürfen gras oder Kartoffel schalen fressen!!"

Comedy - German style! *"Today there is pork soup and ham sandwiches. Jews will be allowed to guzzle grass or potato peelings!!"*
The 'food' queue. Our daily rations comprised: Breakfast, one litre of coffee (Made from burnt acorns and chicory) and a small square of hard, black bread. Main meal (this was also the last meal of the day). One litre of soup, another small square of bread, sometimes a small piece of cheese or a small portion of sausage. The soup was thin and watery, made from potato peelings, leaves and any rotting meat or rotten vegetables that were unfit for use in the staff kitchens. Combined, they were insufficient to sustain life for very long.

It is estimated that 1.6 million people were killed in Auschwitz.

The photos on this page and the following one were taken by Janni on his return Auschwitz-Birkenau in late 2002.

The main gate to Birkenau.

The women's camp seen from the Ramp. Janni tried to find the exact same position from which he had done painting No.2.

The infamous, much-photographed main gate to Auschwitz I, bearing the cynically chosen words (to be found on the gates of all concentration camps) 'ARBEIT MACHT FREI' (Work sets you free). Just to the right, inside the gate, the camp orchestra played marching music every morning as the inmates were escorted to their places of work.

The Roll Call area in Auschwitz I. The strange structure in the foreground is where an SS officer of NCO totalled up all the counts to make sure that the figures were correct.

Inside a typical 'block' originally designed as stables for perhaps 30/40 horses. By the end of 1944, as many as 500 people were crammed into each of these blocks. In late 1942, Janni slept three to a bed; by 1944, eight men shared the same bed.

The two remaining ovens from the four that were in the original crematorium and gas chamber in Auschwitz I, less than 100 metres from the house in which the commandant, Rudolf Hoss, lived with his wife and children.

Auschwitz I. The Railway track to the left of the picture served two purposes. Before Birkenau became operational, the transports came directly into Auschwitz I. The same line was used to send sorted, recycled items, taken from the transportees on arrival, to Germany along with munitions and other items manufactured within the boundaries of the Auschwitz-Birkenau complex.

Another attempt by Janni to photograph from the same point as he had done painting No.3. He didn't get it quite so accurately this time!

The 'Black Wall' where so many early morning executions were carried out, situated between block 10 to the left and 11 to the right. Those executed here were mainly Gestapo prisoners; most of them had been tortured for many days or weeks prior to being brought before a 'court', sentenced to death and summarily executed, naked, by an SS officer who shot them, one after the other in the back of the neck or head.

CHAPTER THIRTY-TWO

After a second cup of coffee and a couple of rounds of toast, I headed for my meeting in the park where I followed the pre-arranged plan.

He was standing at the designated spot and I walked past him without showing any sign of recognition, left the park and walked towards Gdansk bridge. I stopped a couple of times and leaned over to look at the river, looking up and down as far as I could see while scanning the boulevard for my contact. No one was following him and as he passed me, without turning round, I whispered "all clear". He turned, raised his hat and said, "Good afternoon, such beautiful weather." He offered his hand and as I shook it, I felt him press something into my palm. " Lovely to see you again, but I can't stop. Do give my regards to your friend," he said, raised his hat and strolled off over the bridge.

I made a play of opening my bag, looking in my mirror and applying some lipstick then put the note and the mirror back into the little zipped compartment.

I headed for the market feeling much more comfortable in my new bra than I had yesterday in the old one. It must have added something to my figure since I attracted more than my usual number of wolf whistles and cheeky comments.

The vegetables were excellent and plentiful and there were some good apples, pears and plums. I bought as many as I was allowed then went over to the meat and poultry section where I managed to buy a small chicken, some eggs and a reasonable amount of stewing beef. They cost way over the going rate but if you wanted extra, you had to pay for it.

My shopping had been accomplished far too quickly and the prospect of spending the next two hours killing time until Alex had rested held no appeal. It was different when Hedwig was with me, we could always find something to amuse ourselves and to be honest, by now, I was not only tiring of them, but also becoming increasingly concerned and wary of the attentions of the soldiers. At times, I'd felt like responding with a mouthful of abuse but that was fraught with danger. Instead, where before I used to smile back at the soldiers, I now kept my gaze to the ground and showed no outward acknowledgement. This tactic usually produced calls of, "Stuck up little cow " or "Who the fucking hell does she think SHE is?"

It was very intimidating and I wanted to get home quickly.

My arms were aching from the weight of the shopping and it was with great relief that I let myself into the flat as quietly as possible. Alex was still in bed and I took off my shoes in order to move about without disturbing him. Preparing the vegetables was easy, then, as Hedwig had taught me, I browned the onions, floured and seasoned the meat and browned that too before adding the stock, some diced celery, carrot and a bay leaf. It all smelt very good and once it was all simmering on a low heat, I spent the next ten minutes trying to rid my hands of the smell of onions!

The washing was dry and I folded it into the laundry basket. The sun was very warm and the roof hot under my bare feet. I sat down, back against the wall, hitched up my skirt and opened the top of my blouse. It was very peaceful and relaxing and I must have nodded off because the next thing I was aware of was Hedwig gently shaking my arm and saying, "Sorry darling. You looked so happy and relaxed I really didn't want to wake you." I held my hands out to her and she gave me a tug to help me to my feet. Immediately, I put my arms around her and held her very close, not saying anything then went over and picked up the laundry basket and returned to the flat.

"That was really lovely Janni, thank you," Hedwig said with a warm smile and then she added, "Oh and thanks for doing the washing and preparing the meal. It smells delicious."

Alex came out of the bathroom smiled and said,

"You look gorgeous apart from your mucky feet."

I looked down and sure enough, my feet were dirty from the roof with here and their little spots of tar. "I hadn't realised," I began, but Alex was already advancing towards me with a cloth and a bottle of methylated spirit.

"Sit on the stool and lift your right foot up," He commanded and when I complied, he gently cleaned the tar first from one foot, then the other.

I thought he'd finished, but he surprised me by filling a bowl with warm water and washing each of my feet in turn. It was a very pleasant sensation and I was enjoying it immensely. He washed them thoroughly, even between the toes, then dried them. Still not done, he lifted them to his mouth and kissed them one at a time, very lovingly. It was brilliant and if Hedwig had not been at home, I'd have dragged him off to bed there and then. I could tell from the look in his eyes that he felt the same way. "Be a darling and put the potatoes on," Hedwig's voice brought us back to reality and I left Alex to it since he would need some time for the bulge in his trousers to go down!

I put my shoes on and sat with Hedwig on the settee.

It no longer felt strange to sit and indulge in 'girl talk' and she brought me up to date with all the office gossip with such vivid descriptions of the various parties that it was as if they were all known to me. She had a way with words and in addition, she would reinforce descriptions with brief visual caricatures of each character and their mannerisms. She was a keen observer of life and had an amazing memory. Whenever she brought Alex up to date on what we had been doing, she remembered everything in precise detail and could even report lengthy conversations absolutely verbatim. She told me that it came about through learning the small parts she played in the theatre where she learned the entire script, not just her own little bit. It was quite a gift.

Suddenly, I leapt to my feet and said, "Oh Shit! The note!"

Hedwig looked on puzzled as I opened my bag and withdrew the folded paper from the mirror pouch. I read it briefly then handed it to Hedwig, who read it out loud for the benefit of Alex who had just joined us, minus visible protrusions!

"Have your people ready to move five nights from tonight. At that time, they should be waiting inside the sewers close to your exit point. Wait for me there every night from then on at nine o'clock onwards. I shall have company so don't be alarmed. It's simply that we cannot hide everyone in one house, so your friends will be taken individually, via several stopping places to the eventual destination. The time taken will depend entirely on the prevailing circumstances but should take no longer than a week, ten days at the outside. You will need to pay me, (he specified a very large sum of money) and I shall pay each of the escorts. It will not be necessary for you to pay them any further monies. Till Wednesday, nine pm."

Alex erupted. "Christ Janni, are you bloody mad or what? How bloody stupid can you get? You've been carrying that round in your bag all day and for all your observation skills, if people had been watching him and seen him shake hands with you they would have searched you and found that note in seconds flat. Even in a spot check and search, that note would have been your death warrant. You stupid little fool. This whole business has got to stop now. Take all the money back and tell them you can't do it."

I prepared myself for a monumental argument as I replied,

"Yes I was stupid, thoughtless, call it whatever you like and yes, I was lucky not to be stopped and searched, but that's another lesson I've learned and I'll never be that stupid again. I know that you want me to stop because you care so much about me, but I have to do it. To all intents and purposes, we are talking about my parents, my brothers and my sister, all of whom I love very much and I couldn't live with myself if I had the chance but didn't try to save them and much as I love you, they have to come first."

To my surprise, he didn't start shouting, waving his arms or even look angry. On the contrary, his expression softened, he put his arms round me and said, "Of course you must carry on, I was just frightened for you. Everyone should have a friend as loyal as you. But please darling, be extra careful." With a sudden twinkle in his eye he added, "Otherwise I shall have to strip search you every time before you go out and you wouldn't like that. Would you!"

The sound of pans boiling brought us back to reality and Hedwig dashed to the kitchen, hastily turning down the heat under the potatoes and putting the vegetables on to cook. On the way back she picked up three glasses and the plum vodka and we set about it with relish. It had become something of a habit!

I broke the appreciative silence by saying,

"I'll have to see the boys later and arrange my last trip. I want to set up a stash of food in the sewer so that if the family have to hide for any length of time, there will be sufficient to see them through. Don't look so worried Alex, it'll only be for the one day then I'll be back with you forever. Really, it's best if I go tonight. The more time they have to prepare for a sudden departure, the better. They'll be able to bring so little with them that they'll have to decide on what to leave behind. It's heart-breaking, isn't it?"

Reluctantly they both agreed that it made sense although they protested that I didn't have to go back, that the boys could convey the necessary details without me taking any more risks. I pointed out that once the family were collected from the sewers, any further contact would be impossible. I may never see them again or at best, only for a few moments in the ruins to say our goodbyes. Their leaving would tear my heart out and I needed to spend a last night with them. Hedwig and Alex both knew that I could not be dissuaded and acknowledged my motives. We ate our meal and had another drink, then I collected my bag, a heavier cardigan and a bag of provisions from the kitchen.

Alex put on a jacket and to my surprise, Hedwig said,

"I'll come with you. The air will do me good."

Within moments of our arrival, Moishe and Solly appeared. They greeted Alex with a handshake, Hedwig with a kiss on the cheek and when they came to me, they hesitated, unsure of how to greet me. To my surprise, Moishe said, "What the hell!" held my shoulders and kissed me on the cheek. We all laughed and seconds later, Solly followed suit.

I handed my bag to the boys, hugged Hedwig, gave Alex a long, passionate kiss and said, "We had better go. See you tomorrow, same time."

As Solly, Moishe and I entered the sewer. I looked back and blew a kiss to Hedwig and Alex, they acknowledged in similar fashion.

It was the last time I would see either of them.

CHAPTER THIRTY-THREE

It was about half past nine when I arrived at our flat. I knocked on the door and called, "It's me, Janni."

Seconds later, the door was opened by Aaron who gave me a brief hug before we walked into the main room. After the usual hugs and greetings, I sat down and told them of the instructions I had received. Their reaction was one of excitement and delight. In anticipation of this, I had brought a bottle of plum brandy with which to celebrate and once drinks had been poured, everyone began to talk quite animatedly.

Rachel said,

"As far as packing is concerned, we have done that already. We thought we might have to move at very short notice one way or the other and we have sorted out our priorities."

Julius added,

"We don't want our benefactors to know what we have in the way of valuables and before we leave the tunnels, we shall all swallow equal numbers of the remaining precious stones. Your mother and I have wrapped each one individually in cotton wool and when we come to swallow them, a quick dip in olive oil and they'll go down very easily. You don't need me to explain how we recover them!"

"Won't it seem strange if you three don't turn up for the work detail? Won't it arouse suspicions?" I asked.

"Not really," Isaac replied, "So many people are dying they'll hardly notice a few more absentees." "It's easier for Mum and me," Rebecca said, the women where we work are hiding their families in the back rooms of the factories and they've learned not to ask questions."

Aaron, who had spent most of the time since my return sneaking glances at me from time to time, spoke up saying,

"Seriously, the deportations are happening at such an alarming rate and they are so close to us now that I don't think we ought to wait five days. We ought to go down the sewers tomorrow, take a few blankets and a change of undies, plus as much food as we have and wait down there for Moishe and Solly to bring us Janni's signal. It will be much safer."

Julius stood, put his arm round Aaron's shoulder and said,

"That makes a lot of sense son. I agree with him whole-heartedly. We'll go tomorrow night if Janni can arrange it with the boys."

They all looked at me, waiting for my response and I replied,

Give me a few minutes to get this make-up off and change my clothes and I'll go to see them now before it gets any later. The more warning they have of our intentions, the easier it will be for them to make the necessary arrangements."

They all protested,

"You can't go out again now, it's too dangerous and besides, you've only just got here." "It's O.K., nobody will see me. I know my way round here blindfold and in fairness, we can't just spring it on them at the last moment. Hell, there will be six of us with a fair amount of baggage and we can't all go over at once. We will have to stagger our departures, two at a time throughout the day. Any more than that would arouse suspicion. Even then, we'll all have to go via roundabout routes." I replied. They all saw the sense of this and I left them to go and change.

It felt strange and uncomfortable back in boy's clothes and I comforted myself with the thought that after tomorrow, I shouldn't have to wear them again.

Back in the main room, the family couldn't help looking as though they had seen a ghost when Janni, the boy, reappeared in their midst and Rachel said, "You don't look very happy in those clothes darling. Never mind, it won't be for much longer."

She came over, put her arms round me and said,

"Janni, when you first came to us you endeared yourself to all of us and as you know, we have all come to love you very much. Over the last three years, you have done so much, taken so many risks for us that we would never have survived without you. But, it's not for this, but the overall pleasure you have given each and every one of us, the love you have shown to all of us, that I say, you are the most wonderful thing that ever happened to us. God bless you child."

I felt the familiar prickling behind my eyes and turned towards the door as I murmured,

"Thanks Mum, that's the nicest thing anyone has ever said to me and I only hope I prove worthy." I left before anyone could reply because I was embarrassed and about to blubber. The boys were surprised by my late visit but they too had realised that time was now very short and were anxious to help in any way.

It was arranged that my family would move over, two at a time and wait in an empty flat near Solly's apartment until we were all ready to move after dark. The first two would go over at about nine a.m., followed at two-hourly intervals until all six of us were together. Both boys said that it would be better if I remained dressed in my boy's clothes until the actual time of departure to the sewers since, according to Solly, I was far too pretty to go unnoticed in my girl's role and bound to be approached by young men for all the wrong reasons. We laughed, said our farewells and I returned home.

It was very late when we all turned in, everyone was so excited and I was glad that after tomorrow, I would no longer have to lead a dual existence, I would leave this dreadful place for good and go to live with Hedwig and my beloved Alex.

I fell asleep with these happy thoughts.

CHAPTER THIRTY-FOUR

Violent banging on the door at about half past six the next morning awakened us. The banging was incessant, accompanied by shouts of, "Tr offenen. Schnell machen." Julius opened the door to two S.S. men. There were a further two on the landing below and two Ghetto policemen. They told Julius that we should all get dressed immediately, pack suitcases weighing no more than twenty-five kilograms per person and be ready to leave in half an hour. In the meantime, no one was to leave the apartment and a guard would be posted to make sure that this last order was complied with.

We were all very frightened and dumbstruck and Rachel was the first to say, "Come along then, get dressed all of you, there's nothing we can do about it now. Each of you put some bread and sausage in your pockets and come to the kitchen to swallow your little 'pills' while we still have time. Be quick now, all of you."

We all did as she told us, dressing very quickly. I was the only one who hadn't packed anything and it was with great sadness that I left all my pretty clothes, packing only two of Aaron's cast-off shirts, cast-off trousers and some underpants, shoes and socks, two jumpers, toothbrush and comb and that was about the extent of my possessions in this place, everything else being at Alex's.

The half hour went very quickly and in what seemed more like a few minutes, the banging started once again on the door "Alle raus. Nach unten gehen. Schnell! Schneller!" The guttural, shouted orders were accompanied by pushes, kicks and blows from rifle butts. We almost tumbled into the street where more of the same treatment awaited us.

There were hordes of S.S. with dogs and whips, herding us like cattle towards canvas-covered trucks into which we were packed like sardines, with only sufficient room to stand. We were crammed, so tightly, into the limited space, that it was virtually impossible to turn round.

Julius called our names in turn and we all answered. At least we had not become separated. They were so well organised, everything had happened so quickly that we never had a moment to think and everyone of us was hurting somewhere or other from the blows that had been showered upon us. The trucks moved off and in no time at all, the same barked instructions accompanied the lowering of the tailboard and we were dragged to the ground in terror as we suffered still more blows. The snarling guard dogs savagely bit some.

Then we were at a siding in the station, we were quickly marched to the open doors of cattle trucks and made to climb in to the accompaniment of still more vicious blows. Again the truck was packed to bursting point and as the last three people were forcibly pushed in, the guards slammed the door shut and we could hear the bolts shooting home. It was only then that I became aware of the screaming, wailing, crying and the pleas to God for deliverance.

It was as if everything that had happened before entering the cattle truck had taken place without a sound apart from the shouted orders. Now, it was truly as if we were in Bedlam. Finally, the shouted orders ceased, a whistle blew and the train lurched forward. We had no idea where we were going but it soon became apparent that we were not heading in a northeasterly direction, but south. This knowledge brought some measure of reassurance since we were heading away from the direction of Sobibor and Treblinka.

By any standards, the journey was slow with frequent stops lasting many hours. During these stops, we were kept penned inside the terribly cramped wagons.

In the best of conditions, twenty or so people would have been the maximum in any one wagon, but there were three or four times that number crammed into the available space. The only means of going to the toilet was to use one of the two buckets, which had been placed in opposite corners. To get to either of them required a major re-shuffle of bodies and then, having accomplished this difficult task, one had to attend the call of nature in full view of those in the immediate vicinity. Needless to say, we all held off from these essential functions for as long as possible. Sooner or later, we all had to succumb to this indignity. This nightmare journey, which, as the crow flies, was somewhere in the region of two hundred and fifty to three hundred kilometres, lasted for hours on end. During which time, we had no exercise, no food and nothing to drink. Sleep was well nigh impossible due to the lack of adequate space. It was intensely hot with little or no ventilation and we were very thirsty. The smell of perspiration and fear was everywhere, a pungent, acrid stench becoming more foetid and foul by the kilometre. At least four people died and we had to travel with the bodies until we reached our final destination.

Oswiciem. Auschwitz.

CHAPTER THIRTY-FIVE

The bolts were noisily withdrawn, the doors opened and yet again, the cries of, "Raus, Raus. Verfluchte Juden. Schnell machen!" (Out. Quickly. Damned Jews). We jumped or were dragged out of the trucks onto the ground where we were made to form a line assisted by men in striped clothing, Jews who performed this duty over and over again as their full-time job. 'Kapos', mostly hardened criminals armed with heavy wooden clubs 'supervised' with unbridled brutality. Later, we were to learn that the Kapos did their work with such efficiency and enthusiasm that for the most part, the S.S. gave them a free hand and they virtually did all the S.S. dirty work for them. Indeed, on many occasions, they bludgeoned scores of people to death. They were totally depraved.

One aspect of their behaviour, which was later to cause more concern to me, was the fact that they preyed on the younger, good-looking men and boys for sexual gratification. Of these, it is fair to say that some volunteered the use of their bodies for the rewards of extra rations and I am in no position to criticise or condemn them for resorting to this tactic as a means of survival.

Several S.S. officers separated the old, infirm and women with young children from us and formed them into a column to the left, which was then marched off. We had no idea that within an hour, they would all be dead as they headed towards Brzezinka and the gas chambers and crematoria. Next, they separated the remainder, men in one column, women in the other. One Kapo pushed me into the line with the women.

"He's a boy, not a girl." Aaron shouted

On the platform, an S.S. officer stood leaning on a stick. He pointed it at me and said.

"Up here you, now, quickly."

I climbed up onto the platform and the officer lifted my chin with his stick, stared for a long time at my face and into my eyes and then said, "Drop your trousers."

I took him at his word and I detected a hint of admiration for my spirit when he added,

"Unterhosen auch!" (And your underpants too).

I complied to the raucous laughter of some of the soldiers. One shouted,

"You're right, it's not a girl." and another shouted,

"Und er ist auch keine Jude!" (He isn't a Jew either.) Guffaws of laughter greeted this last remark and the officer said,

"Pull your trousers up boy and stand there". He indicated a spot.

As soon as the two columns were in order, the women were marched away, then as the men were about to be marched off, the officer, in quite a kindly tone said, "Go and join your friends boy."

We were marched to a long hut where we were made to hand over whatever we were carrying. We had been told to leave our 'luggage' in the boxcars. They took everything from us, even our toothbrushes and combs. They left nothing to doubt in their body searches and those who had not had the foresight to swallow valuable articles, lost everything in a few seconds. Stupidly, some still wore gold watches, gold and diamond rings and cufflinks. Amazingly, at least two carried gold and silver toothpicks in their waistcoat pockets. More barked orders and we were on the march again, this time to 'Bathing and Delousing'.

We all sat in rows on benches and Kapos with clippers came along and cropped our heads. I could have cried as I saw my lovely locks falling onto the concrete floor. How strange one's priorities are! Next, we were told to strip off. This was the moment I had dreaded and I said to Julius and the boys, "Please stand round me while we do this so that they can't get a proper look at me." Without hesitation, they complied and although Julius and Aaron knew of my 'development' and Isaac didn't, the expression on all of their faces as I removed my shirt was one of total incredulity and I had to say to them, "For Christ's sake, the way you are all gaping, you'll attract more attention than my tits." We were herded through a corridor to a large room where we all showered and were then sprayed with a stinging fluid, presumably the delousing agent, with particular areas being targeted: Head, armpits, crotch. Still naked, we were marched, yet again, to another room where yet more striped inmates issued us with striped clothing. Julius and the boys had done an excellent job of concealing my female characteristics and made an issue of holding up their garments, struggling with them, until such time as I had covered the offending articles! To our great surprise, the next stop was for food, if you could call it that. It comprised a bowl of watery soup, which looked and tasted as though it had been made out of grass and a small square of hard, dark bread. Despite the awful taste, we finished it off because we had no idea when we would be fed again. We were told to keep the battered bowls.

Immediately after the 'food', we were taken to another room where we were asked our names and date of birth. In response to this, I cobbled together a bit of a mixture and answered, "Janek Kowalski, eleventh of the fourth, nineteen twenty-six."

The clerk duly entered these details on a sheet and wrote a number beside it and moments later, my arm was held on the table by one man while another tattooed this number on the inside of my left forearm. They were very rough and it hurt.

From here, we were herded towards rows of barrack huts, referred to as blocks, so many being allocated to each one. Luckily, Julius, Aaron, Isaac and I were in the same group and we entered what appeared to be a vision from Dante's inferno. A passage ran down the middle, the length of the barrack and either side, were what at first appeared to be storage shelves, but which turned out to be bunks. They had only wooden laths on which to sleep, three to a bunk. Such were the cramped conditions that it was impossible to sit upright in the confined spaces and only very few of them had a little straw for comfort. Julius and the two boys were assigned to one such space and I was placed in the one directly above them with two complete strangers. All around, gaunt, haggard people with hopeless expressions on their faces hardly took any interest in our arrival and after only a momentary glance, shrank back into their world of despair. All this was accomplished under the supervision of the senior inhabitant and his assistant. The senior inhabitant had a cubbyhole all to himself with a single bed, table, chair and locker.

An officer and several NCOs entered the room. Everyone had to climb out of their bunks and stand to attention while we were all counted then the officer reeled off 'The Rules', any of which, if ignored, would result in immediate execution.

We were told where the latrines (endless rows of holes cut into wooden boards over deep, concrete and earth pits) and washing facilities (a couple of taps, cold water only) were situated and the times we could use them. At night, there were portable facilities within the block which we should take turns to empty before the morning roll call. The next morning, we would all be allocated work duties after the morning parade and count. When addressed by any of the military personnel, we must always stand to attention and remove our hats. After more warnings of the dire consequences of disobeying any order given by any member of the staff, he and his NCOs left.

The silence which followed their departure was finally broken by newcomers asking questions of the 'old hands' from whom we discovered that our camp was next to the Gypsy camp to our right. To our left were three more enclosed camps. The latrines were at one end of the rows of huts and at the other end, across the railway lines and 'Selektion' ramp was the women's camp and medical barracks. It was from the older inhabitants that we learned the fate of all those who had been diverted into the left hand column, the rest of us would live, for a while at least, until they had either worked us to death or had no more use for us when we too would disappear up the chimney.

Julius, Aaron and Isaac and I talked in low voices, wondering if we would ever see Rachel and Rebecca again before we all fell silent, exhausted by our journey, the beatings and all the rapid marching and indignities we had suffered. Still, we could not sleep. There was insufficient space in the bunks to turn round and soon, one side would become completely numb. The smell of unwashed bodies was overpowering and men, with stomachs bloated from starvation, broke wind repeatedly throughout the night. Compared to this, the ghetto had been paradise.

CHAPTER THIRTY-SIX

Everybody was up very early to use the latrines and limited washing facilities before the six-o'clock a.m. Apelle (roll call) when we were all counted again. This was to become the norm and could last anything from twenty minutes to several hours while numbers were checked and re-checked. We had to stand, without moving for the full duration of the count, no matter how long it lasted and regardless of weather conditions. We could see the women being paraded and counted over in their barracks and strained our necks to see if we could spot Rachel and Rebecca, without success.

Several more officers and their staff appeared on the scene as soon as the count was complete and the new inmates were allocated to work parties. Amongst the officers was the Obersturmbannfhrer (Lieutenant Colonel) who had made me remove my trousers. I noticed that the piping round his epaulettes was a different colour to the others although I didn't know the significance of this at the time. He walked with a very pronounced limp and supported the weight of his right leg with the heavy cane he had used to lift my chin.

He spoke to two of the other officers for a few moments and after what seemed to be a general agreement between all three, he said, "I need a new messenger who will also act as my orderly. All those of you who speak fluent German step forward."

Some inmates, less than one might have imagined, shuffled forward and I joined them. The officer walked along the line, asking questions in German, some he did not even bother to address, dismissing them with comments like, "Too old" or simply "No."

In seconds, he stood opposite me. He looked me up and down, stared hard at my face and then, staring directly into my eyes he asked,

"What's your name, boy?"

"Janek Kowalski Herr Obersturmbannfhrer", I replied

"Are you Polish, boy?" he barked.

I thought very quickly and replied,

"No sir. As far as I know, I'm German."

For a moment I thought he was going to pursue this line of questioning but suddenly, he appeared to relax and said,

"Right. You'll do." He turned to the other officers and said,

"I'll take this one."

The taller of the other two officers shouted,

"Name" and after I had told him and he had written it on his clipped pad, he said,

"Number?"

I wasn't sure what he meant and an NCO grabbed hold of me very roughly, pulled up my sleeve and read out the number, which had been tattooed there. The officer appeared to do a cross check of the details and then said, "Very well, follow the Obersturmbannfhrer."

I fell into step beside him and was glad that he didn't walk very quickly as I still had a tendency to slip into my girlish walk and indeed, I had needed to be very careful about my voice too. "We'll need to get you a proper outfit," he said, breaking in on my thoughts and we headed to a clothing store where I was issued with a pair of riding breeches, black boots, a white shirt, blue blazer and smart cap. "May I change in the toilet?" I asked.

The Kapo issuing the clothes looked as though he had just been shot and glanced at the officer with great fear in his eyes.

The officer looked at me and from the Kapo's reaction, I expected to see a face suffused with rage. Instead, he was actually smiling as he said, "My God. You've have got some cheek. Go on then, in there and don't be too long about it." I breathed an inward sigh of relief and went into the toilet to change. I thought it prudent to leave the door part open as I changed very quickly.

Everything was on the large side for which I was very grateful since they did an excellent job of concealment. The only thing that needed to be changed was the pair of boots, which was several sizes too large. I tried on two more pairs before finding something comfortable.

Finally, attired in my new 'uniform', I accompanied the officer through the gates of the four metre high-electrified fence. We turned right and walked past some watchtowers to the gates of the S.S. Barracks. All I was told at this time was that the officer was in the camp administration department and was principally concerned with staff discipline, welfare, transport and a host of other duties. My function was not clear at this point. The officer took me into the administration block, showed me his office and after a few moments talking to members of his staff, he said, "Come along, boy. There are other duties which you will have to perform including, cleaning my boots and equipment, making sure that my laundry is attended to, keeping my quarters clean and generally doing as you are told. Is that clear?"

"Ja Herr Obersturmbannfhrer," I responded.

He smiled and said,

"You make a very convincing German!" implying his doubts about my claim but to my relief, probing no further.

We arrived at his quarters and he showed me where everything that I would need to fulfil my duties was stored. Then, the small bathroom and toilet which I was expected to keep in spotless condition. The short tour completed, he sat down in an armchair and asked me to help him take his right boot off. I stood in front of him leant over and made several clumsy attempts to pull it off and he winced a couple of times as a result of my exertions.

"Stop!" he said. "Don't you know how to do this?"

"I've never done it before Sir," I replied.

"Right, there is a first time for everything. Turn with your back towards me and stand astride my right leg. Now, bend down and pick up my boot with your hands under the heel. Got that? Good. Now, pull upwards and forwards at the same time."

I did as I was instructed and felt the boot begin to slide, very slowly off his foot. Then, to my great surprise, he placed the sole of his left foot on my bottom and pushed. His boot came off in a rush and I almost overbalanced, but still managed to laugh. When I turned round, clutching the boot in both hands, he was smiling. "It's easy when you know how, isn't it? He said.

He stood up and without the cane, limped round the room a couple of times, stopping from time to time to massage his thigh and to raise and lower his knee. It looked a very difficult process and it was apparent from his expression that it caused him great pain. Finally, with the aid of his right hand, he lifted his knee, placed his foot into the boot and pulled it on with both hands.

"I have to go to my office now," he said, and continued, "Just give the place a good buff-up and before you ask, yes, you may use the toilet. I'll be back in about two hours. Under no circumstances are you to leave these quarters until I get back. Is that clear?"

"Yes Sir." I answered.

Being able to use the toilet was a godsend since it would be much easier to recover the precious stones, a task which would have proved very difficult in the 'open plan' latrines.

He left and I set about my cleaning duties. We had all had various duties in the Lipschitz household and I quite liked cleaning. In the other household Hedwig often remarked that she only had to turn her back for a few minutes and I'd have cleaned everything in sight.

I did a thorough job, even cleaning the insides of the windows. The cleaning products for the bathroom were very poor quality and it was very hard work to remove some of the stains but I kept at it and eventually, I was satisfied that he would be pleased with my efforts. It was essential to be able to take pride in something and I'd already decided that

I was going to make myself indispensable!

You have to remember that I was well aware of the strange effects my physical attributes engendered in members of either sex and I was experienced enough, despite the limited number of my lovers, to recognise an interest that was other than clinical. Such an interest had been apparent in this officer's appraisal and I knew, instinctively that the selection routine was a charade for the sole benefit of the other officers and NCOs and that he had already made up his mind that he wanted me as his 'messenger'.

My future depended on this officer and the fact that he had a sense of humour, had been kind to me in such difficult circumstances and was, to put it bluntly, interested in me, gave me a great deal of hope. Added to this, he was extremely good-looking, apparently easy to get along with and I knew that if I played my cards properly, without taking liberties and giving cause for disenchantment, I should be well protected. It was nearer three hours before he returned. He looked round his quarters and expressed his surprise at the transformation of the bathroom and the general state of order and cleanliness of the whole place. He was even more pleased when he opened his wardrobe to see everything neatly in place and his spare boots highly polished.

"You've done well," He was about to say 'boy' but checked himself and said, "What do they call you?"

"Janni, Sir," I replied.

"Very well Janni. As of tomorrow, immediately after roll call, you will be allowed to proceed to my office unaccompanied and from there on, anywhere in the confines of the camp subject to the limits I shall explain to you. You will carry this card and produce it if challenged. That way, any queries will come directly to me. You will go nowhere without my expressed permission. Do you understand?" He looked at me very earnestly.

"Yes, Sir", I answered and he continued,

"You will only enjoy my protection for as long as you obey these instructions. If you deviate in any way and are caught, it will be out of my hands and I shall be unable to help you. Please be sure that you understand the seriousness of what I am telling you."

I knew exactly what I was doing when I lowered my eyelashes, and after saying,

"Yes Sir, I do understand and I'm very grateful to you", I opened my eyes wide and looked directly into his eyes with the most smouldering look I could muster.

He flushed slightly and was the first to break eye contact.

After a moment he said,

"I have to take fairly long rest periods because of my injuries and an orderly will come for me if I'm needed. Help me off with both boots."

I applied the technique he had taught me and removed the right boot, giggling a little as he placed his left foot on my bum. When it came to the left foot, he couldn't use his right foot for leverage and he gripped the arms of his chair as I leant forward, pulling simultaneously on the heel and the boot came off in one easy movement. "Well done!" he exclaimed, "You are a quick learner."

I stood his boots at the foot of the bed and turned to face him.

"Sit down Janni," he commanded, indicating the other chair, "And tell me about yourself. How old are you?

Where do you come from? What do your parents do? Where did you go to school? I want to know everything." "It's very difficult to answer these questions Sir," I replied and told him, with certain omissions, of what had happened to me during the Blitzkrieg on Warsaw and concluded.

"So you will understand, Sir that I cannot answer your questions truthfully because I do not know the answers myself and when I said to you that I thought I was German, this was because I understood and spoke German very easily but my knowledge of Polish was not so extensive and it is only fluent now because I have been using the language daily for the last three years."

He looked at me quite compassionately and said,

"How terrible for you, and then to be caught up in all this."

"I think I'm about seventeen Sir," I ventured and then, taking my courage in both hands, I added, "I'm not even certain about this Sir because it cannot have escaped your attention that I'm different from other boys and, to be honest, I was dreading this morning because I had been told throughout the night of Herr Doctor Mengele and that I was the sort of unusual person who would excite his interest. I was so relieved when you picked me for this job Sir. To be honest, I was terrified."

"You don't have to worry about that now, I can promise you," he said.

I took my courage in both hands and said,

"It's not that easy, Sir. It's worse than you think and you really don't know what you are letting yourself in for."

"That sounds ominous. What is there that I should know about?" he asked. "You will probably get rid of me now Sir, but you have been so kind I cannot deceive you and I shall understand if you sack me." I turned my back towards him, took off my blazer, unbuttoned my shirt and turned to face him. "Do you see my problem?" I asked.

His eyes were like organ stops and I heard a sharp intake of breath as he contemplated the unexpected sight of my 'tits'.

He stared, speechless for several moments before saying,

"Oh my God! You do have problems, don't you!"

Judging by his campaign medals and badges, he must have seen all sorts of sights but he'd never seen anything like this before and it took him some time to regain any degree of aplomb. At last he asked, "How long have you been like this and what do you feel about it all?" I told him when it had started; about the way I had lived half the time as a girl, but only admitting to doing it to gain extra rations and omitting to tell him about Alex and my relationship with him. He laughed unashamedly when I told him about Gunther and Werner and concluded by saying, "You're either very brave, very stupid or both."

He appeared to be thinking very hard and finally, he said,

"Under my command, no one will question you without me being present so you won't have that worry, but you must not be seen unclothed anywhere, not even in your own barracks. You may use the washing facilities here and with my permission you will be allowed to take a bath, but only when I'm here. I'm taking a terrible chance on this and I hope you appreciate it."

I knew I'd got him and quite brazenly and deliberately, although letting him think it was an instinctive response to his kindness, I put my arms round his neck and hugged his head, knowing that since I was standing and he was sitting, as I pulled him towards me, his face would finish up against my bare breasts and said, "Oh thank you Sir, Thank you. Thank you."

He didn't push me away and after a moment, I moved away as though suddenly aware of the enormity of what I had just done and said, "Oh Hell, I'm sorry Sir, I'm so sorry."

He was having difficulty with his breathing and in quiet tones he managed to mutter,

"It's O.K., but don't do it again!"

I refastened my shirt and tucked it into my breeches.

"Put your blazer on and let me have another look at you", he commanded.

I did as I was told and he eyed me up and down very critically.

"In the top drawer of that chest of drawers you will find some clean, wide bandages. Take some into the bathroom and bandage yourself as tightly as you can manage comfortably and let's see if we can disguise your, er, abnormalities," he commanded with a half smile.

I found the bandages, stripped to the waist and bound the offending articles quite tightly. The result was fairly satisfactory and following his inspection he merely said,

"That's better."

He removed his jacket, stretched out on the bed and lifted his right leg into a comfortable position.

"What happened to your leg?" I enquired

"I caught the blast and some heavy shrapnel from a shell and I'm no longer fit for front line duty. That is why I'm here in this Godforsaken hole. I'm a soldier, not a bloody prison warder," he said with a terrible bitterness.

I was surprised to hear myself saying,

"I'm so sorry. It must have been awful for you." I was even more surprised when I realised that far from continuing my game, I really meant what I had said.

After half an hour's rest, during which time he asked me so many questions about myself that the time passed very quickly, he pulled on his boots yet again and said, " Lunch time. Come with me."

We walked to the back entrance of the officer's mess where the kitchens were situated. He spoke to one of the staff and I was placed in an ante-room, given a bowl of soup, a slice of bread and a large portion of sausage. The orderly told me that the officer would be back to collect me in about three quarters of an hour, possibly sooner.

There was very little to occupy me once my meal was finished and until I knew more about the other locations I would be permitted to enter, there was very little forward planning possible. As it was, I had already achieved far more than I'd thought possible and was happy with my correct assessment of the officer's interest. The officer came to collect me and we walked first to his office, where I sat waiting while he read and signed some papers, issued a string of instructions to soldier clerks, spoke to someone at length on the telephone and finally, gave me a sealed envelope to take to the vehicle workshops. "Come, I'll show you where to go. Do NOT run. Walk fairly briskly and then return to my quarters," he ordered. We went outside and he indicated with his cane the route I had to take to the workshops at Auschwitz. "Off you go then," he commanded.

I did as he instructed and walked fairly quickly, getting used to the boots, and eventually arrived at the barrier to the compound. A youth in similar attire to mine stood in the gatehouse and he called, "Wait there."

An Unterscharfhrer (Corporal) came out of the guardroom and asked, "What have you got there," indicating the fat envelope in my hand.

I stood to attention, took off my cap, handed over the envelope and said, "From Obersturmbannfhrer von Schulenberg, Sir," He took it from my hand, looked at it, called to the youth and gave him instructions. The youth took the envelope and headed off at a fast pace.

"There will be no need to wait. Report back to the Obersturmbannfhrer", the corporal ordered.

"Thank you Sir," I said and returned to the quarters as quickly as possible. On the way back I mused that it was a good thing that there had been a name board on the Colonel's desk otherwise I would not have known his name. His initial was 'E' and I determined to find out what it stood for. The door was ajar and as I approached, I caught the sound of muted music.

I knocked and waited and his voice commanded, "Herein."

I entered and he was sitting in an armchair listening intently to the music. He looked up and said, "That was quick. Do you like music Janni?" he asked "Oh yes sir, particularly Mozart. This is his piano concerto number twenty three isn't it Sir?" I answered, deliberately showing off.

He raised his eyebrows and said,

"Very good. Do you play a musical instrument?"

"Yes Sir, the piano" I replied.

157

"Excellent, you can play for me some time. There is a very good piano in the mess. Sometimes I play to amuse myself but I'm not very good," he said with a deprecatory smile.

We listened to some more music together; the reproduction from the small portable gramophone was really quite good and more than adequate for the small room. He invited me to look through his record collection and there were lots of piano pieces which I recognised and could play.

Finally, he stood up and said,

"Right. That's enough for one day. I'll walk back to your barracks with you as I have some business to attend to over there."

I headed to the door and he suddenly stopped me, handed me a small package and said,

"This is for yourself. Keep it out of sight and don't let the other inmates see you eating it or you could be in for a fight. Be careful."

"I shall be, and thank you sir, I'm very grateful to you." I responded.

He smiled and said, "Come on, then."

CHAPTER THIRTY-SEVEN

Some other work parties were returning and I had to wait with them for the remainder to return before we were counted into the barrack where watery soup and a piece of bread was 'served'. It seemed that our total food ration for one day was to be two slices of bread, a small portion of sausage or cheese and two issues of a litre of 'grass' soup.

I was relieved to see Julius and the boys and they were all delighted with my new status and impressed by the uniform. By contrast, they were in their striped 'pyjama' suits and all showed signs of heavy stubble. After 'dinner' we sat around or lay on our bunks and I learned that, for the time being, they had been allocated to scrubbing and disinfecting the cattle trucks which brought the new arrivals before they returned for their next grim cargo.

In a huddle, I produced my little package and opened it, concealed from the remainder of the inmates by the boys. There were a couple of slices of bread, two large pieces of sausage and a square of cheese. I divided everything into four and we wolfed it down very quickly.

"My God. He's only been here twenty four hours and already he's providing for us again!" Julius whispered. "My boss is a soldier, not, as he puts it, a bloody prison warder and is quite kind. I don't know whether he'll give me something every day, but he did warn me not to let the others see it lest it provoked fighting. So, we must all be extra careful." I concluded.

I went for a pee, splashed water over my face and rubbed water over my teeth and gums. Tomorrow, I vowed, I would ask my officer for a toothbrush.

Back in the barracks, I told Julius about my officer's wounds and the difficulty he had exercising. "Are there any special exercises you could recommend, particularly ones that I would be able to assist with?" I asked Julius.

"Why would you want to do that?" He asked sternly.

"He is kind to me. He will look after me and to be honest, I quite like him," I replied truthfully and before Julius could take me up on this latter point, I added, "Besides, if I get into his good books, I might be able to get some toothbrushes, a piece of soap or anything else that might be useful. He's already very pleased with the cleaning I've done and appears to trust me." "Janni, I told you on several occasions before to look after yourself and you took no notice. Look where it has landed you. You are not, I repeat not, to take any more risks on our behalf. Do you understand me?" Julius admonished.

I smiled at him and gave him a cuddle, saying,

"I'll do my best!"

It had occurred to me many times over since we were dragged out of the ghetto that, if only, those two awful words, if only I had followed the advice of the whole family, I would be with Alex and Hedwig right now, enjoying plum brandy and looking forward to bed-time!

Thoughts of Alex made me miserable. The thought of the terrible anguish he and Hedwig would suffer when they learned that we'd all been deported made me cry silent tears.

In my misery I almost forgot to enquire whether they had any news of Rebecca and Rachel and was very relieved when they told me that for now, they were in a compound called 'Kanada' doing work, sorting the clothes and other items the prisoners had been forced to abandon on arrival, prior to being herded to the 'showers'. We talked some more but after a short while, by tacit agreement, we climbed into our bunks.

Julius, thoughtful as ever, whispered,

"I'll change places with you Janni. It's better if you sleep with the boys just in case any of your bunkmates notices or feels anything unusual about you."

I didn't protest, just gave him a hug and climbed in between the boys. We shuffled into a comfortable position, Isaac with his back to me and me with my back to Aaron. I draped my arm around Isaac, and as he snuggled in towards me, Aaron put his arm round me and in no time at all, we slept. We managed to turn a few times during the night without losing too much sleep and I was very conscious of the fact that my thin shirt had ridden up to my stomach. In any event, it provided very little in the way of padding between the boards and me and I was acutely aware of the tightness of my bandages in this situation. The pattern was set and we continued this awful existence without change, week in, week out. During this time, I had been able to obtain two toothbrushes, one for the family to share and one for myself, which I kept in the officer's bathroom. In addition, I brought back the small pieces of left over soap and scraps of food from the mess kitchens.

CHAPTER THIRTY-EIGHT

Julius gave me instruction and practise in the correct exercises and when I judged it to be the right time, I would apply the techniques to the officer.

He and I were getting on very well and he'd even told me something about himself. He came from Hamburg, had been studying law, but joined the Waffen SS where he rose swiftly through the ranks to major and had been promoted to lieutenant colonel in the field when his commanding officer was killed. He said that he was one of the luckier wounded who had been brought back. Many had not been so lucky. He was twenty-eight and had two sisters younger than himself and a brother in the Luftwaffe. His father, who had been badly wounded in the First World War, losing an arm, was a senior Rechtsanwalt, a barrister, who hoped shortly to be made a Richter, a judge and, he told me his name. Emil.

Several weeks after I had begun working for him, during his morning break, he took me to the mess hall, pointed to the piano and said, "Let me hear you play."

I sat at the piano, raised the lid and ran my fingers over the notes in a series of quick scales. Satisfied with the 'feel' of the instrument, I played "Du bist mein ganzes Hertz" then Liebestraum followed by Wie still ist der Nacht. He was very quiet, listening intently so I finished with Beethoven's 'Moonlight', which I loved playing, and it showed. I finished playing, stood up and turned to him and gave him a mock bow. He smiled and clapped his hands together very lightly, so I bowed a second time and he said, "You play awfully well. I'm quite envious" "There is just one thing Sir, you will have to tell me which composers I'm allowed to play and what light music is permitted. I don't want to get either of us into trouble." I said, trying to make it sound quite conspiratorial. "Good idea," he nodded.

The main door opened and the Camp Commandant, Rudolf Höss (Not to be confused with Rudolf Hess) came in with his adjutant. Emil stood up and gave the Nazi salute, but was unable to click his heels due to his wound.

Hss returned his salute and enquired,

"Who was playing the piano just now?"

I didn't know whether or not we were in trouble, but I needn't have worried. Emil was more than equal to the occasion and very cleverly, he replied.

"This prisoner was playing Sir. An excellent performer, I'm sure you'll agree and I thought that it might be a good idea to have him play some good German music, some good old favourites during mealtimes. It would work wonders for the staff morale."

"Excellent idea Schulenberg," Hss responded, pointedly dropping the 'von' from Emil's surname.

He turned to me and asked,

"Can you play Fr Elise?"

I stood to attention and said,

"Yes Sir."

He pointed to the piano and said, "Get on with it then."

I played it right through and when I finished, stood to attention facing him. He didn't compliment me on my playing, but then I hadn't expected it from this odious little man. He simply turned to Emil and said, "Very well Schulenberg, I'll leave the arrangements in your capable hands." They went through their Heil Hitler routine again which made me want to laugh and I struggled to keep a straight face as the self-important little bastard turned on his heel and left, adjutant in tow.

Emil whispered,

"Sorry Janni. I've landed you with another job, but it was all I could think of on the spur of the moment. He can be an awkward, objectionable son of a bitch."

We walked back to his quarters and I noticed that his gait had not improved over the last few weeks, if anything, it seemed to be giving him more trouble than ever.

This was the opportunity to further his dependence on me for various things. Once in his room, I automatically took his jacket and placed it on a hanger and then helped him remove his boots. It was a fixed routine by now.

He sat on the edge of the bed and half turning, swung his left leg up and onto the bed then reached over to lift his right leg up beside it. He was struggling and without being asked, I went over and very gently lifted his leg onto the bed.

"Thank you, Janni. That was kind of you." he said.

"I can't help noticing that it doesn't seem to be getting any better Sir," I ventured

"Time Janni. In it's own good time." he replied.

"Do you ever get a full day off Sir?" I began

"Of course. Why do you ask?" He answered.

"The mother of one of my friends was a doctor and she specialised in fractures, particularly compound ones of the femur and hip bones and she had a whole series of exercises especially designed to combat muscle wastage. They were very effective. I learned them and used to help out with the more difficult cases," I lied.

Before he could say anything, I continued,

"You'll think me very presumptuous Sir, but I thought that on your day off, you could take a hot bath to loosen your muscles, I could show you these exercises and help with some of the more difficult ones. It has to be worth a trial Sir." Deliberately, I lowered my voice slightly and in a very concerned tone, I added, "I can't bear to see you going through so much pain every day."

He was quiet for some time before answering,

"That's very thoughtful of you. I'll have to think about it."

I didn't push it and left the next round of the conversation to him. He didn't disappoint me.

"When do you want to take another bath?" he asked.

Knowing precisely what I was doing, I looked deeply into his eyes and said, "On your day off Sir!"

I'm sure he blushed as he said,

"You really are a little devil aren't you? I'll think about it and we'll just have to see." I turned away, after giving him a wicked smile, took his jacket from the hanger and gave it a good brushing before replacing it. Next, I quickly polished the boots we had removed and placed them conveniently within his reach. I was aware that he was watching every movement that I made as I went around the room tidying and polishing. I hummed quietly and from time to time, lapsed into some mildly girlish mannerisms. I was surer than ever that I had him firmly on the hook.

He went to his office, then to lunch while I ironed his shirts and handkerchiefs, folded everything neatly away, then sponged and pressed his other uniforms before stripping the bed, changing the sheets and pillow cases and folding them up with the other items to go to the laundry.

He was away all afternoon and when he finally limped in, he looked exhausted. He sat down heavily on the bed, not bothering with the armchair and as I removed his boots yet again, he pointed to his locker and said, "There's a bottle of brandy in the locker. Bring it over here with a glass, please." He was always so courteous now, but then, it's as hard to shake off good manners, as it is bad ones. I took it over and helped him off with his jacket and then after assisting him onto the bed, I leaned over to plump the pillows behind him and said, "Excuse me Sir. My bandages are a bit tight. Would it be all right if I took them off for a little while? This is the only place I can do it in safety."

"Yes, of course. It must be very uncomfortable for you at times." he responded. I didn't go to the bathroom. First, my blazer and then, prolonging it just a little, I unbuttoned my shirt and removed it. Finally, very deliberately, I turned to face him as I started to undo the bandages and when they were completely removed, I stretched my arms out sideways then above my head, leaning back, the better to show off my flat, smooth tummy as well as my tits.

"Ah! That's better", I said as I continued my exercises, making them as provocative as possible.

"I used to wear a bra out there. It was more comfortable," I added matter of factly. He was speechless and he couldn't take his eyes off my body. The silence continued and I was not going to be the one to break it.

In a slightly hoarse voice, very earnestly, he asked,

"Please be very honest with me Janni, did you have a special friend on the outside? I'm sure you know what I mean."

"Yes Sir, I did and I miss him very much. I don't want to talk about it Sir if you don't mind." I answered truthfully.

"Alright, I just needed to know," he responded then, after taking a deep breath he said,

"Come over here and sit on the bed beside me." and when I looked at him enquiringly, he said, " That's not an order, it's a request and you don't have to comply."

Now he was being clever, testing my reactions.

I went and sat on the bed. In reality, only one cheek of my bottom was on the bed. As I turned to face him, I kept my eyes downcast, not making any move at all and after what seemed like a lifetime, he tentatively reached out and stroked the back of my arm before becoming just a little bolder, extending the stroking to my side.

I stood up and he looked surprised and disappointed when I moved away. I walked round the other side of the bed and said,

"Move over." I forgot to say Sir!

He moved to the right hand side of the bed and I pulled off my boots and breeches, locked the door and went and lay down beside him.

He rolled onto his good side, facing me and began stroking me all over. It always provoked the same response and this was no exception. I heard the sharp intake of breath as he said, "My God! Your skin. It's like silk. It's incredible. Your whole body is so beautiful" "You should have seen me with all my hair," I said, ruefully running my fingers over the short, new growth. "I did see you with all your hair, that first day on the ramp when I made you drop your trousers. I haven't forgotten how you looked," he said, confirming my suspicions.

By now, he had one of my tits in his hand and I reached up, put an arm round his neck and gave him one of those wonderful, electric kisses Alex had first taught me. I felt him shudder all over. I turned fully towards him, and unbuttoned his shirt, pressed myself against his bare skin and took his right hand and placed it on my bottom.

Slowly, I unbuttoned his trousers and exposed his erect penis, which I proceeded to titillate with moistened fingers, all round the tip, letting my hand slide right down to the root from time to time. Eventually, I turned him onto his back, straddled him, sitting on his chest. He held my breasts, as, behind me, I continued to massage his penis with one hand while holding his testicles with the other. The familiar tightening of the scrotum and the thrusting movements told me exactly what was going to happen and I increased the tempo and gently squeezed his balls. In seconds, he exploded with a series of jerks and low moans. I kept on fondling, using the ready lubrication to slide gently up and down from tip to root, provoking a series of involuntary shudders until finally, he whispered,

"Stop, for Christ's sake stop. You're driving me mad."

I stopped, climbed off him and walked to the bathroom with my girl's gait and returned with a damp face cloth and towel. As I finished washing and drying his naughty bits, I leant over and kissed him, gently and for only a short duration.

Back in the bathroom I washed and dried myself, re-bandaged my tits and got dressed. In the room, he was sitting up, shirt and trousers back in place and a brandy in his hand. He was quiet for so long that I thought he was too embarrassed to say anything; that he had instantly regretted what had happened and didn't know what to say by way of excuse.

I couldn't have been more wrong as he looked up with a wonderful, lazy, slightly sleepy smile and said, "Thank you Janni. That was wonderful. I cannot believe that body of yours, it's just amazing."

I smiled and said,

"I'm glad I made you happy Sir. But I'm afraid you will get rid of me now." I looked down, not meeting his eyes as though ashamed.

"Don't worry your head about that. But, one thing I beg of you. Do not mention this to a soul; we could both end up in serious trouble if any hint of this got out. You would be shot and I would be kicked out and sent to a camp like this. In a way, we hold each other's fate in our hands," he said urgently. "I'd better go now Sir it's almost check-in time."

I bent over and kissed his forehead, picked up my little package of scraps and said, "See you tomorrow, Sir."

I walked to the barracks well pleased with the day's work.

A week, maybe ten days went by without him making any reference to what had happened or making any further advances and I was beginning to wonder if he had had second thoughts about it. One thing was certain; the next move had to come from him.

I had been very busy taking messages all over the place, then attending to my cleaning duties and it was late afternoon before I saw him. He had obviously had another very busy day and looked drawn and tired. He poured a brandy immediately he came in, without asking for his boots to be removed, sat in the armchair and said, "I have a day off tomorrow. You can have your bath and we'll give those exercises of yours a trial shall we?" "Thank you Sir, " I said with the slightest hint of a smile and added, "Do you wish me to take your boots off before I leave Sir?"

"Um, Yes. Good Lord, is it that time already?" he queried.

I nodded, said "'Fraid so" removed his boots and started to unbutton his jacket.

He clasped his hand over mine and said,

"I'll do that, you had better go or you will be late. Go on, off you go and I'll see you tomorrow. Oh and by the way, you start playing the piano next week. I just thought I'd tell you".

Since the first day, he had always brought some food for me and today was no exception. I'm sure he knew that I was sharing it and for the last couple of weeks, he had brought, two small packages which were easier to conceal in my inside pockets than a single fatter one.

I was beginning to like this man very much.

164

CHAPTER THIRTY-NINE

While I was leading a relatively secure life, others were suffering dreadfully. The crematoria were working nearly all day, every day and those who were not being murdered by this expedient were being literally worked to death as slave labourers in the various industries nearby, the most notable being about five kilometres away at Auschwitz III near Monowice. There, the slaves worked for I.G. Farben, a massive company, who manufactured amongst other things, buna, the synthetic rubber, cement and a range of chemicals and paints. The death toll of workers was very high and even if they didn't die at their place of work, the moment they were no longer capable of assisting production, they were dispatched to the gas chambers. The selection for this final journey 'up the chimney' was made by the simple method of parading the workers every so often and making them run over a measured distance with their trousers removed. This ghastly 'trot past' was overseen by one or two doctors in the company of an officer, who between them judged, from the ability of the inmates to keep pace with the rest and the amount of fat left on their thighs and buttocks whether or not there was any work left in them.

Inside the barrack compounds too, the brutality continued, not only with savage beatings and whippings, but also with 'on the spot executions'. These 'encouragements' also applied in the women's barracks where the female guards, were, if anything, more brutal and sadistically violent than their male counterparts.

A number of women who could no longer cope had thrown themselves onto the electrified fencing in order to commit suicide. After several such occurrences, the guards resorted to a terrible tactic to discourage any further attempts. They made it clear that the following procedure would be followed after every such attempt, successful or otherwise and demonstrated it there and then at roll call.

The guards walked along the ranks and indicated that alternate prisoners should step forward three paces. When this had been completed, the remainder were made to step back four or five paces. Those who had been selected were then made to close up into a single column, shoulder to shoulder facing the outer fence. They numbered exactly one hundred. Guards walked behind them with Schmeisser sub machine guns slung over their shoulders by a strap, barrels parallel to the ground, left hand forward, right hand holding the pistol grip. Once they were all in place, at a command from their officer, they turned, opened fire, and shot a number of the women where they stood. The officers walked along the line of crumpled bodies and any sound or movement and they would dispatch their victims with a single bullet in the head. The remainder of the hundred who had been selected were marched off to the 'showers' and within an hour, had been reduced to little piles of ashes. Rachel, my lovely, wonderful adoptive mother, whom I had loved so dearly, was one of them. Murdered in front of her own daughter.

Julius, Aaron and Isaac were inconsolable and although I had loved her desperately, my loss was in no way comparable to theirs. They had all expected to die here one way or another, but the men folk anticipated that they would die first. It took them a long time to come to terms with what had happened. Regrettably, some women, although fully aware that the consequences of further attempts would result in the deaths of a further hundred women, selfishly still tried to throw themselves on the wire. Charitably, one has to believe that they were so thoroughly stressed and deranged that they were unaware of the horrendous results of their actions. I reported for duty the next morning as arranged and Emil realised that I was very distressed. Tears kept welling up in my eyes and I couldn't look him in the face. I felt so ashamed of what I had done with this man who was, after all, no matter how kind he had been to me, the enemy. I wanted to kill him. "Whatever is the matter Janni?" He enquired very solicitously.

"You bastards have killed my mother and I hate the fucking lot of you," I shouted.

He stood, very quietly, uncertain of himself. At length, he said,

"Janni, surely you know me well enough by now to know that I should never do anything to hurt you and I thought you could tell the difference between me and those animals. I don't condone what is going on here. I really am very sorry about your mother, please believe me."

I looked up at him and he appeared genuinely distraught and ashamed of being a part of this awful regime. He took a pace forward, arms open and I moved towards him. He enfolded me in his arms and held me as I sobbed uncontrollably against his shoulder. It was a relief to let it all out, something I couldn't do in front of the others, it would have only made their distress worse. I had been indifferent to death for so long, I'd seen so much of it that it left me completely unmoved and it was a relief to know that I still had the ability to grieve for a loved one.

Emil stroked my head and patted me gently until my sobbing subsided. He poured some brandy in a glass and said,

"Here, drink this". He kept his arm round my shoulder and held the glass to my lips until I took it from his hands.

"I'm sorry I called you a bastard Sir. That was unfair of me," I snivelled. "It's not for you to apologise to me Janni. I would have said the same thing if our roles had been reversed. Christ, I hate this bloody place." He finished quietly.

The roles were reversed for a moment as, quite unexpectedly; he went over, put on his tiny kettle and made a cup of very poor quality coffee for each of us. He then placed the warm cup in my hands and sat me on the edge of the bed. He sat beside me, arm still round my shoulder, encouraging me to drink. I started blubbering again and in response to the worried look on his face, I told him that his actions had reminded me of the first time I met Aaron. Two frightened young boys, dragged from the rubble with bombs and shells falling all around us and how he had held me and helped me to drink my first cup of coffee. It brought so many memories flooding back. I told him of poor Rebecca who had witnessed her mother's execution and had no other member of the family over there to comfort her. I was sick with worry about her. "Tell me about her," Emil said, trying to get me talking to occupy my mind. I told him how beautiful she was, what good fun, my pal. How we played music together and what a wonderful clarinettist she was. I told him nothing of our love making activities.

We finished our coffee in silence and after a while, he said,

"We'll forget about those exercises for the time being. Go and wash your face in cold water. I've brought some sheet music for you and we can walk over to the mess where you can run through a few pieces in preparation for next week. It may help keep your mind off these sad events.

I liked him again.

We walked to the mess hall and I played for over an hour, losing myself in the music and because of the depth of my grief, playing the more sombre pieces with intense feeling, expressing my emotions. It helped me to think that I was playing them only for Rachel and very quietly, almost under my breath, I recited Kaddish while I played.

Emil thought I was humming and he asked,

"Can you sing Janni?"

"Oh yes Sir, but I daren't," I replied.

"Why ever not?" he queried.

"Because when I sing, I sound exactly like a girl Sir," I mumbled.

"Oh! I see," he answered.

"No Sir, you don't see at all. Until I came here, I'd been living as a girl most of the time. I preferred it that way, in fact, I loved it. Now, I have to be so careful of my voice, the way

I walk, my mannerisms, everything. I'm terrified of anyone other than you knowing about it and worry about what I might do in my sleep lying next to a man while I'm dreaming of my boyfriend or you Sir. I know it's impossible, but I wish I could sleep with you." "So do I Janni. So do I," he said wistfully.

I stopped playing and said,

" I think we ought to see about your exercises now Sir."

"Are you sure you want to?" he asked gently.

"Yes Sir. Quite sure," I answered.

Back in his quarters, he stripped off and went into the bathroom where I had run his bath. He had a lithe, athletic, very pleasing body but it took my breath away when he turned to step into the bath. The wounding was on a massive scale running from below his right knee, right up his flank and up to the middle of his shoulder blade. There were three or four wide, livid cicatrices so close together that they almost constituted a continuous scar with smaller, equally livid scars scattered around. The back of his arm revealed similar wounding on a smaller scale. All the scars were raised, varying in colour from sickly, pinkish yellow to deep purple, the undamaged skin and flesh puckering grotesquely, stretched so taut in places that it was easy to imagine that the slightest strain would wrench open these terrible wounds. I felt very sorry for him. Without thinking I went over and helped him into a sitting position and gently washed and sponged his back, being particularly sensitive to his reactions when I washed the scars with the sponge. I put it down and continued the washing with my hands.

"Oh that is so good Janni. You're so gentle and careful. Thank you."

I helped him to stand and was tempted to continue washing him all over. Instead, I handed him the soap and face cloth and said,

"Call me when you're ready to get out Sir".

In his bedroom, I placed the pillows on the bed so that he would lie almost flat with the pillows to support his right thigh, and placed the jar of ointment, which he had to rub into his wounds on the bedside table. He called, "Help me out please Janni."

I went to him, steadying him as he lifted his right leg over the side of the bath and supporting him as his bad leg took all the weight when he lifted the left leg. The effort made him tremble and I held him until it subsided. Gently, I dried his back, more in a blotting motion than conventional rubbing. The rest, he managed unaided; I pointed to the bed and helped him onto it, indicating that he should turn on his left side. He didn't argue and once satisfied with his position, I began to apply the ointment to the horrendous scars, working as gently as I knew how but at the same time, making sure that all the most sensitive areas were adequately covered. I was still fully clothed apart from my blazer and my sleeves were rolled up to the elbows. From my position, perched on the edge of the bed, I continued the gentle rubbing movements until I could feel the ointment losing its oiliness.

"Turn onto your stomach please sir," I said and without waiting, helped him to turn over. I massaged ointment into his flank and shoulder blade, then, using all the naughty skills I had learned from Alex, I massaged his bottom. Finally, I turned him onto his back and cruelly; I ignored the fact that he was becoming very erect.

"Exercise time!" I said.

"Oh Shit! Do we have to?" He begged.

"Sorry Sir. It really is important that we do this now while your muscles are still receptive." I answered a trifle sadistically.

"Move down the bed so that your legs overhang the edge Sir, Please." I said.

"Oh. Very well," he responded.

"Now Sir, I'm going to lift your leg, place your foot against my chest and hold your knee with both hands. I'm going to lift your knee and then I want you to try to push me away with your foot. I'll help by pulling your knee towards me. Please try very hard sir," I

167

almost commanded as I was in charge now. He did try very hard and we repeated the exercise several times. After a brief rest, holding his heel, I made him lift his knee to his chest and then extend his leg, trying to get it as straight as possible, pushing upwards towards the ceiling. Next, with his heel on my shoulder and my hands over his knee, I asked him to try and bend it. He couldn't manage it but I could feel the effort he was putting into it and knew it would do him good. "It's not over yet I'm afraid Sir, but these exercises are easier. I promise you Sir." I cajoled. I made him get off the bed and stand, feet apart, arms up, elbows out to the side, forearms parallel to the floor, finger tips almost touching in the centre of his chest. From this position, I made him half rotate his body; to the right, to the left, right, left, as many times as he could cope with. After this I made him stand, legs astride, right arm straight down his side, left arm in an arc over his head, from which position, he had to keep his body from bending forward at the same time as he bent to the right, trying to reach further down his leg each time with the objective of reaching his ankle. The exercise was repeated to the left. "Back on the bed. Rest time Sir." I said, and added, "Don't lie down Sir. I'll prop up the pillows behind you so that you sit upright, legs flat. Don't look so cross. It's the last part now."

With both hands together, I made him reach as far down his leg as possible and then try to touch his forehead to his knee. First one leg, then the other as many times as he could manage comfortably. Everything considered, he did awfully well and I was full of admiration for his compliance and tenacity. "I know it hurts Sir but I promise you it will become easier," I ventured sympathetically and continued, "Just lie flat, on your stomach now Sir. Please."

He did as I asked and lay, face down, his forehead resting on folded arms. Starting from his neck muscles, I massaged every inch of his body down to his waist, skipping his bottom to move down to his thighs. Working back up from the knees, I began the probing massage of his buttocks, the way Alex used to do to me and I had done to Hedwig and Rebecca. Parting his legs slightly and with a little ointment on my fingers, I gently played around, teasingly pressing, stroking, caressing his anus and allowing my little finger to penetrate occasionally.

"Lift your midriff," I commanded and as he complied, I continued my ministrations with one hand while, with the other; I alternated between holding his testicles and running my hand up and down the length of his penis.

Eventually, I said,

"Turn onto your back." Again, I failed to say Sir!

He did as I asked and lay looking at me, totally besotted. I've never experienced such a feeling of power. Total control.

In a very leisurely manner, I removed each item of clothing until, stark naked, I climbed onto the bed, straddling him, with my bottom pressing down on his erect willy.

I leant forward taking the weight on my elbows, one either side of his head and proceeded to apply all the kissing techniques Alex had taught me, starting with the ultra cool, electric kisses and progressing to the longer, more searching, passionate extremes.

He could not keep his hands still. They were all over my body; stroking, squeezing, clutching, holding my bottom tightly with both hands, one tentative finger exploring the most secret place while his pelvis moved rhythmically against me.

When I judged the moment to be right, I reached over with my left hand, delved into the pot of ointment, sat upright and, reaching between my legs, preceded to apply a liberal amount to his penis and a similar amount to my bottom. I took his throbbing member in one hand and lowering myself, carefully guided him inside me. His breathing was almost out of control and as I started to move up and down, his hands moved frantically all over my body. He squeezed my breasts and nipples very hard, slid his hands up the under side of my thighs until he held both cheeks of my bottom then held my waist, moving me up and down to suit his tempo. Once again, at the strategic moment, I speeded up the movement and reached round to give full attention to his testicles. He increased the pace still more, panting, muttering wonderful endearments as we both exploded together, him inside me and me all over his stomach and chest.

Our movements gradually subsided and I straightened my legs, lying the full length of his stomach as I kissed him gently, and, because I knew how concerned men were about the quality of their performance, I told him he was wonderful, that it was the best ever!

He held me for a long time and I had to wrestle away as I said, "I'd better take my bath now Sir and if you come in, I'll wash you too." "Janni, I don't know what to say. That was wonderful. I've never known anything quite like that before. You're amazing and your body is so beautiful," he stammered.

"You are not being one hundred percent truthful with me Sir," I ventured and as he raised his eyebrows and looked at me for an explanation, I continued, "You might not have gone that far before Sir, but this was most certainly not your first experience with another boy. I'm not daft Sir", I concluded.

"You are very perceptive Janni. You're also right, but I've never done that before, only a bit of mutual masturbation at boarding school, university and the military college and to be honest, until you, I've never wanted to, but since that first day with you, I've thought of nothing else, wondering what it would be like making love to you. You're fantastic."

"You are only the second person I've done it with and it was very nice Sir," I responded, even though I'd only been thinking of Alex the whole time!

I took my bath and he washed. We both dressed and sat listening to his records and drinking his awful coffee, which was still like nectar to me.

I had been thinking hard and said,

"I think it would be a good idea if we kept our clothes on when we go through your exercises each day Sir. On your day off, it's different, nobody would dare to bother you, would they?" "You are absolutely right. It would be all too easy to get completely carried away." he replied with a lecherous grin.

I stood up, collected my little packages which he had so thoughtfully collected from the mess kitchen after I had played the piano, leant over and kissed him on the forehead and said, "I'd better go, otherwise I shall want to stay here all night. Till tomorrow sir. Goodnight." That night, I didn't want Julius to feel alone and desolate, so I swapped places with him so that he and the boys could be together.

CHAPTER FORTY

A couple of days later I played the piano in the mess during lunch for the first time and to my surprise and delight, received a round of applause from the assembled officers. For these efforts, I was given extra food, not much, just a few scraps which, together with Emil's daily contribution, helped sustain my family and me. Some days later, Emil really surprised me. Quite suddenly, he said, "I've seen your 'sister' Rebecca. I agree with you, she is very beautiful." "Oh. Is she all right Sir? I've been terribly worried about her." I asked excitedly. " I have had her moved to play in the camp orchestra and if I can arrange it you will be able to play with them and rehearse with them on occasions," he answered and it was fortunate that we were in his quarters when he told me, because, ever impulsive, I reached up, hugged him, did a little dance and then kissed him murmuring, "Fantastic. Fantastic. You are so very thoughtful Sir. I love you."

Suddenly, I became fully aware of what I had just said and happily convinced myself that what I had meant was, I loved him for helping Rebecca. I didn't question myself any further! That night, Julius and the boys could hardly conceal their delight when I told them and Aaron said, "This officer must be a lot different to the rests of these bastards. He is extraordinarily kind to you, and through you, to our family. You must have him totally bewitched Janni."

This was so close to the truth that I half turned away from them as I answered,

"I told you before, he only wants to be a soldier and is basically a very decent, kind man. I had no idea when I expressed my concerns about Becca that he would respond so wonderfully. I like him very much." True to his word, Emil took me to a little hall one morning and there was the camp orchestra, getting ready to rehearse under their conductor, a very daunting, lady.

Suddenly, there was a yell, "JANNI!"

Becca put down her clarinet ran towards me and in seconds we were hugging, stroking each other's heads and crying out of sheer joy at being reunited. The other members of the orchestra looked on indulgently and when I looked at Emil, I mouthed the words "Thank You" at him; He smiled, looked a little uncomfortable and turned to look out of the window.

Becca and I only had a few moments to talk before the conductor called everybody to attention. "Please take your positions," she said.

Emil and I listened to them play. Everything considered, they were not too bad, but then most of them had been professional musicians.

After their first break, I went over to the conductor and asked if they had the music for the Mozart Clarinet Concerto. She hadn't, but asked the members if they knew the score. Most did and the rest said they could improvise. Becca agreed to play and I went over to Emil and whispered, "This is just for you." I walked to the piano and we played, the orchestra gaining assurance with every note Becca played. Her tone was brilliant, haunting, subtly stimulating the whole gamut of emotions and I let the tears role down my face, unashamedly as I recalled the first occasion we had played it together. When we had finished, everybody clapped and the severe looking conductor hugged Becca, saying, "Wonderful, truly wonderful."

I was still holding Becca's hand when I heard a cough. I turned to see Emil standing to one side. He gave a barely perceptible bow to Becca and said, "Thank you Frulein. That was beautiful. You are very talented." Then, turning to me, he said, "Come Janni, we have work to do."

I squeezed Becca's hand, kissed her briefly and said,

"Love you, see you soon." and very reluctantly let go of her hand and followed Emil from the hall.

Outside, I fell into step beside him and said,

"Thank you so much Sir, I can't tell you how much this means to us. We appreciate it very much." "I must be getting soft," he said with a smile and added, "Seeing the joy on your faces and listening to you both playing made me feel very emotional. I could tell that you love each other very much. God, these are dreadful times that we are living in Janni."

We went through his exercises every day and he admitted that they were doing him a lot of good and he could feel the strength returning to his leg. In mock alarm I said,

"Oh Hell, we'll have to stop."

"What do you mean, stop? Whatever for, when they are doing me so much good?" he queried. "If I help you to get really fit again, you'll be off, back to the fighting, probably get yourself killed and I'll never see you again." I answered.

"You really do care, don't you Janni?" he said thoughtfully.

"Yes Sir I do and also, I'm afraid that if you go, there will be no one to look after me. I feel very safe with you around Sir. To be honest Sir, homosexuality is rife here, and the longest serving 'members', the block seniors and the kapos are the worst offenders. I have to be on my guard against their advances all the time," I answered truthfully.

"I hope I'm right in believing that those are not your only reasons and that I mean more than that to you," he said with just a hint of sadness. He needed reassurance and I waited until we reached his room before saying, "Stop fishing Sir! You know damned well that I love you and not just because you look after me and are so kind and considerate." I reached up on my toes and kissed the tip of his nose. He smiled and folded me in his arms and started to laugh.

"What's so funny Sir?" I asked.

"This whole situation. It's so incongruous to hear you calling me Sir all the time, even when we are having sex, nearly all your endearments end with Sir. Don't YOU think that's funny?" he retorted. I laughed with him and said, "I know your christian name, but if I once start calling you that, I might forget and call you Emil in front of another member of staff and they would be sure to report it. You'll just have to imagine that when I'm calling you 'Sir' in those particular circumstances, I mean 'lover', dearest, darling or just Emil. It's something I've had to get used to."

"I know you're right, but it still seems so odd," he chortled.

We went through his exercises and I could tell that he was improving daily. On 'bath days', I noticed that his scars were softening and the puckering easing. He was able to move about with much more confidence and agility although he still relied heavily on his cane when walking anything over sixty or seventy metres. In our lovemaking, he was becoming more and more adventurous and he said he got a tremendous thrill out of holding my penis or testicles while he made love to me and with the strength returning to his leg, he liked to try a variety of positions so that he could indulge his latest passion for playing with my naughty bits. I wasn't complaining. I liked it too.

Once and once only, he didn't ask directly, but in a round about way, suggested that oral sex would be nice.

"I don't want to do that Sir," I said reproachfully.

"I would never force you to do anything that is disagreeable to you Janni," he said contritely and continued, "I just assumed, no, I mean I imagined that you probably did it with your boyfriend because you obviously loved him very much."

I didn't answer and left him to draw his own conclusions.

171

CHAPTER FORTY-ONE

Over the next six months, I did a lot of cleaning, carried many messages, played the piano nearly every day and met Becca at least once a week. She had told me that a part of the orchestra's duties was to play light music, Strauss and Viennese operettas while the people were undressing to go to the gas chambers. It was all part of the deception, just like the instructions to place their clothes in tidy piles and remember where they had put them so they could find them quickly after their showers. Another duty was to play marching music when the working parties left for work each morning.

Occasionally, the whole orchestra, or just a few members would have to play at functions for the officers and I played with them on a number of occasions. Several times, we played 'drinking' songs. I particularly remember two elderly Jews who had been provided with tailed suits. One played the accordion and the other the violin. They were very good and sometimes, a euphonium player, a trumpeter, Becca and I would join them to play lilting, Bavarian songs. At such times, the seated officers would link arms and sway from side to side in time with the music and join in singing the choruses and get very drunk. It all seemed so terribly normal and such good fun!

One day, Becca told me that a number of women were having sex with some of the guards. She said how much she despised them for giving themselves to the enemy. I hadn't got an answer to that! We had got through the winter fairly well although the barracks were very cold and we had no blankets. Quite a few people died during the coldest spells but their places were rapidly filled by new arrivals. Lice were a real problem and everyone would shake their clothing, run a flame round the seams of everything, and when we managed to acquire razor blades, everybody shaved their heads, armpits and crotches in addition to the more conventional areas.

I was lucky in as much as I had no hair under my arms, very little pubic hair and I could have a strip wash and wash my hair every day in Emil's bathroom. In addition, he had obtained some powder for me, which kept the ghastly things at bay. Whenever I did the ironing for Emil, I ran the hot iron along the inside creases of my clothes just to be on the safe side.

Julius and the boys, along with several other inmates, were transferred to work in the armaments factory in Auschwitz I, by the SS workshops and at first they were marched across each morning and then back again in the evening. Although the work was more skilled and they were on their feet the whole day, it was not as arduous or upsetting as the work they had been doing and my concern for their health eased a little as distinct signs of improvement became evident. I let them have all the food that Emil gave me each day since he had become well aware of what I was doing with it and frequently provided extra for me. He took a lot of chances on my behalf, even giving me little parcels of food for Rebecca whenever we had the chance of playing in the orchestra together.

I had become a familiar figure from my messenger duties round the camp and from playing the piano in the mess and at concerts. Most of the guards treated me good-naturedly, some even asking if I could play special songs for them. In the circumstances, my hopes of survival were reasonably high and my spirits were rising. Although it was always rewarding to see Julius, Aaron and Isaac, I hated returning to the barracks each evening and, surrounded by the gaunt, haggard, hopeless faces, it was very easy to sink back into the depths of depression and despair.

Then, after a few more months, my depression hit rock bottom. I returned to the barracks and my 'family' were not there. I was frantic with worry and although I was relieved to learn that they were not dead, merely transferred to the barracks in Auschwitz I, it meant that I could no longer provide the extra food which was so vital to their survival.

Additionally, it meant there was no other member of the family in the same barracks as myself. I missed them dreadfully. Occasionally, I caught a glimpse of one or the other of them when I had to take packages or messages across, but I never got to speak to them. For some weeks, I didn't see anything of them. Then one morning I saw them with a load of other inmates in the back of an open lorry. They were heading to Monowice and I.G. Farben, Auschwitz III.

I didn't pass this information on to Rebecca. It would have destroyed her.

I told Emil what had happened and he was genuinely upset for me.

"I wish there was something I could do Janni but it's just not possible. I could help your sister because the orchestra comes within the administration and entertainment departments, but this, I am afraid, is totally out of my department and it is impossible to intercede or help in any way. I'm so sorry," he concluded miserably. We consoled each other in our usual way and on my way back to the barracks; I very nearly came to grief. I was whistling a piece of music that I'd been asked to play and for which I had no sheet music. I often did this within the confines of Emil's quarters while I was cleaning or ironing, but on this occasion, I forgot where I was. A sudden bellow "Warum pfeist du. Vergiss nicht wo du bist, du blde affe."(Why are you whistling? Don't forget where you are, you bloody ape.)

I stopped, stood to attention and removed my hat. One had to do this whenever a member of staff addressed you. He marched up to me and said, "What was that you were whistling and why were you doing it. Come on, speak up boy." "I have to play it tomorrow for one of the officers and I have no sheet music nor am I quite certain how it goes Sir. I was just trying to refresh my memory Sir." I replied, trying to conceal my trembling. "Where are you from boy?" he asked.

Without thinking, I replied,

"I'm German, just like you sir. The only difference is you know why you're here but I don't" He cuffed me hard round the ear, making it sing and for good measure, brought his hand back again to strike the other side of my head as he looked menacingly into my face. He could see that I was shaking and after a moment or two, his expression softened a little and gruffly, he said, "Consider yourself lucky it's me you are talking to boy. Anyone else and you would have been shot by now. Bite your tongue in future and don't be so bloody stupid or you won't last long. Do you hear me boy? Now, be on your way before I change my mind and don't start whistling again."

"Thank you Sir," I said humbly and turned, military fashion and headed for the barracks as quickly as I dared without running.

CHAPTER FORTY-TWO

At least I had plenty to keep me occupied and the time did not hang as heavily for me as it did for others, particularly as I had my weekly reunions with Becca to look forward to. Dear Becca was becoming much thinner but was still as beautiful as ever. Somehow, she even managed to appear elegant despite the tattered clothing and the cropped hair. I had loved her since the first time we washed together in the kitchen, which seemed like an eternity ago.

Another winter to get through, sometimes sharing a warm bed with my lover during the day and a freezing cold bed with smelly, lice-infested, unwashed strangers by night. The ritual of recovering, washing and swallowing my diamonds and emeralds had become second nature by now and it was one of the few things that Emil did not know about me.

He was very busy organising labour for the works department to build another crematorium. Apart from the main ones there were already two temporary gas chambers, one in the woods by the disrobing house beyond crematoria IV and V in the KANADA compound and another disrobing house and temporary gas chamber in the corner of the woods, where the mass graves and cremation pits were situated. It was common knowledge that in these same woods, were mass graves of thousands of Russian POWs, who against all known conventions, were worked to the point of death and then brutally murdered.

The reason for increased 'production' soon became apparent, as the barracks immediately to our left as we faced the railway platform, began to fill with thousands of Hungarian Jews who were being transported from Budapest to extermination camps at the rate of ten to twelve thousand per day. The crematoria were operating to their maximum capacity, non-stop, the air full of the acrid, black, oily smoke and the cloying stench of death everywhere. It was impossible to get an overall picture or number of the daily rate of gassings and cremations or deaths by other means because no one wanted to talk about it, contemplate their own destiny or even hazard a guess about anything. It was not a subject I could discuss with Emil either. It was rumoured that they were 'processing' between twelve and fourteen thousand per day.

After a particularly busy period when Emil had not had a full day off for ages, he had worked flat out in the morning so that he could at least have a half-day, and back in his quarters, he surprised me by producing a small wireless set. He fitted a plug and a wire for an aerial and switched on. After it had warmed up, he fiddled with the controls and after a series of whistles, howls and lots of static noise; he managed to locate a number of stations and jotted the dial locations onto a pad. During his fiddling, I heard a very English voice reading a news bulletin and Emil turned past the station very quickly.

"Can you find that station again Sir," I asked excitedly.

"Yes, but I don't understand English and if we were caught listening to it, we should probably both be shot," he replied.

"I understand English Sir and it did sound very interesting. Couldn't you turn it down very low so that we can find out what is happening Sir." I persisted.

He turned the volume down and very tentatively tuned in to the English station. We huddled round the set and I translated for him, telling of the success of the Normandy landings and how the Allies had landed in great strength and were sweeping all opposition aside as they raced towards Paris.

Before commenting on the news he said,

"You never cease to amaze me. What else is there that I should know about you? How long have you been able to speak English for God's sake?"

"I've always been able to speak English Sir. Don't ask me why or how, I don't know sir," I replied. He was very thoughtful for some time and when he eventually spoke, he made

174

no further comment about my linguistic ability.

"Our war was lost from the moment we procrastinated and failed to invade England, abetted by invading Russia at the wrong time of the year and extending our supply lines too far, too quickly. Early, rapid successes are fine so long as you consolidate with proper back up and supply lines, but the stupid little corporal always thought he knew more about military strategy than his generals and military advisers. He rode roughshod over their protestations and his actions have resulted in the deaths of hundreds of thousands of our soldiers and the capture of hundreds of thousands more."

I forgot my rule about calling him Emil and with alarm in my voice I said,

"Emil, for God's sake be careful what you are saying. Please be quiet. If anyone hears you ranting like this, you will be shot for treason."

Quickly I leant over and changed the radio station, grabbed hold of him and started kissing him so that he couldn't say anything further on the subject.

"What would I do without you? You really do care about me don't you?" he commented, and I was surprised and a little hurt to think that he still harboured even the slightest doubt about my feelings for him. I didn't answer him but gave him a very reproachful look as though to say, "How could you doubt me." He smiled; ruffled my hair and we went through our bath and exercise routine, a lot of loving and a bath and clean shirt and bandages for me.

From then on, we listened to the news regularly and excitement mounted as we reached the end of September and the reports were coming in of how close the Russians were and how, to the west, the allies were advancing at a fast pace on all fronts.

Over the next few weeks, the whole place became a hive of even more frantic activity and in answer to my questions, Emil told me that we would all be evacuating this place and that a party of engineers would be the last to leave after they had destroyed the gas chambers and crematoria. The Russians were very close now and the 'selections' had long ceased.

Finally, the big day arrived, all preparations had been completed and the remaining prisoners were lined up in massive columns, guards on foot, on motor cycles and trucks, officers in cars, some guards had acquired horses and with much shouting, beating and whipping and urged on by the savage, barking dogs, we marched out of Auschwitz Birkenau being joined by the survivors of Auschwitz I and a handful from Monowice. It was from these few that I later learned that Julius, Aaron and Isaac had all perished.

CHAPTER FORTY-THREE

That first day, we walked until dusk, all of us exhausted. Calls of nature were allowed, out in the open under watchful eyes, then one had to run to catch up one's place. Those who flagged, stumbled and finally, through sheer exhaustion, collapsed, were shot where they lay and left at the side of the road. There was no mercy. One would have thought that since they already knew the war was lost and had gone to great trouble to demolish the evidence of their crimes at Birkenau, they would have shown a little restraint. On the contrary, some indulged in great excesses of murder and on one occasion, Emil's Sergeant major had to threaten one guard with immediate execution if he did not keep a rein on his orgy of killing.

It was bitterly cold and prisoners would drag the dead bodies along with them as they stripped them of their clothes to provide extra warmth for themselves before callously casting the bodies of their fellow sufferers aside like scrawny, broken dolls. Some prisoners were put on trains at Gleiwitz, many of us were marched away and we heard later that of those who came after us, a few thousand or so, were marched off into some woods where pits had been dug and were immediately killed by raking machine gun fire. There was little or nothing to eat on that first day and in subsequent days there was barely a mouthful of anything per person and this inadequate sustenance could not replace the energy sources being lost through the continuous marching. Some, a very few, managed to take whatever opportunities presented themselves and escaped. We froze at night, sleeping out in the open and from the warmth of their vehicles and fires; the guards would emerge, fully rested and whip us back into motion.

My precious stones were still inside my stomach and it was just as well that, through lack of food, I did not feel the need to perform the usual function. It was the first time that I had suffered real hunger by comparison with the others who had not been lucky enough to have a guardian like Emil. I lost weight rapidly and since I was not very heavy to begin with it was extremely worrying and called into doubt the chances of surviving much more of this endless marching.

We must have covered some eight hundred kilometres by the time we passed to the north of a town called Celle and finally arrived at Bergen Belsen. In our path we had left roads and ditches littered with bodies and we were no strangers to death on a massive scale, but the sight that greeted us when we entered the gates of Belsen defied belief and sent shivers of fear through all of us. Mounds of naked, broken corpses lay everywhere and as we were separated into men's and women's camps, further bodies were being thrown out of the barracks by other inmates and left to lie where they had been tossed. Typhus and dysentery were rife, the sickly sweet smell of decomposing bodies hung in the air so thickly that it caught, like something solid in the back of the throat and made us retch. We had nothing inside us to vomit and our diaphragms and ribcages ached from the fruitless automatic responses of our useless bodies.

All attempts to work had been abandoned and sallow, incredibly thin people with dead eyes, ambled about, without direction, some almost naked, oblivious to anything and everything. Together with some of the others, I strolled slowly along the wire which separated the men and women's compounds. The women did the same on the other side, seeking out the faces of loved ones, asking if anyone had seen such and such a person, eyes darting from face to face in this desperate search. Finally, Becca and I spotted each other simultaneously and, overjoyed, we almost ran to the wire, touched hands and cried. I could not believe that she had survived that march of death.

She was dreadfully emaciated and a ghastly colour, doubled over from stomach cramps and breathing in quick, shallow gulps. I had forgotten that she had always been mildly asthmatic, but under these conditions, it had really got a hold of her and she was serious-ly ill. A woman guard came over, pushed Becca away from the wire and told me to get away.

We had to comply but Becca and I spoke in Polish and arranged to keep a lookout at the same place at certain times each day.

This place had not been intended as an extermination camp but as a concentration and slave labour camp. It had none of the extermination facilities of places like Auschwitz Birkenau, with the exception of two small cremation ovens but still managed to kill thou-sands upon thousands of its inmates through malnutrition, illness and sheer brutality. A lot of the guards at this stage of the war were soldiers, like Emil, recovering from wounds, unfit for frontline duty and for the most part, they tended to leave us to our own devices. Nevertheless, many carried out their duties with extreme brutality, taking revenge on us for the imminent loss of the war.

Throughout the cold months of February, March and early April people were dying at an alarming rate. The typhus and dysentery were out of control, we were given hardly any food and there were some reports of cannibalism. I had only seen Emil twice in the first week after we had left Auschwitz and one of the kinder soldiers enquired for me and found that he had been sent to join a unit not far to the west of here. Becca was barely able to walk and when she struggled over to me, we sat, uninterrupted as the guards, from the evil Commandant, Auschwitz trained Josef Kramer, his equally evil henchwoman, Irma Grese, and down to the lowest Sturmann (Lance Corporal) were keeping well away from the dis-ease ridden compound, looking after their own skins and as the sound of guns rumbled in the distance, making panicky preparations for their own getaway.

The guns were getting louder and closer and Becca had to be supported by two colleagues as she came over each day. We were both so thin, filthy and lice infested. Poor Becca had suffered far more than me because she had been constantly losing weight over the last two years where I'd been lucky in having plenty of food from Emil. Even so, I was quite small, measuring about one metre sixty-five and my girlish figure was approximately eighty-five, fifty-eight, eighty five centimetres and I weighed about fifty -three kilos when we first went to Auschwitz. Now, I weighed about thirty-seven kilos, suffered from dysentery, was crawling with lice and smelt like a drain. I recalled dear Alex saying to me "I'd love you even if you were covered all over in cowshit" and wondered what he would say if he could see me now and if he would remain true to his word!

Becca broke in on my thoughts saying,

"There's just the two of us now darling and I can't last out much longer. I hope help gets here before it's too late." "They will darling, they will," I answered with as much confi-dence as I could muster, "They'll be here any day now."

"This may seem silly Janni, but in case they don't I want you to marry me. Say you will, please darling?" Becca asked beseechingly.

"Of course I will darling, I should be very honoured and you know I'll always love you." I responded earnestly. Under normal circumstances, this would never have been allowed without lots of instruction and a change in religion on the part of one of us but in the cir-cumstances, the Rabbi was prepared to give it his blessing and two days later, the guards let us through the fence and we were married amid strangers, who like ourselves were on the verge of death. We had token rings made of string and when the little, shortened cere-mony was complete, we sat, Becca leaning against me as I encircled her frail body with one arm and with my filthy lips, kissed her filthy, beautiful face.

Under cover of our embrace, Becca pressed a tiny package into my hand saying,

"These are my stones. You had better look after them for us Janni, I can't manage any more."

I took the package from her, pushed it down my boot and said,

177

"Don't worry darling, I'll keep them safe for us so that we have a start when we're out of here and we are better." At half-past six that night, she died in my arms. I shouted and raved screaming to God that if indeed he did exist, he had a funny way of protecting his chosen people. That he was the most sadistically evil-minded bastard imaginable, far worse than the individual commandants of all these dreadful establishments, because he was in overall charge of them and sanctioned it all. I couldn't stop crying.

Regardless of my wild rant against God, I couldn't let Becca go to meet her maker without the appropriate prayers and I found the Rabbi who had married us only hours earlier. Now he was saying Kaddish for her.

CHAPTER FORTY-FOUR

They had all gone. Aaron, so witty, charming and caring. Little Isaac, always a trifle unsure of himself but whose generosity knew no bounds and who loved everybody unconditionally and Julius and Rachel who could not have treated me with more love, affection and tenderness if I had really been one of their own. They never differentiated between their own children and me in any way. I loved them all very much and of course, dearest Rebecca who had always been so special. We had always loved each other intensely, even before the events during the last few weeks in the ghetto and now I held her in my arms, my wife of a few short hours, long after she had died, refusing to relinquish my hold on her rapidly cooling body, until finally, some other inmates forced us apart and covered her face where she lay.

I was desolate. Loneliness engulfed me and I realised that I was totally alone. I didn't know if I would ever see Alex or Hedwig again, or Emil. Everyone I had ever loved was dead or gone and I hadn't any family left. I have never felt so low in my life and I sat, waiting for death to catch up with me. I had nothing left to live for.

The next morning, the sound of fighting was very close and Kramer went out of the camp with a white flag. He returned only a short while later under escort, accompanied by an English Officer, a lieutenant colonel I think, several other officers, NCOs and ordinary soldiers, all armed to the teeth and looking very grim and purposeful. When they came through the gates and were confronted with the sights and smells of the compound, littered with about twenty to twenty-five thousand unburied corpses, they stripped Kramer of all his accoutrements and placed him under guard while they went round to secure all the other guards. Unbelievably, to the rear of the latrine block two of them were shooting inmates in full view of the British soldiers and the colonel dispatched them instantly with a couple of well aimed shots. Some of the inmates, with all the strength their feeble frames could muster, began attacking the guards and the soldiers did nothing to prevent it until at least three of the guards had been beaten to death.

It was the fifteenth of April 1945; I had been married and widowed in less than two days. A medical team came in very quickly, all of them wearing masks over their mouths and noses as they went about the business of trying to save the survivors. Mobile kitchens were setup and hot food, only very small quantities because our stomachs couldn't take it, was issued along with hot drinks. Apart from eating a few stalks of grass, this was the first food many of us had had in more than a week. People continued to die and the British colonel made the German prisoners start to collect the bodies on hand trucks and place them in obscene mounds while a contingent of soldiers marched into the nearby town and returned with all the townsmen and women, led by all the senior dignitaries. They were made to walk round to see for themselves the evil that had been going on under their noses.

To a man, they all denied that they had any knowledge of it. Neither before nor since have I ever had seen such an example of collective lying. The Officer made them help with the loading of bodies, men and women alike and we all applauded his sense of justice and hoped that these fat, smug liars would become infected with the diseases that were still rampant. It all took time; a large mobile laundry and bath unit arrived and with the help of the engineers, got hot water supplies going and found clothing for us. We were all treated with DDT and slowly began the long road to physical recovery. Now I had to swallow all the stones and although my dysentery was abating thanks to the excellent ministrations of the army medics, I was still passing them daily, washing them and swallowing them again.

Bulldozers arrived and, after digging enormous pits, masked drivers used the blades of their vehicles to push the mounds of bodies into them. Even those of us who had become so used to seeing death on a massive scale were shocked by the obscenity of seeing these twisted, lifeless shells being bundled, over and over, amongst flailing arms and legs, into their communal graves. For the poor soldiers who had to drive the vehicles, the images must have haunted them for the rest of their lives and my heart goes out to them.

As soon as we were fit enough to be moved, we were taken to displaced persons (DP) camps and it was apparent that some of the German guards had donned prison uniforms, hoping to pass themselves off as inmates and get away without being made to answer for their crimes.

In our contingent, they were weeded out very quickly and the soldiers took them away. The DP camp was still like being in prison and although we were well fed and had clean clothing and medical treatment, we were treated with suspicion and a certain amount of harshness. We were in fact an enormous nuisance, and nobody had the faintest idea how to deal with us.

It took many months for us all to be sorted into nationalities and to be screened. The latter process was not very efficient and virtually ceased altogether, allowing many S.S. thugs and murderers to pass themselves off as genuine victims.

My screening was difficult because I insisted that I was English but had no way of proving it and for a long time I was employed as the camp interpreter, speaking German, Polish, English and a fair smattering of Russian. Eventually I was, shall we say half-released on the condition that I joined the MSLO (Mixed Service Labour Organisation) an organisation to utilise the skills of inmates for the benefit of the occupying forces. The Duties ranged from highly skilled occupations in building, joinery, electrical engineering, mechanical and motor engineering to the more menial tasks of interpreting and performing guard duties on small military units. I fell into the latter two categories, serving as interpreter and having to do frequent guard duties on minor military installations.

We wore navy blue battledress, blue shirts and navy blue berets with the initials M.S.L.O. in red on shoulder flashes, offset by black boots and gaiters and black webbing belts. You would have been hard pushed to find a more motley crew anywhere else in the world.

First, we guarded establishments in Minden, then at Bad Oeynhausen, The headquarters of the British Army of the Rhine. On to Detmold, down to Lbbecke, then to Osnabrck. We covered an awful lot of ground but, in essence, we were still prisoners. In all this time, no one had tried to check my story and although, in view of the number of people involved, it was understandable for I was but a small cog, it was nevertheless extremely frustrating and I saw no end to this eternal incarceration.

Many of my fellow workers were extremely talented and supplemented their income by carving exquisite horses, dogs, deer and all sorts of other animals from soapstone or alabaster, while others, with gas flames and an assortment of long-nosed pliers made dachshunds, more horses, lions, in fact, anything, from empty bottles of various colours. They sold these mainly to members of the occupying forces and accumulated substantial amounts of savings as a result of their endeavours. Alas, I hadn't any of their talents.

CHAPTER FORTY-FIVE

One of the places we guarded at night and at weekends was a sort of military bank situated in Osnabrck on the corner of Katerinen Strasse. By day, there were only two officers, a sergeant, a private and an army driver, helped by two German clerks and a German driver.

By night, there were only the sergeant and the two other ranks on the premises but the floor above was occupied by some QARANC (Queen Alexandra's Royal Army Nursing Corps) nurses who shared their bathroom with the soldiers. To the rear of the building, enclosed within the yard was a tiny cottage and an elderly German couple who lived there were responsible for cleaning the premises and cooking and washing for the other ranks. I remember their name because it was so strange, Karl und Louisa Saueressig (Sour vinegar). The ground floor comprised the main office and a smaller office directly behind it, hallway with steps leading down to the cellar, which had been converted to a vault, and three other rooms. One was the sergeant's bedroom and this was separated from the soldier's bedroom by another room, which served as the guardroom. Here, four of us would take up our posts for guard duty. Two on duty, two off at regular intervals throughout the night. At least, this was the theory, but in fact we just lolled about, stretched on the beds, played cards, read or listened to music. Nothing ever happened.

The sergeant and I became very friendly and after a while, we went shopping together and I bought some civilian clothes, which he allowed me to leave in his locker. We MSLO types were not allowed to wear civilian clothes and on my days off, before any of our people went on duty, I would walk down to the office, change in the sergeant's room and the two of us would go out round the drinking dens and clubs. I hated my tattooed number and at first, I used to cover it with a plaster but a tattooist suggested that it might be possible to remove it by re-tattooing with neat bleach. I gave it a try. After each session, I had to wait a week or two before he did it again. It was a fairly lengthy and uncomfortable process, but eventually, I was left with only the barest trace, hardly detectable and easily covered with a rub of stage make-up. Oddly enough, this 'treatment' was not as efficient as I had thought and many months later, my tattoo re-emerged.

Before long, I was playing the piano in one of the clubs, dressed quite normally and at weekends, playing and singing in another, in my female role. The sergeant was tickled pink when we used to return to his quarters and some of my MSLO colleagues would be there on duty and they never recognised me. They would wink knowingly at the sergeant as though to say, "No marks for guessing what you'll be up to tonight!" In fact, they couldn't have been more wrong. The sergeant and I were just pals and with another of his friends, an Intelligence Corps staff sergeant, he set in motion the events which would finally result in me being accepted as English. But that was a long time hence.

Eventually, I was released from the MSLO and for a while I continued to play in one small, crowded, dingy club but my earnings were pretty low and I could see that it was going to be difficult to make both ends meet. There was a thriving black market and all my old skills, honed to perfection another lifetime ago in Warsaw, made me a very successful player in this shady game.

I lived in one small room and although I had a kitchen, I shared the bathroom with a youngish couple and they were none too happy seeing me as a girl one minute and a young man the next; apart from confusing their visitors, it added a degree of unwelcome notoriety to the house! I had never taken anyone back there, with the exception of the intelligence corps guy, and no one had seen him.

Apart from my gender bending, I'd done nothing to warrant the decision of the owner to terminate my agreement. As it happened, since leaving Auschwitz and Emil, I had been

181

totally celibate. Not from lack of opportunity, but I'd never been promiscuous and I had to be seriously attracted to someone before I would even think about him or her in a physical way. Having said that, there were one or two occasions with the intelligence corps chap, Michael, when I almost let things get out of hand. I had better let Michael tell this story himself!!

CHAPTER FORTY SIX

MICHAEL'S STORY

It must have been towards the middle of nineteen forty six when I was posted to Osnabrck and since I was the only member of my corps, apart from my commanding officer serving in that area, I knew no one as I entered the sergeant's mess on that first evening. After dinner, three other sergeants and I played snooker, drank some very indifferent beer and exchanged details about ourselves.

My companions, like myself, were from independent corps rather than from any of the main regiments garrisoned in the town and since we had our own functions to perform, we did not have to do any of the usual regimental duties like orderly sergeant or guard commander, which the others were committed to from time to time. Perhaps it was this that created an 'us and them' atmosphere and caused us to gravitate towards one another; it wasn't long before we became something of an exclusive little group, set apart from the main force. Very occasionally, we were joined by a fifth member who neither lived nor dined in the mess but instead, lived in quarters at his place of work, a sort of army bank, right in the centre of the town.

He and I soon became friends and, because he used the mess so infrequently, we would meet two or three times each week at his office and proceed from there to the various drinking haunts in the town.

One Saturday evening, instead of meeting at his office, he asked if I would meet him at a particular club because he was bringing someone else along whom he would introduce upon their arrival.

Inside the club my eyes quickly adjusted to the dimmer lighting and I spotted Tim sitting alone at a corner table. As I approached, I noticed another glass, half empty on the table directly opposite Tim's chair. He waved as he caught sight of me, indicated one of the vacant chairs beside him and turned to beckon the waiter with whom he seemed to be on excellent terms. The waiter and I arrived simultaneously and after I had seated myself, he took my order and left.

Tim had been very mysterious about his guest and since he was generally quite forthright, I had been intrigued when, in response to my question as to the identity of his friend, he had replied in a deliberately vague manner, "Oh, just a friend."

The waiter returned with my cold beer and after taking a deep draught, I asked Tim where his friend was. "Just coming," he said and as he did so, he turned slightly, looking past me and, smiling, half rose from his seat.

I looked in the direction he was facing and out of the smoky gloom, a figure glided gracefully towards us.

My face must have said it all because Tim said,

"Down Boy. Keep your eyes and your hands to yourself, this is an unusual, exceptional and very special friend!"

As she approached the table, Tim and I stood up and he performed the introductions.

"Mike, this is Janni (He pronounced it Yanni), Janni, this is Mike."

I couldn't take my eyes off her but somehow managed to stammer,

"I'm delighted to meet you. Tim's something of a dark horse, he's been keeping you under wraps and I can't say that I blame him."

She smiled and if I hadn't been captivated before, I was now completely enslaved as she said, "Tim has told me about you and I've been looking forward to meeting you." I suddenly realised that I was still holding her hand and rather self-consciously, I let go and held the chair for her until she was seated.

"Thank you Mike," Janni said in her delightful, slightly husky voice. As I returned to my seat, I caught sight of Tim looking at me with great amusement and I grinned at him as I said, "It's O.K., I remember what you said."

We finished our drinks and I called the waiter over to order refills. There were so many questions I wanted to ask. Here in this slightly seedy club, was this incredibly beautiful girl with an absolutely stunning figure looking so completely relaxed and at the same time conveying the impression that she was unaware of all the admiration she was attracting. Her voice was very upper crust, slightly 'plummy' and everything about her was effortlessly, exquisitely, deliciously feminine. There was just a hint of fragility about her, which, even though I could sense an elusive, powerful, underlying strength, aroused my protective instincts.

Tim and Janni deftly fielded all my questions, which caused them great delight since I was in the Intelligence Corps and the principle job for which I had been trained was that of interrogation!

The waiter returned to the table, whispered in Janni's ear and left.

Janni stood up and said,

"Sorry, you'll have to excuse me for a while," and with a slightly mocking smile, she added, "I have to go and earn my living."

Tim and I both stood as she left and my eyes were riveted to her as she glided away, her long dress split to the thigh, revealing incredible, sun-tanned legs perched on ridiculously high-heeled sandals, her bare back tapering to a narrow waist above an exquisitely formed little bottom. She turned this way and that, smiling, acknowledging customers with a wave or mock curtsy. Her self-assurance was remarkable.

She disappeared through a side door and I turned back to the table. Tim was already seated and was grinning from ear to ear. He must have read my mind, sensing the anxious thoughts going through my head about the manner in which she earned her living.

Laughingly he said,

"My God! You're totally smitten aren't you?" and before I could reply, he added, "Forget it Mike, things are not what they seem in more ways than one." His enigmatic smile was beginning to annoy me and he must have realised this as he said, "Don't worry and stop scowling, the process of revelation is about to begin." He turned and nodded towards a miniscule stage at the end of the room.

I followed the direction of his eyes, just in time to see Janni appear through a curtain at the back.

She walked to the microphone at the front of the stage and addressed the audience in flawless German, told a few, cleverly linked, risqu stories and as the laughter died down, she walked over and sat at the piano, taking the microphone and stand with her.

You could have heard a pin drop.

She played a couple of pieces, which were currently popular and then sang three or four songs.

Her voice was not very powerful, but sultry and her natural huskiness made it very sexy.

She finished the song, and with a truly wicked grin, she said,

"And now, for the small minority whose minds are on a higher plane, something completely different."

Some good-natured, derogatory shouts greeted her words, causing her smile to widen. She looked at them with mock disdain, turning her eyes upwards as she said, "What am I supposed to do in the face of such ignorance?" It was obviously a routine with which the whole audience was familiar and in which they loved to participate.

There were shouts of:

"You know what we want; Dance for us; Get your kit off. Go on, give us all a treat." Janni was in total control and it was apparent that they all adored her. She hooted with laughter and said, "I've never come across such a lot of lecherous, dirty minded buggers in one place. Now be quiet or I shan't stay."

Obediently, the crowd quietened down and Janni played 'Clair de Lune'. There was utter silence as she played and I was aware that this girl was quite an exceptional pianist.

When she had finished, thunderous applause broke out as she stood up. She bowed several times, more a slight inclination of the head than a full bow and said, "There, I knew you could behave yourselves if you really tried. I'll be back later." With that, she went to the curtain at the rear of the stage, turned and waved amidst more applause and disappeared from sight.

Moments later, she reappeared through the side door and wended her way towards us through the tables, stopping here and there to squeeze an outstretched hand, touching a finger to her lips and brushing it on the mouth of a customer, raising her arms and giving an exaggerated sway of her hips and bottom and occasionally ruffling someone's hair. She didn't discriminate between the men and women, the girls being just as enraptured and captivated as the men. Tim and I were the object of very envious looks as she headed towards our table.

We stood as she approached and I suddenly found myself extending both hands towards her.

She responded quite naturally, took both my hands in hers and gave them a squeeze as I said, "That was a wonderful performance."

She inclined her head, did her mini curtsy and said,

"Why thank you kind Sir," at the same time, letting go of my hands. Then, knees together, she hitched up her dress slightly as she sat down.

We ordered more drinks and I plied her with all sorts of questions about her performing skills, how long she had been in this business, what her ambitions were and so forth. In some areas she was quite forthcoming and in others, very evasive and when I asked her if she had a boyfriend, adding that I couldn't imagine anyone as beautiful as her being without one, I could have kicked myself when her smile vanished to be replaced by an expression of utter desolation and sadness as she said, "No, there is no one. All my family are dead and I think my friends must have died too. I haven't had a boyfriend since the end of nineteen forty-four and I think he was probably killed in the last months of the war. Before you ask, I'm not ready for any new relationship; I just want to get on with my life without added complications. My last boyfriend was very special, in fact, I owe him my life and until I know what happened to him I can't feel free to love anyone else. Please don't ask any more questions about him." "If you tell me his name, what unit he was with and where you last saw him, I might be able to find out about him for you," I volunteered.

Her head tilted back, she looked me straight in the eyes and very defiantly, she said, "The last time we saw each other was in Auschwitz Birkenau, I was a prisoner he was an Obersturmbannfhrer, a Lieutenant Colonel in the S.S. He was not concentration camp staff, but from the Waffen S.S., on temporary duty unconnected with the treatment of prisoners. He was very badly wounded fighting on the Russian front and he was recuperating by doing a desk job. "We loved each other very much for two years. Then, together with hundreds of other inmates, I was marched off to Bergen Belsen and he went to join a unit fighting on the western front. I haven't seen him since."

She looked quite sad as she finished her tale and I glanced across at Tim, his look giving all the confirmation I needed that this was the first he had heard about her involvement with an S.S. officer.

Poor child, I thought and I reached over and took both her hands in mine saying,

"There are still a lot of officers interned all over the country just waiting to be given the final clearance before they can rejoin their families. I really can make enquiries for you if you would like me to."

She smiled wanly and said,

"You really are very kind but you do not know all the circumstances and I don't think he would like it to become known to his family or friends that he had been, shall we say, sleeping with an inmate, particularly one like me."

She let go of my hands, placed her own on the rim of the table and, using her bottom, pushed her chair away from the table.

"Time to do another spot," she said and without waiting for us to stand, she stood up, turned and walked away.

Tim and I looked at each other and I felt sure that he was regretting his invitation to me. Very slowly he lit a cigarette and after several deep drags he said,

"Christ Mike, can't you forget your interrogation routine just once in a while? You should have been patient and I'd have told you everything I know about Janni although I have to admit I didn't know about her S.S. lover. That came as something of a surprise."

I thought for a moment and said,

"I can't see that it matters, particularly if what she says about him being in the Waffen S.S. is true and why should such a beautiful girl have to worry about his family's and friend's opinions. Is she Jewish or what?"

Tim looked me squarely in the face and said,

"Oh, what the hell. You're going to find out sooner or later and I had rather hoped that it would be later. Now, since you are so smitten, I think it's as well that you know now."
"Know what?" I asked.

Tim took a deep breath and said,

"Mike, there is no easy way to tell you this, but Janni is a guy, a bloke, a fella. She's not a young girl but an extraordinarily beautiful young man who just happens to have this incredible figure, tits and all and I have to confess that I've never met anyone quite so love-ly. I couldn't believe it at first but I can assure you that it is indisputable, she uses my quar-ters to change and I can confirm every detail. That's why I told you right from the begin-ning to forget it, that things were not what they seemed. But, with your incredible conceit, thinking that you are God's gift to all women, you pressed on regardless and as a result, you have seriously upset this very tragic, very lonely, very loveable child. I hope you can make amends."

"Oh shit!" I thought as I turned to Tim and said,

"I really am very sorry Tim but if you had told me beforehand without being so bloody secretive, this need not have happened. Tell me, how do I set it right? Come on, you're the one with all the answers."

Tim looked hard at me and said,

"Yes, on reflection it was silly of me not to have told you before we came, but I wasn't sure what your reaction would have been if I had told you we were going to see a pretty young transvestite who happened to be a very good friend of mine!"

We both laughed and he continued,

"Now that you know, it's as well that you also know that I always refer to Janni as her or she or young lady because that is what she prefers and that, to all intents and purposes is what she is.

"If you have a problem with that, now is the time to tell me." I thought hard for a moment, searching for the right words to reassure Tim and said, "I've never met anyone like her before and what you have just told me doesn't make any difference to me. As far as I am concerned, she is just a very beautiful young girl although I promise not to try to make a date with her!"

Tim laughed out loud and said,

"Christ, until I told you, you were virtually undressing her with every look you randy bas-tard and all it takes is one little thing for you to change your mind."

186

We both laughed at his choice of words and he said,

"By the way, before you ask, I am not involved with her. As a matter of fact, she's in the MSLO by day and does guard duty some nights at the office with three other guys. To them, she's a young man and they haven't a clue about her other existence. By day, she works as an interpreter. We got to know each other because she wanted to practise her English, which she had hardly spoken for seven years. We spend hours talking together and playing chess and I lend her my books and give her my newspapers."

I was trying to make some sense of what Tim had just told me and I said,

"Hang on a minute Tim, If she's hardly spoken any English for seven years, we are back to nineteen thirty nine or thereabouts and she speaks it so beautifully with quite a posh accent that she must have gone to an exceptionally good school. Christ, she speaks it better than us. Then, I can't quite work this out, she can only be about eighteen or nineteen and that means that she would only have been eleven or twelve in nineteen thirty nine, much too early to have gone to a secondary school."

"Confusing isn't it?" Tim conceded and carried on,

"Now we come to the main reason for me wanting you to meet her. She says that she is about twenty years old and believes herself to be English. She needs help to find out about herself.

"You immediately sprang to mind as the man for the job. In fact, I've sort of volunteered you! It is going to be very difficult because she has no memory of anything before being blown up in Warsaw during the Blitzkrieg. Even her name, Janni Kowalski is just a made up name." "Some challenge," I said thoughtfully.

We had been so engrossed in conversation that we hadn't looked towards the little stage and suddenly I was aware that Janni was singing again. She sang in English and although the tune was familiar from the AFN and BFN radio broadcasts, I couldn't put a name to it. The rest of the band, drums, double bass, saxophone and trumpet, accompanied her at the piano in a slow, soulful, slightly melancholy blues number and the customers danced to the smoochy rhythm, arms round their partners' waists or necks, cheek against cheek, virtually swaying on the spot, bodies pressed closely together. As the music finished, Janni stood, gave a little bow in acknowledgement of the applause and left the stage through the curtain. The band struck up with a faster number and Janni emerged from the side door and headed towards us.

Tim and I stood as she approached and Tim held the chair for her until she was comfortably seated.

Seconds later, the waiter appeared with a bottle of Deinhard dry Sekt in an ice bucket, three flutes and three large brandies.

Tim and I looked at each other enquiringly and Janni, interpreting our bafflement said,

"Don't look so mystified. It was my round and I felt like something stronger now that I've finished for the evening. Will you do the honours please Tim?"

Tim picked up the bottle smiled at me gleefully and said,

"Certainly, but only on the condition that you will dance with each of us in turn."

Janni grinned and said to Tim,

"You sneaky bastard. I'll bet you've told Mike all about me and you're determined to see if he has any misgivings about dancing with a tranny."

She turned to me and said,

"Do all Englishmen take malicious delight in trying to embarrass their best friends or is it the sole prerogative of this cheeky sod?"

All three of us hooted with laughter and I was suitably impressed by Janni's vocabulary. I said, "Yes, he had told me about you and as far as I can see, nothing has changed. You're still Janni, you're still very beautiful and I should be delighted to dance with you."

She grinned her impudent grin and said,

"You're a bit of a smooth bastard too!"

The three of us laughed a lot and I said,

"You only get away with your impudence and bad language because you are so lovely and so very feminine, but don't push your luck. If Tim lets rip with his repertoire of swear words, we'll all be thrown out into the street."

She laughed and said,

"I don't believe you. Tim never swears do you darling?" She had reached over and taken his hand whilst she said this and it just seemed so natural that I found myself doubting Tim's revelation and Janni's own confirmation.

The more I observed her, the more difficult I found it to believe that she was anything other than an exceptionally beautiful young girl. There was nothing exaggerated in her movements, they were all so delicate and completely natural. She had slim arms and small, sensitive hands which would have looked totally out of place on a man. The same was true of her small, dainty feet and wonderful legs and her shoulders lacked the muscular defini-tion of all but the very youngest of boys. It was quite clear that she didn't shave and she wore only the minimum amount of make-up. And then, there was the voice. It was not in any way contrived, not a man trying to sound like a girl. Most of the homosexuals I've encountered who strive to sound feminine just end up sounding fairly ridiculous and their attempts at female mannerisms appear nothing short of grotesque, right down to the minc-ing, little steps which they misguidedly believe make them more convincing, alluring, or both. From the red-blooded male point of view, they all fail miserably. Not so with Janni. When she walked, it was with the sheer elegance of a catwalk model. She was indeed truly beautiful.

Janni broke in on my thoughts saying,

"You look very contemplative Mike. What's going on inside that head of yours?"

I drank some Sekt and replied,

"I was just thinking about your identity problem and by that I don't mean gender prob-lem. You will have to give me as much information as you have to enable me to make a start and from what Tim tells me, that does not amount to very much."

Janni reached over and squeezed my hand saying,

"You are going to help me then?" and when I nodded, she continued,

"If we are all free tomorrow, can we leave it till then? We can finish our drinks, take a couple of bottles back to Tim's place and chat there till all hours. They will be closing here in about ten minutes."

Tim and I both agreed and we called the waiter over to order a couple of bottles of sekt. Tim said that he had brandy, whisky, vodka and some 'thinners' in his room. Janni left us for a moment or two and returned wearing an open, three quarter length camel coat. She slung her bag over her shoulder and said, "Come on then. Let's go."

Tim and I each picked up a bottle, put on our berets and headed for the door. Once on the street, Janni moved in between us and tucked her arms into ours. I thought, "I really like this girl" and despite the revelations, that is how I continued to think of her. Back at Tim's place, I was highly amused by the ease with which we entered the place unchallenged. The MSLO guards were sprawled in chairs and on the two beds. The air was thick with smoke and they had a radio playing quietly. They smiled as we entered and said, "Good evening sergeants, good evening Frulein, and then addressed Janni in a different language which I recognised as Polish. Janni spoke to them fluently in their own language for a few moments, laughed with them and turned to Tim saying, "They want to know if you have any cigarettes to sell them?" Tim said he had forty they could have and he disappeared into his room to return seconds later with two packets of Senior Service. He sold them very cheaply to the guards and they were suitably grateful.

We chatted to them for a few more minutes in a mixture of English, German and Polish and then retired to Tim's room.

Janni took off her coat and propped herself up on Tim's bed and asked, "Have you any brandy left Tim?" and continued, "I'm absolutely shattered, I've been up since five o'clock this morning."

Tim poured a stiff brandy, handed it to Janni and said, "What will you have Mike?"

I settled for scotch and water and Tim followed suit.

We drank quite a lot and talked into the small hours and finally Janni said, " I'd better get off home. It's terribly late."

Tim stood up and said, "I'll take your case up to the bathroom for you so that you can change up there then you can leave without the others seeing you."

Janni laughed and said, "Oh I am sorry Tim, I should have told you. I finished with the MSLO on Wednesday and I have a room in town all of my own although I have to share the bathroom with a young couple. It's only small, but it's the first time I've felt free in seven years. It's quite wonderful."

Tim put his arms round her and said, "That's great news. I am so pleased for you. Look, why don't you both come over before lunch tomorrow and we can have a proper celebration. We can have an evening meal together and take the rest as it comes. O.K?"

Janni and I both replied together, "Sounds fine."

I turned to Tim and said, "If Janni doesn't mind, I'll walk her home. It's late and there are always a few unsavoury drunken characters about in the small hours after a skinful on Saturday night. Is that alright with you Janni?"

She smiled and said, "You are very thoughtful and yes, I really would appreciate the escort even though it's only a few minutes walk from here. Thank you."

I helped her on with her coat and Tim walked us to the gates, which he unlocked. We said our goodnights and as Janni and I walked away to the sound of Tim re-locking the gates, she slipped her arm through mine and said, "This way."

We walked in silence until Janni suddenly said, "Here we are. I told you it wasn't far. I hope this hasn't been too much trouble for you and taken you out of your way."

"Really, it was no trouble at all and I'm heading in the right direction for the barracks," I responded.

Janni studied my face and said, "Please don't take this the wrong way, but I can't invite you in for a drink. No, that's not right, I can do as I please, but this is my own private domain, my very first and if I spend too long in a room with people, I become very claustrophobic. It's a legacy of Auschwitz and Belsen. I need my space, my privacy all to myself, added to which, I don't think the other people would appreciate me taking a soldier into my room at this hour of the morning. They would jump to the wrong conclusions and I should hate to acquire a bad reputation within days of taking up residence."

We both laughed and I said, "I'm not the least bit offended and I do understand. Anyway, it's very late and if we are going to do a bit of partying tomorrow, we ought to get some sleep. I seem to remember you saying that you were up at five o'clock yesterday morning and you must be exhausted. Go on, off you go and I'll see you at Tim's tomorrow."

It seemed so natural as she stood on tiptoe, put a hand round the back of my neck, brushed her lips lightly over mine and said, "Goodnight Mike and thanks for everything. See you tomorrow." She opened the door, turned and waved and was gone.

CHAPTER FORTY-SEVEN

Sunday was a glorious day and as I set off for Tim's place, it really was too warm to be wearing battledress but it would certainly be cool coming home late. In view of this, I had dressed in 'shirt sleeve order' and put my tie and battle dress blouse in a small bag. On the way, I called at the NAAFI shop and bought a couple of bottles and some salad things for later. Tim was outside with the driver giving the unit Volkswagen a polish. On seeing me, he said, "I thought we might all go for a spin later so I booked the car for recreational transport."

"Good idea," I said and continued, "I've brought some salad things and a couple of bottles. We can make up a nice picnic and head off into the countryside somewhere. I'll leave that to you since I'm new to the area."

Tim put his leather into the empty bucket, handed it to the driver and said, "O.K. That will do. You won't be needed for the rest of the day but if you are going out, don't forget, in by twenty three fifty nine hours."

The driver said,

"O.K. sergeant," and left to go to his room.

"Let's put these things somewhere cool Tim," I said indicating my bag of goodies. Tim placed my things on the floor of a cool outbuilding and we went inside to his room, passing through the small guardroom where four MSLO men were doing weekend guard duty. They all said, "Good morning sergeant," and as I acknowledged them, almost as one, they asked, "Have you any cigarettes we can buy please?"

Although I didn't smoke, I always collected my NAAFI ration and I sold them a packet each.

Tim laughed and said,

"Don't sell any more to anyone else at that price, give them to Janni, she can get a hell of a price for them and for tins of Lyons ground coffee or Nescafe." "By the way, how did you two get on last night?"

The question seemed innocent enough so I said,

"Fine, she only lives about five minutes from here and as we set off, it seemed quite natural for her to slip her arm through mine and I didn't object, but I was quite unprepared as I was about to leave her at her door when she put her hand round my neck, kissed me lightly on the lips and said goodnight. As I walked home, I said to myself, "There's a first time for everything, and I've never been kissed like that by a man before!"

Tim laughed and said,

"Sorry, I should have warned you, she greets and bids farewell to all her close friends like that and don't read any more into it than that. However, you are one of the privileged few to be regarded as a friend otherwise, she'd have just offered her hand. I'm very pleased. Oh, I see you've bought the Sunday papers, you can busy yourself with those while I go and clean up and organise the picnic stuff. By the way, give me your jacket and I'll hang it up so that it doesn't get creased in that bag."

I sat by the open window scanning through the headlines and enjoying the balmy air.

A voice suddenly said, "Hello, may I come in please?"

Janni was standing outside looking amazing in a light summer dress, her bare arms and legs golden brown and sun-bleached streaks in her hair. She had a small sling bag and a loosely folded cardigan and, typically Janni, ridiculous high-heeled shoes with no backs and open toes.

I had to admit that she looked gorgeous.

"Just a minute, I'll open the gate for you," I replied.

I went out, withdrew the bolts and opened the gate.

Janni came in, said "Hi Mike," and just as Tim had predicted, she kissed me lightly, the way she had done earlier that morning.

I felt no embarrassment whatsoever.

"Tim has just told me off for selling some cigarettes too cheaply and instructed me to give the rest to you," I said with a laugh.

Janni laughed too and said,

"Great, I'll be your agent on commission."

We both chuckled and Janni said,

"Come on, I'll make a pot of tea, I suppose Tim's washing and shaving. He is a fuss-pot, he takes longer to get ready than I do."

She busied herself making tea and setting out the cups and saucers. I felt sure that these latter items were her own contribution, because we soldiers had become used to brown enamel mugs, which, to the uninitiated, posed a real threat: sometimes, the mugs were so hot, they could take the skin off your lips!

I couldn't help watching her every movement trying to detect some outward sign that 'she was really a 'he'. To no avail. There was nothing the remotest bit masculine, not the slightest hint.

She could obviously read my mind and I was thoroughly disconcerted when she said,

"My friend Hedwig in Warsaw fell about laughing when we both needed a pee rather desperately. We went into some bombed out buildings and I lifted my skirt and peed against the wall. She told me that it was very unladylike and I should have to learn to do it in the conventional way, sitting down, or in that case, squatting demurely."

She giggled slightly in her husky way and said,

"I hope I haven't shocked you, but I do know that people find it hard to believe that I'm not what I appear to be and normally, I don't enlighten them. You're different, you have to know and before you ask, I'm happier as I am, I like my body the way it is and if you saw me dressed as a man, you'd know why I choose this life. I can't imagine being a man and having a boyfriend. It would seem very strange."

"You are very frank," I said and continued, "Have you always been so beautiful or did you have to work at it?"

She smiled her devastating smile and said,

"That was a lovely thing to say Mike. You're sweet, but in answer to your question, when they pulled me out of the rubble in Warsaw, they thought I was a girl and the family who took me in thought the same thing. Now that bit is spooky because the parents were both highly respected doctors, the mother being a paediatrician and it wasn't until I got undressed in the kitchen to have a wash when the bombing and shelling finally ceased that the daughter, Rebecca, pointed out the difference as she called for her mum!" At this point, Tim arrived which effectively put and end to the conversation. Janni greeted Tim with a big hug and the light kiss on the lips. He wasn't put out in any way, in fact, he held Janni by the shoulders at arm's length, looked her up and down and said, "You look absolutely ravishing today. I don't know how you manage it after such a long day and late night."

Janni smiled and said,

"It must be catching. You've both been so very complimentary. With two such attractive guys saying such nice things about me, I could easily become big-headed."

She did her mocking curtsy and kissed us both on the cheek.

"Do you take sugar Mike?" she asked.

"One please, " I replied

Tim sipped his tea, complimented Janni on its quality and said,

"I've asked the old dear who looks after us to make up a picnic with the things you brought Mike and she's putting a load of ice cubes into thermos flasks for us. She's wonderful, does all our cooking, cleaning and laundry and doesn't object to doing the odd bit of black-marketeering!"

Janni was just like a young child, suddenly becoming very excited, saying, "What a lovely idea, where are we going?"

"I thought we would go through Bad Salzuflen, stop off there for a cold beer and then head off towards Detmold and go and have a look at Hermann's Denkmal. It's quite an impressive sight and there are acres of lovely space in which to have our picnic. How does that sound?" Tim enquired. Janni was almost jumping up and down with excitement as she said, "That sounds wonderful. I always wanted to go to see the Denkmal. Then, there's another first for me. I've never been in a motorcar before. What with having my own room and leading my own life, then being invited out like this, it's almost too much. You can say that this will be my first totally free day for seven years. It's really lovely of you both." Impulsively, she came and kissed each of us in turn and gave us a big hug. I had become used to it very quickly and responded by hugging her back and Tim did the same.

We were all very happy.

Janni turned to me and said,

"Mike, I've written down everything I can remember and as far as the age bit is concerned, that was Dr Lipschitz's educated guess and because of my physical differences, it could be out either way by a year or so. I thought I'd give you these details now then we won't have to talk about them and spoil our day. Take my notes home and read them and then you can make notes of your own about any questions you think might be important and then we can discuss it one day next week. Is that O.K?"

She handed me a little folder and as I put it in my bag I said,

"That is a very good idea and you are right. We don't want to spoil the day by raking up unpleasant memories. I'll just say this Janni, in the short time I've known you, I have come to like you very much and for many reasons, my heart goes out to you. I can't begin to imagine all the horrors you have experienced and it's a great tribute to your courage, determination and resilience that you were able to survive. I promise you now that I shall do everything possible to discover your true identity, no matter how long it may take and you can always call on me to help with any problems you may encounter until we've got it all sorted out. Oh, and I'm sorry for introducing an element of solemnity."

Janni didn't say anything but her lip trembled just a little and I thought I could see tears in her eyes as she gave me yet another impulsive hug and whispered, "Thank you so much Mike. I'm so glad Tim volunteered you for this job."

CHAPTER FORTY-EIGHT

We collected all our picnic things and packed them into the car. I attended to the gates as Tim drove the car into the street. After I had closed them I said to Janni, "Since this is your first time in a motor car, let me get in first in the back and you sit up in the front with Tim."

She was overjoyed at receiving such consideration and attention and I remember thinking, "There is no way that this delightful child can be anything other than a girl," and from that moment on, that was exactly how I thought of her.

Tim was a good driver and obviously knew the area well; in next to no time, we were clear of the town and speeding through the countryside.

Janni was absolutely delighted, keeping up a non-stop commentary, gasping in surprise at some of the country sights and wanting to stop here and there to inspect a particular object or gaze into the distance over the fields. It was a pleasure to watch her simple enjoyment and the expressions on her lovely face.

We stopped at a small, very cosy 'bierstube' and drank wonderful cold beer after waiting in anticipation, almost drooling as the bartender poured from the fonts, stopping every so often to remove the excess froth with a spatula.

It was so good; we just had to have a second one and then resumed our journey, arriving at the large car park near Hermann's Denkmal after about half an hour's drive. Lots of people had had the same idea as ourselves and many families were out in force, young and old, all carrying their picnic baskets and hampers, seeking out suitable spots. In addition there was no shortage of military personnel of all ranks, fraternising with the locals and visitors and generally enjoying themselves.

We stood and gazed in awe at the towering statue of Hermann and I vowed to find out more about the character who merited such an enormous monument. It was very, very impressive. Finally, we selected a spot on a gentle slope, facing south into the warm sun. Janni spread the cloth and we started opening the little packages. Thoughtfully, Tim had brought a large bowl and into it, he tipped the ice from the thermos flasks and placed the bottles of sekt to chill down. It was all very civilised and we made the meal last out. Tim's 'old dear' had packed some apple cakes and honey cakes and we washed these down with the second bottle of sekt.

All the sitting in the hot sun was alright for a while but soon, one became aware of how thoroughly uncomfortable it can be, just sitting on grass, so by mutual consent, we packed up our empty dishes and bottles and strolled to the area where the waste bins were discreetly placed, disposed of our rubbish and as one, felt the need to attend the calls of nature. Janni headed off in the direction of the 'Ladies' followed by a lot of admiring glances from many of the young men, military and civilian and I have to admit that every inch of her was worth watching. She walked so beautifully, almost as if her feet didn't touch the ground, her back curved inwards making her beautiful little bottom more pronounced and I could almost read the minds of the men who were ogling her every move. I really couldn't blame them! Tim and I were both waiting for her and as she arrived, she linked her arms through ours and said, "This is a lovely day, I don't want it to end."

We drove the twenty-five miles to Bad Oeynhausen at a leisurely speed and parked a short distance from the main 'spa' buildings.

It was far too early to think about food and, being Headquarters of the British Army of The Rhine, plenty of shops were open, even though it was a Sunday.

We strolled through the streets window-shopping and Janni, hooting with laughter, announced that we were not to accompany her into one shop because she wanted to buy some underwear and bras, which she would have to try on.

Dutifully, we waited outside for her and when she rejoined us, she said,

194

"If I tell you the colours I like, will you buy me some nylons from the NAAFI or Richard Shops? They are so expensive in the German shops, even if you can find any."

Tim and I both volunteered our services.

I spotted a quaint little toyshop and I whispered to Tim,

"Keep Janni busy for a few minutes, there is something I want to do."

Tim took Janni's arm and headed towards a shoe shop and I entered the toy store. I soon found what I was looking for, a beautifully made teddy bear about fourteen inches high with a small velvet bow round his neck. He was very cute and seemed to have a personality all of his own. The assistant placed him in a box and wrapped it very professionally, saying, "He should make someone very happy."

"I hope so", I replied, thinking to myself, "That was a very expensive impulse!" The assistant placed the box in a stout brown paper carrier bag, thanked me for my custom and held the door for me.

Tim and Janni had similar bags, both having bought shoes. They told me what they had bought and Janni was delighted with her purchase since there were far more styles to choose from here as opposed to Osnabrck. Tim agreed saying that he had found the most comfortable shoes that would not look out of place with his uniform.

"What have you been buying?" Janni asked.

"Oh, just a little present for someone," I said.

"Anyone like a tea or a cold beer?" Tim asked.

As one, Janni and I replied,

"Cold beer please!"

We sat at a table on the pavement outside a bar and soon, we had ice-cold beers in front of us.

Janni undid her package and showed me the shoes, tiny, skimpy things that would undoubtedly show off her dainty little feet to great advantage. Up until that moment, I had never considered feet to be particularly attractive. But I was experiencing something new every day at the moment!

Tim followed suit and showed me his new shoes, which, as he said, looked, very comfortable and serviceable.

They both looked at me, and looked pointedly at my carrier bag.

I handed it to Janni and said,

"It's for you."

The excited child took over and she took the beautifully wrapped box from the bag and slowly unwrapped it, prolonging the surprise as she carefully folded the wrapping paper before placing it in the bag. Finally, she took a deep breath and opened the box.

She gasped, her face an absolute picture of delight as she reached into the box, lifted the teddy bear out and held it to her cheek. She turned to me and said, "Oh Mike, what a lovely, lovely surprise. He's a beautiful little bear and I shall love him to bits."

She continued to cuddle the bear and Tim looked at me as though I had lost my senses.

By way of explanation for my impulsive action, I said,

"It's a sort of symbol of the childhood you lost Janni and the one we hope to find. Don't go and lose it again."

They both laughed and impetuously, Janni put her arm round my neck, held the bear between our cheeks for a second then kissed me full on the lips and said, "Thank you so much, I'll treasure him for always and I promise to take good care of him."

Suddenly, she gave a little shiver and said,

"It's become quite chilly, look, I'm all goose pimples."

Tim responded by putting his arm round her and saying,

"Come on, let's run to the car. We'll go and get something to eat, which should warm us. Then, we can drive home at a steady pace."

He and Janni started to run for the car and there was nothing for me to do but to follow suit. I hate running, even the shortest distance because, even though the doctors don't know it, I have a heart problem and anything too strenuous gives me severe chest pains, that is why whenever I went dancing, I always stopped after a slow waltz. Anything quicker or more prolonged and I would have been in trouble. I slowed to a walk, giving my heart a chance to stop pounding before reaching the car.

Janni was already in the back of the car with her cardigan round her shoulders and the little bear on her lap. She was stroking it's back and talking to it, apologising for being away so long and promising it a nice drink of brandy at the next stop!

"What's the plan now?" I asked as I climbed in the front beside Tim.

"If it's O.K. with you two and since it's still early, we can go back via Lbbecke which is only a minor diversion. There is a nice little place there called Terrassen Cafe just on the way down into the town and we can have a decent meal before driving home," Tim suggested.

"Teddy and I would like that very much," Janni said laughingly

We set off on the direct route from Bad Oeynhausen to Osnabrck and about two or three miles out of the town, we turned right onto the main road to Lbbecke. It was a journey of some eight miles and in no time at all, Tim pulled off the road into a turning on the left and we drove up to the cafe.

The waiter found us a table, brought our drinks and three menus.

The choice was fairly limited but what we had was very good and since the town had it's own brewery, we drank the local beer which was excellent. The other customers were quite amused to see the bear sitting in the vacant seat next to Janni who would bend over, from time to time, talk to it and kiss it on the head. They probably thought she was either slightly retarded, a bit tipsy, or both.

Suitably replete, we settled the bill and strolled back to the car.

Janni had linked her arms through ours and held the bear in one hand as we walked.

"That was really lovely. Can we all come here again some time please?" she asked.

"We are only poor sergeants so we can't do it too often on our wages," Tim replied. Janni laughed and said, "That's no problem, just get me some cigarettes, coffee and nylons and I'll get plenty of money for us."

We all laughed and I said,

"Tim. This girl could get us all into serious trouble without even thinking about it, but it sounds like a bloody good idea to me."

They both laughed and Tim said,

"Yeah, to me too."

Tim unlocked the doors and I asked,

"Would you like to sit in the front again Janni?"

"No, it's O.K. I can snuggle up very cosily in the back thanks Mike," she replied. I held the door for her and true to her word, once inside, she took off her shoes, tucked her feet under her and, still holding the bear, she made herself very comfortable. We headed down the hill to the T-junction in the main street of the town, turned left and drove the thirty miles back to Osnabrck fairly quickly. No one spoke much and I turned round to ask Janni if she was all right. She was fast asleep, her unusually long eyelashes on her cheeks, her feet still tucked underneath her and both her arms round the bear. It seems ridiculous, because this was, after all, a bloke, but a great wave of tenderness swept over me and I resisted the impulse to reach over and stroke her head. She was simply breathtakingly beautiful and I tried to imagine how I would have handled the situation if it had been me enclosed in that fantastic body. I soon gave up trying since it was impossible to visualise myself in the same role or to have experienced a fraction of what she must have had to go through.

I had been so deep in thought that it came as a surprise when Tim announced, "Here we are," as he pulled up beside the gates to his office.

I got out and opened the gates, closing them again after Tim had reversed the car into the yard.

Janni was stirring as I opened the rear door and said,

"Come on sleepy head and don't forget your shoes."

She put her shoes on and held out her hand to me to help her from the car, shivered at the change of temperature and pulled her cardigan round her shoulders.

As we went in to Tim's room, I said,

"You had a nice little sleep, you were well away."

Janni smiled and said,

"I don't remember going to sleep. I just recall feeling warm and cosy and the next thing I was gone. I was dreaming, " she concluded.

"Anything interesting?" I asked.

"It was a bit sad really," she answered, and continued, " At times, it all seems so long ago and at others, it's just as if it happened yesterday. Once, in Warsaw when I was a bit tiddly, I bought two little teddy bears and I gave one to my boyfriend Alex and the other to his mother Hedwig. They were lovely people and I hope that they and the little bears survived." There was no adequate response to this so I just put my arm round her and gave her a comforting squeeze.

She turned to Tim and said,

"You were very good, drinking so little, you deserve a large brandy and I could use one too."

Tim smiled and said,

"I was just thinking the same thing myself but I'd like a decent cup of coffee with it. Anyone else?"

"Good idea," I said and Janni put the cups on the table while Tim filled the kettle and set it to boil.

We drank our coffee and brandies slowly, enjoying them to the full and when we had finished, Janni said, "Thank you both for a truly lovely day. I can't remember the last time I felt so happy."

Impulsively, she kissed us both on the lips and then said,

"Would you walk me home again please Mike?"

"Of course," I said and added, "I'll need tomorrow to read through your notes so I suggest we all meet again here on Tuesday at about seven o'clock if that's alright with the two of you." They both agreed and Janni picked up her little bear and gave Tim a hug and goodnight kiss then he came out with us to attend to the gates.

Janni and I walked arm in arm in silence the few hundred yards to her small flat. She stood on the step and holding the bear in her left hand, she placed both arms around my neck and caught me with my mouth slightly open. She brushed her lips slowly back and forth across mine as she breathed in, very deliberately. It was mind-blowing; a combination of icy coolness and electric current flowed through me and made me shudder right down to my toes.

She moved away, leaving me quite breathless and said,

"I'm sorry, I shouldn't have done that. It was such a lovely day and it has been so long since I really kissed anyone. Then you were so sweet and kind to buy me my little bear, I just wanted to say thank you and instead, I've shocked you haven't I?"

I managed to regain some composure and replied,

"Yes, you have shocked me, in more ways than one. First, because it was totally unexpected, secondly, and more importantly, I have to admit that I enjoyed it very much. I've never experienced anything like that from a kiss before. Where the hell did you learn to do that?"

She looked at me for a long time before saying,

"My first kiss was just like that. My first boyfriend Alex taught me. But Mike, it was just a happy impulse to round off a wonderful day and without wishing to be unkind, if I invited you in and let it go any further than this, we should both regret it very much in the morning."

I laughed at her honesty and said,

"Janni, Tim and I both love you in our own ways and we want to see you happy. You are an absolute delight to be with and I wouldn't want to spoil that in any way although I'm learning new things about myself every minute when I'm with you. In fact, if I did spend the night with you, the only thing I should regret in the morning would be the alteration of the relationship between you, Tim and me. Added to which, I don't think you really want to go to bed with me because of your loyalty to your S.S. officer whom you obviously still love very much and I can't see you doing anything for which you would hate yourself in the morning." The familiar, sad smile passed over her face, making her look more beautiful and appealing than ever as she said, "You are absolutely right and very understanding. I've only had two boyfriends and I don't want another one yet. I really am sorry for kissing you the way I did; it was silly of me but sometimes, because I'm an extremely tactile person, I respond to happiness without giving too much thought to what I'm doing. But then, if I didn't react impulsively and had to give everything serious thought before I followed my instinct, all the spontaneity and with it, the genuineness of my response would be false; if you follow me? I'll just have to content myself with practising on my little bear."

We both laughed and I hugged her to me and said,

"You really are lovely and it's been a wonderful day. Thank you very much just for being you. I'll see you Tuesday at Tim's"

I kissed her on the forehead, pushed her away and waited while she opened the door before saying,

"Till Tuesday then, Bye."

"Yes, till Tuesday then and thanks again," she responded and let herself into the flat. I walked back to the barracks deep in thought, still shaken by the effects of that electrifying kiss and astonished by the sudden realisation that I really did want to go to bed with her and screw us both senseless although I hadn't given the mechanics of such a course of action much more than a passing thought! Amazing! There was no way I was going to mention any of this to Tim!

Back in my room, the thoughts persisted and I tried to picture her in men's clothing, without success.

CHAPTER FORTY-NINE

Reveille came much too soon and the wash, shave and teeth-cleaning session went only part way towards reviving me but a good breakfast and several cups of strong tea had me feeling more up to the mark.

I had a busy day ahead of me with three interrogations of displaced persons purporting to be ex-Polish army veterans but whom we believed were actually either ex members of the Ukrainian Galician Division of the S.S., or Ukrainian concentration camp guards. Confirmation of their possible involvement with the Polish army was well nigh impossible since co-operation with the Russians, who were occupying Poland, was virtually non-existent and in any event, a large percentage of the records had been destroyed when Warsaw was practically razed to the ground in the closing stages of the war. None of them had their blood group tattooed on the inside of their elbows, which was customary for members of the S.S. but this was not necessarily conclusive. It occurred to me that if any of these men had served at Auschwitz Birkenau, Janni, who had spent two years there during the period when it was more likely that Ukrainian guards might have been employed, may well be able to identify them. After considerable thought, I decided against asking her since it might rekindle sad, unhappy and unpleasant memories for her.

It was a long day with no progress other than to reinforce the belief that these men were very accomplished liars who had thought out their stories very cleverly and stuck to them without wavering.

I had dinner in the mess, declined a game of snooker saying I still had work to attend to and retired to my room with Janni's notes.

As Tim had said, there was so very little real information to go on and it appeared to me that the only hope was that if Janni was English as she believed herself to be then following the outbreak of war, there would not have been too many English people in Poland at that time, let alone in the capital itself. If this was indeed the case, surely members of the family back in England would have made enquiries of the Foreign Office (F.O.) and records of any such enquiries might still exist. At the same time the F.O. was very busy with countless enquiries regarding many of the immediate danger zones particularly as France too had declared war on Germany and there were many English people living in France who were eager to return home. Added to which, there was an influx of Jews escaping persecution and the office really had it's hands full one way or the other trying to sort out the bogus from the genuine, constantly aware that they could be allowing spies to slip through their fingers, so individual enquiries may not have received the attention they would command under more normal circumstances. Nevertheless, it seemed the best starting point but first, I would have to clear any such enquiry through my superiors and in view of the backlog of interrogations we still had to plough through, I was not confident that they would allow time and resources for Janni's case.

Ours was an odd little unit and in contrast to the more traditional corps and regiments, our discipline was not so strictly adhered to in as much as officers and NCOs called each other by christian names, except in the presence of officers from other departments, especially those of higher rank than our own.

My immediate superior was a captain and on Tuesday morning, I gave him a brief outline of Janni's case and asked his assistance.

As I expected, he said that we had far more important matters on hand and that for the foreseeable future his case would have to go on the back boiler until the situation had eased sufficiently to allow us some leeway. He sympathised with Janni and how desperate he must be to discover his true identity and to see if he could find anything about any living relatives particularly as at the moment, he was, to all intents and purposes, a stateless person.

He promised to review the situation at the earliest opportunity and I had to be content with that for the time being.

Satisfied that I had done all that was possible for the present, I struggled through still more interrogations during the rest of the day.

Back in my room, I washed, shaved, changed my shirt and left the barracks.

CHAPTER FIFTY

It was a good twenty to thirty minutes walk to Tim's, the time varying in accordance with how my heart was behaving itself and the consequent adjustment I had to make to my pace. I suppose all the sitting and constant battle of wits throughout the day in a heavily smoke-laden atmosphere had taken its toll and I walked at a rather slower pace than usual, musing as I walked. It occurred to me that had I stayed with Janni on Sunday night and fulfilled my desires, the physical exertions would probably have killed me or at least brought on a serious attack of angina!

Janni was already there when I arrived and I apologised for being late. Notwithstanding the devastating effect of her last kiss, I was very pleased when she greeted me with her customary kiss on the lips and relieved that it wasn't a repeat of the last one. She was not working that night and the three of us decided we would go to the local army cinema to watch one of the latest Hollywood epics.

Janni loved it, even the appallingly bad supporting film and the Movietone news. She declared the ice cream bliss.

On the way back, we called in for a cold beer and I told Janni what I had done on her behalf cautioning her not to build up her hopes because of all the other work that was going on at the time and that it might take some considerable time to initiate all the enquiries. It might even be that no records existed of next of kin making enquiries as far back as nineteen thirty nine. Even if such records existed we had no idea of how many enquiries might have been made and then there would be the lengthy process of elimination, which would entail tracing all of those families concerned.

In the meantime, some could well have moved from their original addresses and some might have died in the blitz. It promised to be a lengthy and drawn out business. But we would stick at it, no matter how long it took. When I finished my report, Janni reached over and squeezed my hand saying, "Tim was right. You are definitely the man for the job and I feel happier already. I know that it can take a long time, but at least something is happening at last. No one wanted to listen or take anything seriously before and it was not a particularly pleasant experience. You see, at the moment I'm nobody, I don't exist, I have only temporary papers, which state that I am probably Polish and a displaced person. I have no documents or permits to travel to any other country so I cannot travel to England and make enquiries for myself and even if I could, I shouldn't know where to begin."

She held onto my hand for a long time and the frequent squeezes she had given, almost like punctuation marks as she emphasised a particular point were quite endearing. Her hands were so tiny by comparison with my rather large 'hams' and yet again, I felt the surge of tenderness and protective instincts sweep over me.

I extracted my hand from her grip, stood up and said,

"I'll order another drink for us on the way to the loo. Are you sticking with beer?"

They both agreed and I placed my order with the waiter as I headed for the toilet. I always found it somewhat disconcerting to be confronted by a female attendant in the gentleman's toilets, who carried out repeated cleaning operations between 'customers' to ensure the customary high standard of German hygiene. There was always a plate with a few coins of varying denominations strategically placed so that you were left in no doubt that a gratuity was expected. I could just about cope with the idea of a woman listening as I tried to reduce the sound of my performance by urinating on the side of the bowl instead of aiming straight for the water but the thought of her listening to every sound as I blasted away with everything available should more pressing needs of nature arise convinced me that I should walk out of the cubicle, unable to meet her eye with head bowed in shame. No one should be made to feel guilty because they needed a crap!

I washed my hands, placed the expected tip on the plate and beat a hasty retreat. We finished our beers and walked slowly back to Tim's place and allowed Janni, strictly against regulations while we were in uniform, to link her arms through ours. Fortunately, we were not called upon to salute anyone so it didn't matter very much. Once indoors, we settled for coffee and chatted amiably for half an hour or so before Janni and I took our leave and I walked her back home.

At the door to her flat, we were both a bit hesitant, remembering the previous occasion, when, to my great surprise Janni said, "This is silly. Come on up and have a goodnight brandy. Apart from anything else, Humphrey would like to see you."

"Humphrey?" I queried,

"Humphrey bear. He asks about you all the time!" Janni replied, her voice bubbling with laughter.

I laughed with her as we climbed the steep stairs to her little flat. There was a very tiny kitchenette just to the right of the door and the main room to the left. It was medium sized with a decent carpet, old fashioned, but good quality furniture, comprising a table and two dining chairs, a wardrobe and three-quarter bed, a bedside table with a lamp and radio, two armchairs and a couple of rugs. A standard lamp stood in the corner and I have to admit that it was very cosy. Heating was provided by a three-element electric fire, which was set into a marble surround.

Janni told me to sit down, but to take my belt off in case I left Blanco all over her cushions and went into the kitchen. She came back with two cups of coffee went to the kitchen again and returned with two glasses and a bottle of Hine brandy.

"You pour please Mike," she said as she kicked her shoes off, put her coffee on the wide arm of her chair and sat down with her feet tucked under her pert little bottom. I cautioned myself against making such mental observations but it was difficult not to admire the sheer perfection of her wonderful, young body.

"How tall are you Janni?" I asked.

She thought hard for a moment and said,

"I'm so used to doing everything in metric measurements that I have to really concentrate to give my measurements in the old way. I'm not one hundred percent sure of the figures, but when the doctor measured me a few weeks ago, I think he said I was five feet four and a half inches tall, I weigh eight stone four pounds," she paused, sought for the words, giggled and continued, "My vital statistics are thirty -three, twenty-two, thirty-three and I take size four and a half shoes. I'm about twenty years of age, I don't smoke, drink like a fish and I'm definitely not a virgin." She dissolved into hoots of laughter as she uttered the last part and we both laughed even longer when she added, "There, now you know all about me and I shouldn't be too difficult to trace because there can't be that many non-virgins about."

When we had stopped laughing, she asked,

"Now, tell me all about yourself, starting with how old you are, whether you're married and if you like bears."

Her smile was infectious and I must have been grinning as I answered,

"I am thirty one, five feet eleven, twelve stone five, I haven't a clue about my vital statistics. Before the war I used to teach European languages, I'm not married and like yourself, positively not a virgin. I love bears and have been known to have improper relations with them ever since early childhood."

"Ho! Ho! Ho!" Janni roared, turned to Humphrey and, wagging her finger, she said, "I was wrong when I said you had nothing to worry about just because you heard Mike say 'Bugger the bear'. Go and hide, quick!"

She was so funny and delightful and as she wiped laughter tears from her eyes, she stood up and said, "I'm almost peeing myself. Be back in a minute."

She went to the wardrobe, draped something over her arm and slid her feet into a pair of high heeled, backless, fluffy slippers. I heard her going along the landing and as I awaited her return, I realised that it was quite warm so I took off my battledress blouse and hung it over the back of a chair.

A few minutes later, Janni returned. She was wearing a silky, shiny beige gown, crossed over like a double-breasted coat and loosely tied with a matching sash. She carried her day dress on a hanger, which she hung in the wardrobe. I watched her every movement and it was quite apparent that she had nothing on under the flimsy gown.

She resumed her position in the big armchair, feet tucked up and the Japanese style sleeves slid back to reveal her arms. She leaned backwards and shook her hair, turned to me and said,

"It seems to have become so warm all of a sudden, almost clammy. Oh, you felt it too," she nodded in the direction of my jacket.

She jumped up again and went to the kitchen and after the sounds of the fridge being opened and closed, she returned with a small bowl of ice cubes, put them on the table and resuming her seat she said, "I know it's not the normal thing, but it's quite a popular way of drinking 'weinbrandt' here in Germany. Be a darling and pour us a couple of large ones over about three or four ice cubes".

I got out of my chair, took my coffee cup and Janni's and put them on the table. Then as instructed, I placed ice cubes in each glass and poured the brandy over them very slowly. She was right. In the increasingly clammy atmosphere, it was very refreshing. Janni reached out behind her and fiddled with the radio, finally settling for the American Forces Network broadcast which she turned down to make a pleasant background. As she stretched, my eyes followed the line of her neck right down her throat to the curve of her breasts. She was incredible!

As she turned back, she caught the direction of my eyes, pulled her gown a little tighter and said,

"I alternate between AFN and BFN to hear all the latest popular music and to learn the words, then, some mornings or afternoons, I go to the club and if I haven't been able to get the sheet music, I practise playing the tunes by ear before singing along with them. After all, it is my living and I enjoy playing. How do you like the brandy with ice by the way?" Before I could answer there was a blinding flash of lightning, so close you could hear it crackle, followed simultaneously by an incredible, rippling bang, which sounded as though it had torn all the slates off the roof.

Janni's reaction was almost as fast as the lightning; she leapt out of her chair, knocking her drink over in the process, jumped onto my knee and curled up into a tight ball. I put my arms round her, stroked her back and murmured, "It's alright, really, it's alright. Don't be afraid. It's only thunder." There were several more flashes and loud bangs and she flinched with every one, holding me tightly. She was obviously very frightened.

The storm moved further away and I could feel the tension go out of her body. She snuggled against me and whispered, "I'm sorry it was just like being bombed and shelled in Warsaw all over again. Silly me. I'll be alright in a moment."

I continued stroking her and eventually reached for my brandy glass and placed it between her hands.

She took a couple of small sips, handed the glass back to me and said, "Thanks Mike, I'm O.K. now."

She made a conscious effort to rally and her sense of humour came to her rescue as she laughed nervously and said, "You're lucky. During the real blitz I peed myself several times."

I hugged her to me and said,

"Janni darling, you are wonderful and I should have felt both honoured and wet if you had peed on me."

We both laughed and the tension evaporated but she remained where she was, snuggling comfortably against me and I was not about to complain. I loved the feel of her through the flimsy gown, the smell of her and her close proximity. She felt so small and vulnerable and the soft background music, combined with the effect of the brandy made me feel very cosy and contented.

I had continued to stroke her, very lovingly and without realising what I was doing, I bent over and kissed her head.

Slowly, she uncoiled from her tight, ball-like position, stretched her legs over the arm of the chair, squirmed around and put her arms round my neck and before I knew what was happening, she electrified me again with that astonishing kissing technique, followed by a slower, more lengthy series of fabulous, exploratory, very passionate kisses. My senses were reeling and the next thing I knew, my hands were all over her body, feeling every contour through the flimsy gown. I became more daring and slid my hand inside the gown, cupping a firm shapely breast and tweaking the nipple between finger and thumb. She became more passionate as I ran my hand down over the gentlest curve on her otherwise flat stomach.

Holding my face in her hands and still kissing me, she moved around until she sat astride me and opened the front of her gown.

Her body was all that it promised to be and more. To touch her skin was almost as electrifying as her kisses and it took my breath away. Impossible to describe, so fine, so beautiful to the touch, like the finest silk and when, finally, I clasped both cheeks of her bottom, I thought that I would ejaculate inside my trousers.

Quite suddenly, Janni stopped kissing me, and cried,

"Shit! Shit! Oh Shit!" climbed off me and ran out of the room into the kitchen where I could hear her sobbing gently.

Frankly, I didn't know what to do. My instinct was to go to her and offer comfort but I suspected that it would not have been what she wanted. Instead, I picked up her fallen glass and put it on the coaster on the table.

It was a difficult situation. If I put my jacket and belt on and made a move to leave she might feel that I was angry at having been led on and then dumped, unceremoniously with a throbbing erection, dashed expectations and aching balls.

I laughed inwardly at my own appraisal and acknowledged that it was mostly true. It was good therapy and in traditional military fashion, my penis stood at ease, then stood easy and finally relaxed in line with the inner seam of my trousers.

I heard Janni splashing cold water on her face and a few moments later, she came back into the room looking slightly sheepish. She went to the table and poured two more enormous brandies over ice. As she handed one to me, in a quiet, remorseful voice, she said, "I don't know what you must think of me. I've behaved very badly and I'm sorry. When I invited you in, I had no intention of doing anything like that but you were such good fun, it was great having you there during the thunderstorm and when I was on your knee, I felt comfortable, safe and very happy. It has been a long time since I felt any of those things all at the same time and quite suddenly, for the first time in two years, I felt that I could let go. I couldn't. It was as if I was being seriously unfaithful and since I'm not, by nature, a promiscuous person, if I had carried on, it would have been gratuitous sex just for the sake of sex. I felt guilty because I was using you, while the moment it started to get serious, I began thinking of Emil and realised that I couldn't continue. I'm sorry Michael, but I still love him so much and I'm thoroughly ashamed of my behaviour. Please say you forgive me." This was very much what I had suspected and I admired her honesty even if it didn't do very much for my ego. I said, "Janni, I'm not altogether stupid and I'm just as much to blame as you. I should not have let my feelings and my hands run away with me because, if I'm totally honest I suspected that it was all due to the cosiness, the drink and, for me, the fortuitous intervention of the storm. We both let our senses get the better of us and because I was enjoying myself so much, even though I guessed that it wasn't me you were thinking about, it should have been up to me to stop the situation from going that far. I'm not angry, except a little bit with myself and I'm the one who should be apologising for taking advantage of you when you were so vulnerable. Now then, we've both done our little grovelling apology act, Humphrey, who averted his eyes when we were misbehaving has turned round to smile at us again and I suggest we have another strong coffee."

It was a relief to hear her laugh again and the bounce was back in her step as she went to make the coffee.

I had lost all sense of time and when I realised that it was after three o'clock in the morning, it occurred to me that I did not have a late night pass. It didn't matter too much, since I was exempted from having to book in and out of the camp, but awkward questions would be asked by the regimental police, who didn't care for us 'odds and sods' very much, if I rolled up to the guardroom at this hour of the morning. Far better if I rolled up after breakfast, after the change of guard as though I had just been out for a stroll and to collect the newspapers. I mentioned this to Janni when she returned with the coffee. She turned to face me and said, "It's O.K. As it happens, I don't feel tired and to be honest, I don't want you to go yet. I'd rather you stayed and talked until we've put that episode behind us or there will always be a lingering doubt that after my appalling behaviour, you couldn't get away quick enough. But Michael, it's all right for me because I can sleep tomorrow and you'll have a full day ahead of you. You'll be shattered."

"Don't give it a thought," I said, "Many nights we work right through with difficult interrogations and we get used to it. A good shower, shave and shampoo and the other thing beginning with 's' and I'll be as good as new. Now then, you work Wednesday nights and I'll be busy for a couple of days but I do have a sort of half day on Friday. What I suggest is that I pick you up here at lunchtime, take you to meet my boss so that he can put a face, a very beautiful face I might add, to the name. After that, we can have lunch somewhere and then, since it is cigarette ration day, I'll take you to the NAAFI and you can pick out some nylons and coffee and anything else that takes your fancy then I'll drop you back here to get ready for your evening performance. I'll go on to Tim's and we'll both meet you in the club later." As an afterthought, I added, "Safety in numbers is perhaps the best policy don't you think."

Janni hit me playfully on the arm and said,

"Michael, you really are so nice and so thoughtful. It sounds a lovely idea." I had noticed that this was at least the third time she had called me Michael and I found it very pleasing. From then on, she never called me Mike.

We chatted about all sorts of inconsequential things and despite our earlier protestations to the contrary, we were having difficulty keeping our eyes open and many yawns were escaping un-smothered. Finally, Janni capitulated by saying, "It's no good, I'll have to lie down for a while. There is room on the bed for two and I think I can trust you, but if you can't trust yourself, you had better stay in the chair." She climbed onto the bed and moved over close to the wall. I took off my tie and shoes and stretched out on my back beside her.

We lay in complete silence, almost as if we were afraid to move, holding our breath. Janni broke the tension by turning to face the wall and drawing her knees up slightly. She reached backwards across my body with her hand, got hold of mine and almost dragged me onto my side so that my stomach fitted to the curve of her back. My hand was still firmly in her grasp as she drew it round her, my arm over her waist, and held it between both hands against her breasts as she snuggled even closer to me.

I had remained absolutely silent and did not wish to break the spell or this total trust. Moments later, Janni's breathing had changed into a slow, barely perceptible rhythm and I realised she was fast asleep.

The temptation to kiss her head and the back of her neck was not motivated by lust this time, purely out of tenderness. It was a truly wonderful feeling to have this beautiful being, totally trusting, curled up asleep against me like a warm little animal. Again, I was amazed that the fact that Janni really was a man had made no difference to my feelings, yet I could no more have seen myself behaving with any real man in a similar manner than I could have imagined ever meeting anyone like Janni. I was full of admiration for the way in which she handled her physical 'abnormalities' and there was no doubting that as far as she was concerned she was a girl. For my part, I still needed some convincing that she wasn't since every piece of physical evidence, except the one 'piece' I hadn't seen, indicated that she was indeed, a very beautiful young girl.

I must have fallen asleep and the next thing I remember was Janni gently shaking me and saying,

"Michael, we've slept a bit late. Come on, wake up."

As I came to, the first thing I noticed was the smell of toast and Janni said, "Here's a clean towel. Go and wash your face and there will be tea and toast on the table when you get back. Don't be long."

I went along to the tiny bathroom, had a long and satisfying pee, stripped off my shirt and had a good wash. I ran my fingers under the cold tap and rubbed my gums and teeth. It would have to do until I returned to barracks. I had shaved the night before so that after running my comb through my hair and putting on my tie, I looked quite presentable and I must have slept in the one position all night because my trousers had not suffered any undue creasing. All in all, I shouldn't present too questionable a picture when I walked into camp.

Back in the flat, Janni had put plates, knives and a pot of marmalade, one of apricot jam and another of blackcurrant on the table. She followed up quickly with a pot of tea, sugar bowl, a jug of milk and a large plate of toast.

"Best I can do; I wasn't expecting company for breakfast and I don't eat bacon and eggs so early in the day," Janni greeted me.

I sat at the table opposite her and said,

"It's fantastic. I never expected anything like this. By the way, how did you manage to get up and move around without disturbing me?"

She laughed her delightful laugh and said,

"You were so sound asleep, it was as if you were dead and I thought that this was not going to go down too well with the neighbours or your military bosses. Far from being free, I saw myself in captivity once more. At least you don't snore or fart in your sleep." She giggled and continued,

"I just slipped your arm from around me slid down to the bottom of the bed and climbed off. At first, I thought about climbing over you, but my first boyfriend used to pretend to be asleep and if I tried to reach across him or climb over, he would immediately grab me and get all randy, so I was a bit wary of that approach. Not that I don't trust you, but sometimes, when you just wake up, you are not completely in control of your brain cells and do things out of character. Anyway, shut up and eat your toast before it gets cold." We finished breakfast in almost total silence and after a last cup of tea, I put on my battledress blouse, belt and beret, thanked Janni for a lovely time and held her by the shoulders while kissing her on the forehead.

I confirmed the time that I would collect her on Friday and left, going down the stairs as quietly as possible so as not to disturb the other occupants. Fortunately, there were no prying eyes and I didn't encounter anyone as I let myself out. Janni's reputation was still intact.

I felt great and walked at a fair clip, calling in at the 'Toc H' canteen to buy the newspapers on the way to the barracks.

Nobody challenged me and I went to my room to complete my morning ablutions.

CHAPTER FIFTY-ONE

On the Friday, I finished early; in fact, I had a seventy-two hour pass but had spent an hour in the office finishing a report. It was great to have a long soak in a deep, hot bath, wash my hair and let it dry quite naturally after a brisk towelling with clean underwear, shirt and socks, I felt ten years younger. Since I was not on any 'work' assignment and didn't have to bother about looking typically English, I chose cavalry twill slacks, check shirt and knitted tie, hacking jacket and brogues.

Having checked my wallet and identity papers, I collected the car and headed for Janni's flat. There was a small, handwritten card beside the bell push bearing the name 'Kowalski'. I rang and waited. A few moments later, Janni appeared at an upper widow and at first, she didn't recognise me in civilian clothes. She called down, "Ja, kann ich ihnen helfen?" (Yes, can I help you?). Then, as I stepped back a couple of paces "Oh, it's you Michael, I'll be with you in a moment."

Moments later, I heard her high heels clattering on the stairs and she opened the door. She looked absolutely breathtaking. Her taste was impeccable. She wore a knee-length pale cream skirt, a pale coffee coloured silk shirt and lightweight, camel jacket, set off by cream and tan high-heeled shoes and matching shoulder bag. The final touch was a silk scarf of russet, olive and gold tied loosely round her throat. Her lipstick was a sort of copper brown as was the hint of eye shadow and her lashes looked longer than ever, dark and lustrous. I suspected that the gold highlights were not entirely due to the sun but they looked absolutely wonderful against her dark chestnut hair.

She held my shoulders and brushed her cheek against mine saying, "Sorry, no kiss. My lipstick will come off."

I took her arm and walked her to the car. She was surprised and delighted and inordinately pleased when I went round and held the door for her. She settled herself down and as I climbed in behind the wheel, she said, "How lovely. You really are full of surprises Michael and by the way, you look very nice."

I smiled and said,

"I was going to say the same about you only I should have used different adjectives like, wonderful, fabulous, gorgeous or incredible. Come to think of it, I'd have probably used all four."

She giggled delightedly and said,

"I told you once before that you were a smooth bastard and I was right."

We both laughed and as I started the car she asked,

"What are we going to do first?"

"We can't see my boss today because he is very busy, but I'll arrange a meeting soon. So, I thought we could go to the NAAFI first, get our shopping out of the way and then I'll take you somewhere nice for lunch. By the way, I've obtained a special pass for you so that from now on, you will be able to use the NAAFI and any of the other facilities even without me. It's something I managed to convince my boss that you should have and he issued it without hesitation. It also entitles you to buy English money at the English exchange rate from the military bank where Tim works."

She clapped her hands together, leaned across and kissed me on the cheek, and said,

"Oh Michael, that's wonderful. You are so very thoughtful and I never dreamed I would get one of these. Thank you so much. I'll have to meet this boss of yours and thank him personally."

She paused for a moment and suddenly exclaimed,

"Oh shit! I've put lipstick on your cheek. Just a minute." She reached into her bag and brought out a miniscule handkerchief, which she wet with the tip of her tongue, reached over and proceeded to wipe away the telltale smear from my cheek.

It all seemed so domesticated and natural and I must say, I enjoyed this feeling. We pulled in at the NAAFI and walked in arm in arm attracting many admiring glances. I hoped that it was because we made an attractive couple but it was Janni who drew all the attention.

We bought a large amount including nylons, coffee, cigarettes and cigars, brandy, whisky and gin, tonic, ginger ale and soda water. Fresh fruit, meat and poultry for Janni, loads of household cleaning things, soap, toothpaste and for Janni some make-up and perfume. Eventually, she said,

"I think we'd better stop now. I could stay here all day. I've never seen so much. It's wonderful."

She continued, "I suppose we have to pay in English money. If so, you'll have to pay for mine and I'll give you the equivalent in marks."

I had no one back home to worry about had saved quite a lot of my pay during my service and had drawn a fair amount for my seventy-two hour pass. I turned to her and said, "Janni, don't get cross, but today is your day. Your introduction to the new world of the NAAFI. I don't want any money from you for this first treat but, after today, you are on your own."

"Michael, I can't possibly let you pay for all this. It's not right." She had said this quite loudly in front of the cashier. She lowered her gaze and fluttered her eyelashes, looked up and in the same loud voice said, "After all, I hardly know you Sir!"

I roared with laughter, leant over and kissed her and Janni and the cashier joined in with the laughter.

I settled the bill and we struggled to the car, Janni with four shopping bags and me with a large box. We loaded everything on the back seat and floor.

Once inside, Janni said,

"I don't want to be a nuisance, but I think we ought to go back to the flat and put some of these things in the fridge and anyway, I couldn't possibly carry all this stuff up on my own." We returned to the flat and carted all Janni's stuff upstairs and in next to no time she had stored things in the fridge and the cupboards. She took a small suitcase and one bag back to the car in which she had placed her cigarettes and cigars, two tins of ground coffee and two tins of Nescafe.

She put the case containing her change of clothes for the club on the back seat, kept the bag on her lap and said, "If you put your things in here with mine, I'll sell them for us tonight and give you the money later on and, by the way, now that I can buy my own, I won't charge you a commission for selling yours."

"You are incorrigible," I said and asked, "Now then, where would you like to go for lunch?" She was quiet for a moment, apparently in deep thought and rather hesitantly, she said, "If it isn't too far, I'd like to go to Lbbecke again to that Terrassen Cafe. It was nice there." I was very pleased because it had been my intention to suggest the same place and I agreed wholeheartedly.

We drove to Lbbecke quite quickly and Janni said,

"I like it when you go fast. It's very exciting, particularly when you go round the corners. You are a very good driver Michael and I feel totally safe with you. One day, I'll buy a car of my own and learn to drive it."

"What kind of car would you buy?" I asked.

She became all animated and excited as she replied,

"I've already seen what I want. Nothing big, just a lovely little Volkswagen cabriolet, white, with a dark red soft-top. I haven't actually seen the car, only pictures of it because it won't be available for a while yet, but there's no rush. Before I buy a car, I want to get a larger flat where I don't have to share the bathroom with anyone else. I mean, I'm very happy where I am and I have more room and freedom than I've had in my life, but I've always had to share bathrooms or latrines or barrack-room bathrooms and toilets with lots of other people and I want my own bathroom where everything in it is mine."

The meal was a great success but overshadowed by the intensity of my feelings for her and her awareness of the fact that I had fallen madly in love with her. The result was that we avoided all reference to anything regarding the state of our relationship and there were a few uncomfortable silences, which were broken only by the discussion of trivia.

We stopped once for a coffee on the way back to Osnabrck before heading to Tim's place. Tim was all smiles as we arrived, received his usual kiss and big hug from Janni and, as usual, kept a protective arm around her shoulder as we walked into the building and along the passage to his room.

In his room, as he usually did, he held her at arm's length, looked her up and down and said, "Christ! You are looking so beautiful today Janni. Not that you don't always look beautiful, but there is something extra special about you. What have you been doing to effect this subtle change?"

Always ready to shock, Janni laughed and said,

"We haven't been shagging if that's what you think although we have been discussing the relative merits of indoor or outdoor coitus, fully clothed, semi-clothed or starkers. We couldn't make up our minds so we just said, sod it, we'll have more fun if we go and see Tim!" Tim roared with laughter and I thought how clever Janni was in using Tim to trivialise our earlier, earnest discussion. Things were going from bad to worse in a way because I felt an almost proprietorial pride in her wonderful, witty personality and I knew that I was seriously in love with this person, balls or no balls!

Janni went to get changed and soon reappeared looking ravishing. Without waiting to be asked she went to Tim's locker, took out a bottle of brandy and said, "I hope you don't mind Tim, but I need a couple of stiff one's before I perform." She stopped, giggled and continued hurriedly, "Christ, you must both think I've got a one-track mind talking about stiff ones and I was just going to make it worse by asking if anyone would care to join me." She almost collapsed with laughter and pleaded, "Come on you two, help me before I embarrass myself further."

We were all laughing as Tim went to the cupboard and provided three glasses into which he poured pretty substantial measures.

Janni, still in irrepressible mood said,

"We've eaten so much, drunk lots of beer, coffee, brandy and Sekt that I shall be peeing all night and I wouldn't be surprised if I fart during my act. Still, as long as I can manage to do it in key, nobody should notice."

Tim and I laughed, neither of us able to visualise this gorgeous creature actually breaking wind. We finished our drinks and Janni decided that she would walk the short distance to the club on her own. She slipped on her light coat, picked up her bag and gave us both a peck on the lips as she left us at the gates.

"See you later," she called as she turned and waved then she vanished around the first corner.

Tim turned to me and said,

"I've never seen her so happy before; you must have had a really nice day together. Care to tell me about it?"

I told him about obtaining the pass for the NAAFI and her permit to use the facilities of his office which he thought was wonderful and then I told him about our shopping, the drive to Lbbecke, lunch at the Terrassen Cafe and the drive back. I omitted all personal details and he seemed quite satisfied that such a nice day out would account for Janni's happiness. If I'm totally honest, I suppose it was only the fact that I feared Tim's reaction, which prevented me from telling him any more details and admitting that I was madly in love with her. After all, I hadn't known him all that long and he might have reservations about any man who falls in love with another man. I know I had before I met Janni! We sat out in the little courtyard drinking coffee and I mentioned to Tim that Janni wanted to meet my boss to thank him personally and Tim said, "Christ, don't take her into a barracks again, she finds it difficult to cope with anything like that. How the hell she managed in the DP camps and the MSLO barracks, I'll never know but great concentrations of troops and shouted orders frighten her very badly. If I were you, I'd arrange an informal meeting in a hotel bar or anywhere with less threatening surroundings."

I thought, 'I've still got an awful lot to learn about Janni' and replied,

"Thanks for the advice. It never occurred to me that she might have problems like that. I'll do as you suggest and it might make her feel more comfortable if you came along as well. That's if you don't mind?"

"Good idea," Tim replied and continued, "Best not to invite him over to her club. He'll get enough of a shock as it is when he meets her for the first time. After all, I don't suppose you have prepared him for meeting 'Miss Janni Kowalski' when he has her on paper as 'Mr Janni Kowalski'."

I laughed and said,

"I've thought a great deal about that and I decided that he should meet her just as she is, without any prior enlightenment. People are prone to develop pre-conceived ideas about what they regard as sexually abnormal. Oddities to be treated very warily and with distaste, engender revulsion and are usually referred to in the most derogatory terms such as queers, poofters, brown-hatters, shirt-lifters, sausage jockeys or a host of other equally uncomplimentary names. I seriously believe that he will find her as charming as we do and will be very understanding and sympathetic if we do it this way. What do you think Tim?"

He mulled over what I had said and replied,

"You are right, of course. Preconceptions can be a dangerous thing and could create prejudice, even before they have met. Mind you, I'm looking forward to observing his reactions!"

That settled, and leaving me to make the arrangements, Tim and I strolled round to the club where Janni was in mid-song as we arrived.

We made our way to the usual table, which had been kept for us, and ordered drinks for ourselves and Janni who was in great form, her audience, as usual hanging on to every word, joining in with and enjoying the banter and good-naturedly accepting and laughing at themselves when she put some of them down in the most sarcastic terms, never once losing her smile which took all the offence out of her caustic comments. Since it was a German owned club, for the most part, she did her act in German although she sang the latest American and British songs in English. Three soldiers sat near the stage wearing boots and gaiters; web belts and they had tucked their berets under their shoulder straps. They had obviously been drinking for some time and were fairly boisterous, making frequent, loud comments about Janni's assets and what they would like to do to her.

She ignored them completely and I suppose they thought that her knowledge of English was limited to the words of the songs. Whatever, their suggestions and propositions became more graphic and quite disgusting.

Without missing a beat, Janni walked to the front of the tiny stage, stepped down and still singing, walked over to them in her slinkiest way and singled out the leader of the trio who was the most offensive. She held out her hand to him and when he took it, she backed off onto the dance floor, dragging him with her, still smiling. In the middle, she stopped. To the crowd, in German, she said, "We are taught that the English are perfect gentlemen but did you ever see three such sorry, pitiful specimens in your life?" She waved her hand to encompass the other two and amid mounting laughter and with a huge grin, she continued,

"By contrast, you lovely people are princes with perfect manners and although I know, without being big-headed that you would all like to shag me, German good manners prevent you from saying so in as many words. That's not to say that you aren't a dirty lot of buggers, but I love you all for your restraint."

The audience cheered and clapped and laughed and Janni, still holding the soldier's hand, walked round him making him turn on the spot to follow her. She released her hand, stepped back and indicating him and the others with a wave of her hand, she said, "Now these 'gentlemen' have been calling out all evening in the crudest terms about what they would like to do to me for the rest of the night until the early hours. I ask you, take another look at them. I very much doubt that they could muster a good fart between them, let alone a good shag and this one looks as though he's about to piss himself with fright. Some soldier, some fine example of the fearless, fighting, farting 'Tommy'. Hardly the stuff that legends are made from. It's a common term in the British Army that bullshit baffles brains and although I can see plenty of evidence of bullshit, I think we would be hard pressed to find any brains."

The crowd roared with laughter and clapped for a long time as Janni escorted the soldier back to his table and in her perfect English she said, "Thank you so much for letting me make such a complete idiot out of you, the Germans loved it. They don't take too kindly to your boorish behaviour and neither do I. The three of you are a disgrace to the uniform you are wearing and you certainly won't make any friends carrying on the way you have tonight. From now on, behave yourselves. Any more filth from any one of you and I'll have you thrown out so fast, you won't know what's hit you." She smiled her most wonderful smile at them, turned, and amidst thunderous applause, she walked gracefully over to our table with a wicked twinkle in her eyes. As we stood to greet her, she kissed us both on the mouth and I assume, purely for the benefit of the three soldiers, instead of the normal brush with the lips, she gave us longer, more lingering kisses which I enjoyed, but Tim was taken completely by surprise and was left quite speechless for some moments.

"Great performance. That should teach the bastards," I said.

Janni laughed and said,

"I enjoyed myself immensely, the stupid sods hadn't a clue what I was talking about and probably thought that I was saying all sorts of complimentary things about them and that the applause was, in part, for them for being such 'Jolly Good Fellows'. Now they know better and that they've been made to look absolute prats. Good fun wasn't it?" "Yes it was," I replied and added, "Mind you, having said that, you used some pretty colourful language yourself in your put-down. I must say, it springs to your lips very readily and your vocabulary of bad words poses a serious threat to Tim's hitherto unchallenged supremacy in that department."

Tim had recovered from the kiss and laughingly he said,

"Yes, by God Janni, that was very impressive and I particularly admired the alliteration of the 'fearless, fighting, farting Tommy.' That was brilliant. You will have to give me some lessons!"

We all drank quite a lot, Janni sang a few more numbers and the soldiers, suitably subdued, behaved themselves and when Janni had finished, they came over to our table and addressed Tim since I was in civilian clothes. Their ringleader spoke, "Excuse me sergeant, we just wanted to apologise to the young lady."

He turned to Janni and said,

"We are all really sorry Miss. We didn't think you would understand what we were saying and had we known, we would have kept our comments within more acceptable bounds." The other two murmured their agreement with these sentiments and looked suitably shame-faced.

Janni, gracious as ever, stood up and held out her hand to them which they all shook in turn, looking very relieved.

Tim stood up and said,

"I'm glad you had the decency to apologise lads. You were a bit over the top and although Janni can handle herself, as you found out to your cost, she is a very special, very beautiful young lady and should not be subjected to that sort of behaviour. As she said, you didn't make any friends here tonight, like it or loathe it, that is what we have to do these days and such exhibitions do little to advance our cause. Anyway, that's enough of that; just don't let it happen again. Now off you go or you'll be late."

They breathed a collective sigh of relief and their leader said,

"Sorry again Miss. You are smashin' and a great singer. Goodnight Miss, Goodnight sergeant, Goodnight Sir."

We said goodnight to them and they left.

A couple of brandies later and the three of us left. This time, we didn't go back to Tim's place since Janni pleaded tiredness, saying she needed her beauty sleep. Janni and I left Tim at the end of his street and she and I continued on to her flat. At her door, I didn't allow the kissing to go beyond the familiar 'electric' kiss saying that I too needed a good night's sleep. I returned to barracks torn between my need to see her as often as possible and the frustration and torment future involvement would cause.

CHAPTER FIFTY-TWO

The next morning, although it was Saturday, I knew that I would find my boss in his office arranging our schedules for the following week and I approached him in our usual, informal way,

"Good morning Arthur, I thought I should find you here," I said. "Morning Mike, and I thought I'd given you a seventy-two hour pass and didn't expect to see you until Monday," he replied.

"I gave those two passes to Kowalski who was absolutely delighted and wants to meet you to thank you personally. If it's O.K. with you, I thought we could all have a drink together on Sunday," I ventured.

He looked up from his papers and after a moment's pause, he said,

"I must confess to being intrigued by the fella's story and since my curiosity always gets the better of me, I'll take you up on the offer."

"Janni always feels more comfortable if my pal Tim, the Pay Corps sergeant is around so, I've invited him too. I hope you don't mind?"

"Sounds O.K. to me." he responded.

"I think everyone would feel more at ease if we wore our civvies. Poor Tim would feel uncomfortable calling you by your christian name if you were in uniform." I said.

"Yes, you are probably right. I can't stand underlying tension, it doesn't make for the happiest meetings." Arthur replied.

"That's settled then. I'll pick you up at noon tomorrow. Bye for now." I headed for the door as my boss said,

"I look forward to it. Cheers."

That night at the club, I told Janni and Tim what I had arranged and they were both very pleased. As Tim pointed out, once Arthur had met Janni, he'd bend over backwards to help her. I shared his expectations assuming, that is, that Arthur survived the initial shock!

When I took Janni home in the early hours of Sunday, my resolve to limit the kissing broke down and after a lengthy bout of very passionate, extremely erotic kissing; I pushed Janni away and said,

"I'm sorry, I can't go on with this. I'm finding it too difficult to keep my hands off you, to explore your body and become even more physical. Your idea just isn't going to work. For both our sakes, from now on we had better restrict ourselves to a plain straightforward peck on the lips, not even your brief sense-shocker; it's too dangerous."

She put her head against my chest and was very quiet for some time and then in an almost inaudible voice, she said, "Michael, Dear, I'm so sorry. It was silly of me to think that we could be so physical without becoming aroused and I must take the blame for that. I wouldn't let myself go so much, giving you false hope when I know that sooner or later, I would call a halt leaving us both thoroughly wound up and excited without the prospect of any fulfilment. It is cruel to both of us and reluctantly I have to agree to your proposed restrictions." We both fell silent, just hugging each other, still reluctant to break the physical contact from which we both appeared to draw such comfort.

With great effort, I drew away from her and said,

"I love you Janni," as I held her shoulders and kissed her lightly on the forehead. Impulsively, she pulled me to her, arms round my neck, cheek against mine and I could detect a slight wetness as she whispered, "I know, I know. Goodnight Michael. We will see each other tomorrow won't we?" "I'm afraid you will have to put up with me again tomorrow," I said trying to lighten the mood and as an afterthought, I added, "Tim will collect you and take you round to the hotel while I collect my boss. See you there." I turned and walked away, stopping once to look back. Janni still stood at her doorstep looking quite forlorn and I resisted the urgent tugging of my heartstrings to rush back and take her in my arms.

Back in my own room, I decided that from now on, my dealings with Janni would be purely on a business basis.

I would attend the meeting which I had arranged and from then on I would only see her if any new development necessitated her presence. Otherwise, I would just get on with my job. After sleeping on the problem and mulling over all the alternatives in my mind, I elected to ask Arthur for a temporary transfer away from Osnabrck.

CHAPTER FIFTY-THREE
(Janni's life in Hamburg)

I packed my two suitcases and took the train to Hamburg, booked into a cheap hotel and set about finding accommodation.

The savings which I had accrued from my wages in the MSLO and from the clubs and illegal activities would only last a little while and I had determined that I was not going to live in a tatty place like the one in Osnabrck.

With this foremost in my mind, I did the rounds of several high-class jewellers and sold one of my diamonds for a very good price and as a result, I rented a beautifully furnished flat overlooking the Alster.

I spent the whole of the next day adding my own personal touches to my new domain, adding a radiogram and a whole range of kitchen and bathroom items. I hadn't felt so good or so free for years. It was truly wonderful.

Apart from the nice location, there were some wonderful shops nearby, The Stadts Oper (Opera House) just round the corner, two German cinemas and an Army Kinema Company Globe cinema on the corner. A short walk and there was a lovely little restaurant-cum-coffee house called L'Aronge (I think) whose speciality was the most delicious oxtail soup I have ever tasted, it was available thick or clear. Then, I found the most amazing boutique called 'Bei Hilde' owned and run by this very eccentric lady, Hilde. The clothes were of excellent quality and she was always prepared to haggle over the price, it was part of the fun of shopping there. We became firm friends.

Another favourite haunt was a little ice-cream parlour along Jungfernstieg, past the front of a big department store, Peek und Kloppenberg, then down some steps at the side of the bridge to the walkway along the side of the Alster. The proprietor was an 'artist' who sculpted the most wonderful creations in water ices with swans piped in whipped cream on top. Bliss.

That evening, I set off to inspect the clubs to look for prospective employment. Within days I'd been offered jobs in a variety of places, from resident pianist in the cocktail lounge of the Vierjahrenzeit Hotel, within a stone's throw of my flat, to my own singing and playing spot in a few seedy clubs, eventually settling for a twice nightly spot in the Kaskade, a large night club near the HauptBahnhof. The club was divided into two, one part being rather down market and bawdy and the other, very upmarket with a wonderful group called the Blue Five, who were all amazing musicians. Admittedly, there were strip shows in this part of the club too, but by contrast to the other half, the girls were all very beautiful and performed very tastefully. Neither the management nor the girls knew that I was anything other than I purported to be and eager young men frequently chatted me up. It was part of my job to flirt and occasionally to drink with them at the tables, encouraging them to spend obscene amounts of money in the vain hope that I would finish up in one of their beds. I never did, nor did I feel any qualms about encouraging them to spend money. After all, my commission was quite high!

The owner of this establishment was called Gunther Fleischer, a fabulous character who knew just about everyone who mattered. He spoke flawless, accent free English and his manners were impeccable. He was also very generous and we would frequently drink a few bottles of Sekt together or he would invite me to join him and his friends for a late meal and more drinks. Despite my protestations, he never allowed me to pay for anything. He treated all his employees with respect and never ever made a pass at any of us.

I had a reasonable income on which I could live quite well and a lovely home, but I was very lonely and although there were acquaintances and a few friends, whenever they left after a dinner party at my flat, or I left their places, I finished up alone and bored. You can only read so much and only listen to music for so long before ennui sets in.

Just up from Jungfernstieg, one of the narrower streets led uphill all the way to St. Pauli and the notorious Reeper Bahn. On the right up this narrow street, the opening concealed by strategically placed brick walls, there was one of the 'naughty' streets. The soldiers called it Winklestrasse but it's proper name, if I recall it correctly was Ulrikestrasse. It was enclosed at each end by the same brick barriers with enormous out of bounds signs for the benefit of the troops and Military Policemen patrolled nearby to enforce this order, motivated more by concern for the soldier's health than any moralistic reasons, although the women had to be licensed, carry a card and have regular medical inspections. Their cards were appropriately stamped if they were free of venereal disease, which meant very little since their first customer of the new day could re-infect them and their subsequent customers would become infected until the next examination when she would have to withdraw her services! Inside, in the downstairs windows, these prostitutes sat in their underwear and negotiated their prices through holes in the glass, which were opened when they rotated a circle of glass from the inside. I've never seen such a raddled looking bunch of trollops in my life and it doesn't say much for the males of the species who kept these awful creatures in business. I only walked through out of curiosity and was subjected to a lot of catcalling, vitriolic abuse and hisses from the ghastly creatures, illuminated by dim red bulbs in their little 'shop fronts'. I retreated very quickly and continued up the street.

A few minutes walk brought me to a bar-cum-club called the Monocle Bar and I went in, sat down and ordered a coffee and a weinbrandt. It was very lively and a large percentage of the clientelle and the entertainers were transvestites and not very convincing trannies at that. A fair proportion of them were very large, heavy and very obviously male who all must have had a great sense of the ridiculous because it was hard to believe that they took themselves seriously. They were very loud, to the point of being raucous and their jokes very rude and suggestive, their actions and mannerisms outrageously 'camp', but they were all good fun and I joined in their choruses along with the rest of the 'audience'.

I became a regular visitor on my nights off from my job and enjoyed all the friendly banter with these real oddball people. We got on very well together and after hours, I often played the piano and sang for them. Eventually, the boss said I could have a full time job and we did a deal whereby I earned more than I was currently earning.

It was great, not only was it within easy walking distance of my flat but it brought me into contact with all sorts of very influential people who used this strange place to live out their fantasies. For my performances, I had a selection of gowns, slit up the thigh, the halter neck open to way below my navel and the bare back plunging almost to the cleft in my bum. I wore light evening sandals with idiotically high, stiletto heels and when, in fairness to my boss and the other performers I revealed my true gender, they were absolutely astonished. I really did have to flash my willy at them to convince them. We had one hell of a party that night and I had to take a taxi the short distance home. The taxis were an absolute hoot, most of them towed little trailers in which some kind of stove produced gas which was them pumped via connecting tubes to a strange balloon like structure situated on the top of the vehicles in a cage. This coal gas was the fuel. They were extremely dangerous and likely to explode in the event of an accident.

CHAPTER FIFTY-FOUR

The weeks went by and since I worked late and slept late I devoted the afternoons to shopping, black-marketing and research, seeking out all channels of information to track down the whereabouts of so many of the more brutal and vicious of the concentration camp guards. It was a laborious process, consuming all my afternoons and occasional mornings and it wasn't until I met an officer who worked for the justice department of the Allied Control Commission that I made any real headway since it was difficult to obtain access to German military records. He introduced me to an officer who led a team whose sole occupation was to find these criminals and bring them to justice. Alas, although they traced many of them, the prosecutions were few and far between and the authorities seemed reluctant to press charges. Eventually, they gave up any pretence and disbanded this unit but not before I had traced quite a few of the people I most wanted to see brought to justice. I joined forces with a Jewish man who also had many connections and whatever information I gathered, I passed on to him for onward transmission to Simon Wiesenthal.

There was another secret Jewish organisation who had planned to exact their own revenge and although their plan to poison vast numbers of the German population by introducing quantities of extremely toxic poison into the water supplies had been discovered and the persons carrying the poison had been arrested by the British, they had a marked degree of success in Berlin where some of them had infiltrated the bakery supplying bread to the prison in which several thousand former SS men were languishing. Powerful poisons were introduced into the bread and a great number of the SS were killed. The authorities would only admit to a number, somewhere around three hundred, being killed, but if other reports were to be believed, the figure was closer to three thousand.

It was never proved to be the work of this group, but suspicions ran high when a former Dachau guard who had previously served at Auschwitz was thrown from the top of the old Flak towers in Hamburg Altona while a fair was in full swing on the Dom Hof below. I had given the name and address of this man to my Jewish contact!

For all that I wanted to see the victims of the Nazis avenged, I am by nature a gentle, non-violent person, and no matter the depth of my hatred or justification, I could not bring myself to harm another human being. Call it cowardly if you will, but I left these forms of retribution to others.

Now, I was working, sleeping, eating and researching and whilst I was no longer bored, I was still lonely and looked forward to my stints at the club each night where the camaraderie of the others never failed to cheer me. One evening I was just finishing the last number of my first 'spot' when a tallish man came through the doors, shook his umbrella and handed it together with his raincoat to the cloakroom attendant. It was difficult to see clearly from the bright stage through the smoke- laden atmosphere beyond the illuminated circle of the dance floor. There, the tables and their occupants were only discernable as dark shapes.

The newcomer sat at the edge of the dance floor and called the waitress. As he looked up to place his order, I almost died as I recognised him. I left the stage through the rear curtain and sat quietly for a few moments. From the tiny dressing room, I took the passageway towards the toilets and entered the gloom of the club from a direction almost directly behind the newcomer. I approached to within touching distance, then, struggling to find my masculine voice, I said,

"On your next full day off, shall we have a bath and try those exercises together Sir."
He nearly fell off his chair, struggled to stand and then looked at me in total disbelief.
"My God Janni. Is it really you?" he spluttered.
"Yes Emil. I can call you that now can't I? It really is me and I'm so happy to see you,"

I said, taking both his hands in mine and in my feminine voice, I asked, "May I sit down?" "Of course. Of course. Forgive me, it's the shock. I'm forgetting my manners," he responded, still visibly shaken.

He held my chair for me and waited until I was seated comfortably before taking hold of my hands again and saying,

"This is truly wonderful. I can't begin to tell you how wonderful. I've missed you so much and never stopped thinking about you. I was convinced that you were dead, that I should never see you again and because I was interned for a lengthy spell until they were satisfied that I was clean, I hadn't even started the process of trying to find out what happened to you. Oh, and by the way, those letters that you and your family wrote as references for me were very well received and I'm eternally grateful to you all." He said it all in a rush and had to pause for breath.

I called for coffee and asked the waitress to bring a bottle of weinbrandt and to leave it at the table. We talked and talked, bringing each other up to date on everything that had happened since we'd last been together and the whole time, he couldn't take his eyes off me nor I mine off him as he said,

"Janni, I always thought you were very pretty from the first memorable occasion when I saw you on that ramp, but now, you're incredibly beautiful and so very feminine I can hardly believe what I'm seeing."

"Look, I have to leave you for a short while to play and sing a few numbers, then, you'll have my undivided attention and I should like you to dance with me please." I stood up as I spoke and, perfectly mannered as ever, he stood up too, moved my chair back and said, "Don't be too long."

I played and sang my numbers, told a few bawdy jokes in between and then I addressed the audience saying,

"Tonight is a wonderful night for me. I have just been re-united with someone whom I thought had been killed and who thought that I had met the same fate. As a change from the music I usually play, I hope you will indulge me on this special occasion if I play something especially for the man to whom I owe my life."

I played all Emil's favourites, from Beethoven to Chopin; from Rachmaninov to Schubert, Brahms, Liszt and many more. Everyone applauded vigorously and I gave my deep bow, allowing the customers a fuller view of my tits at the end of the performance.

This time, I left via the front of the stage, hiking up my gown as I stepped down to give the customers and Emil in particular full value for money. As Emil rose to escort me to his table, the crowd applauded him. He looked quite embarrassed.

The group had started playing and Emil held my chair as we approached the table. Instead of sitting down, I placed my arms around his neck and said,

"Come and dance with me. Hold me please. I've missed you too, so very much."

"Have you honestly?" he asked and when I nodded and lay my head against his shoulder, he continued, "I suppose you already have a boyfriend?" He said this quite casually, but I could feel the tension in him as he waited for my answer.

"No, Emil, I haven't and, before you ask, there hasn't been anyone since you."

We danced and held each other very close until the early hours while the boss and some of the big, blousy raucous trannies looked on having turned all sentimental and unashamedly shed schnapps-fuelled tears. They could tell I was deliriously happy. I took him back to my flat and we fulfilled our joint wish of so long ago, when I had said, " I wish I could sleep with you", and he had replied, "So do I Janni, so do I."

We could, at long last, let our emotions run riot, use endearing expressions freely and be as adventurous and noisy in our love-making as we wished without the constant fear of discovery and the inevitable outcome. His vicious scars were no longer, raised, livid ropes and he had regained full use of his muscles. This new freedom of movement allowed him to be extremely adventurous and inventive. I told him that I had been so busy settling in, securing a job and working all hours that although I had found the telephone number of his parent's house, I still had not plucked up the courage to telephone.

He was delighted by the fact that it had been my clear intention to find him and as an expression of this joy, he set about lovemaking all over again. We slept well into the afternoon.

CHAPTER FIFTY-FIVE

He had returned to the law profession and worked very hard at it during the day, but most nights, he stayed with me. He wanted me to speak English most of the time so that he could improve his own mastery of the language.

There were so many English, American and Canadian soldiers stationed hereabouts that English was very widely spoken and I would often be invited to officer's messes or the sergeant's club just opposite the Globe cinema where I spoke English the whole time.

Emil's parents were lovely, upper crust, old wealth and they made me feel very much at home and were delighted that their son had found someone so lovely. They hadn't a clue and would have been mortified if they had learned the truth. As it was, I often spent weekends in their lovely house, fronting onto the Elbe at Blankenese, a few miles out of Hamburg on the north side of the river, or slightly longer spells at their summer residence on the Baltic coast between Neustadt, Scharbeutz and Travemnde overlooking Timmendorfer Strand, a beautiful curving beach of soft silvery sand sloping down to the blue-green Baltic, where, like the Mediterranean, the rise and fall of the tide was minimal and quaint; horseshoe shaped, wickerwork beach huts and double, enclosed seats dotted the upper reaches of the shore. I was in my element because I had developed a particularly sweet tooth and a very short distance to the east of Travemnde, lay Lbeck, famous the world over for its obscenely decadent marzipan, especially the one with the rich, dark chocolate coating. I made an absolute pig of myself.

On a more sober note, the border to the Soviet occupied East Germany started immediately to the east of this lovely town, and the town itself, in fact the whole area including Travemnde was a haven for ex SS men. I recognised quite a few faces. I pointed them out to Emil, seeking confirmation of their identities from him. This provoked our first argument. He responded, saying,

"For God's sake Janni, can't you put all that behind you? We have each other now, we are happy and we don't need constant reminders of those dark days."

I rounded on him angrily and in a raised voice, I said,

"They are all around us. How can I ignore them, watching them walking around in apparent luxury, looking like butter wouldn't melt in their mouths, with untroubled consciences after participating in the murder of millions. What sort of unfeeling person do you think I am if you think I can put that out of my mind and not wish to see them punished? Christ Emil, where is your sense of justice or have you, just like the rest, started to make apologies for their barbarity?"

He was flabbergasted by my outburst, astonished at the depth of hatred apparent in my tone and he said,

"Oh Shit Darling, you of all people should know that I could never make apologies for that scum. They make me ashamed to admit to being German and afraid to admit to being in the SS, more especially when people say, "He served at Auschwitz."

"It's very difficult to live with and even though I can justify my own conduct throughout the war, I could never justify the excesses that were committed in this country's name. The whole nation will not be forgiven for many years to come, if ever. I can understand your feelings, but as for me, I just want to get on with my life. Surely that's not too much to ask, is it?"

"You mean that just like the rest of them, you'll stand by and do nothing. Is that what you're telling me?" I accused and added, "And all the time, from the very first time in your quarters, I was struggling with my conscience for falling in love with you, the enemy, and I convinced myself that it was alright because you were different, a man of integrity, of high moral principles who could be relied upon to do the right thing. How could I have been so gullible."?

I turned away from him and began to walk off along the seafront.

He didn't follow and after a while I risked a look back and saw him sitting on a bench looking very dejected.

Back in the house, I poured a large drink and sat at the open window staring out over the blue waters of the Baltic, just a stone's throw away. Remorse was setting in and I admitted to myself that my tirade had been unfair, very hurtful and considering how kind and thoughtful he had been, taking dangerous risks to help my family, and me my attack had been unwarranted. I felt really contrite and miserable.

His footsteps approached the door. He entered, put an arm round me and simultaneously, tentatively, we both began,

"I'm sorry!"

I reached up and put my fingers on his lips and said,

"Shush. Shush. I should never have said what I did. You helped me, loved me and did whatever you could for my family under very difficult circumstances and I know that I should never have survived without you. Please forgive me for saying those horrible things. I really do love you and I'm sorry if I hurt you. Please, can we just forget it and go back to being like we were."

He just hugged me to him very hard and I could feel his silent tears on my cheek as he murmured,

"Janni, Janni darling, I love you to the point of distraction and I don't want anything to come between us, ever. Don't let's fight again, I can't bear it."

I learned that arguments are excellent for increasing the tenderness factor in lovemaking and made a mental note to argue more often!

CHAPTER FIFTY-SIX

Emil didn't like the hours or the environment in which I worked and he regularly tried to persuade me to give it up. He could find me a job in his office as a translator and court interpreter. He also wanted to move into my flat so that we lived together permanently and shared the household expenses. It was strange, I had been lonely, desperately wanting a loving companion, but I was still claustrophobic from my experiences and didn't want any ties imposed on my freedom. I had to be in charge of my own space and while I adored having him at home, even for extended periods, I was not ready to give up this hard won independence.

He said he understood, but he hated having his hopes thwarted and was often petulant. He was becoming more and more possessive and became extremely jealous when he found letters, written to Alex's old address, returned with the notation 'This address no longer exists. No known forwarding location'.

"You're still in love with him aren't you?" he shouted accusingly. "Bloody hell, I thought you loved me."

I didn't answer, nor did I tell him that Hedwig and Alex, if they were still alive, held a small fortune belonging to me.

At the club, he was frequently moody, insanely jealous and gave me filthy looks when, as part of my job, I sat with customers, laughed at their jokes and accepted the drinks they showered upon me.

One evening two English sergeants came in and I was delighted when I recognised them as my friends Michael and Tim from Osnabrck who broke out into the most enormous grins when they recognised me, picked me up and twirled me round before holding me at arm's length, looking me up and down and declaring,

"You look fantastic, fabulous, no, beautiful. I'm still trying to remember you in your natty blue battle dress."

Emil slammed his drink down on the table, got up, said, "Flighty, lying bitch," and stormed out. Deliberately, I stayed late and when I finally arrived home at about four-thirty a.m., he was still up, pacing angrily up and down the living room floor and as I let myself in, he shouted,

"Where the hell have you been till now? I suppose you've been with him haven't you?"

I ignored him, went over to the sideboard and poured a large brandy before sitting down in my favourite chair. I took a deep breath and said,

"Emil, this has got to stop. This petty jealousy of yours is destroying us. I've done nothing to warrant your accusations and to be honest; I'm getting fed up with your surly, aggressive behaviour. I am not your chattel. I love and trust you and I expect the same in return. Instead, you are taking the edge off our happiness and I won't put up with it any more. It would be better if we don't see each other for a while until you have got your priorities right. In fact, you had better leave now. Go home and sort yourself out and when you think you can behave in a more reasonable way, but not until then, you can 'phone me and I might be prepared to give it another chance. In the meantime, I should like my key back please."

He dragged me up out of the chair, spilling my drink, started shaking me and shouting at the top of his voice,

"You cheating, ungrateful little shit, I ought to beat the hell out of you."

I pushed him away and said,

"Only a couple of weeks ago, you were telling me that you were different from all those other SS thugs. We were both wrong. Now give me my key and get out before I call the police and don't bother to telephone."

I walked over, opened the door and held out my hand for the key.

He pulled the key from his key-ring, threw it on the floor and stormed out in a terrible rage.

I got very drunk, fell on the bed and cried myself to sleep.

CHAPTER FIFTY-SEVEN

Over the next few months, I threw myself into my work and moved out of the club which, I finally admitted to myself, was a tatty, sleazy dive and after a short spell back at the Kaskade, I stopped playing in the clubs altogether except to oblige Gunther at the Kaskade occasionally. Because I lived nearby, I was available at very short notice if an entertainer couldn't appear through illness, bad weather or any other reason. He would pay me very well on these occasions.

Dear Hilde employed me as a sales assistant on a small basic wage and a good rate of commission. It worked out very well for both of us. I still had all Rebecca's diamonds and emeralds and all but one of my own. I sold two more diamonds and was agreeably surprised at the increase in value since the last time. Hilde arranged driving lessons for me and I invested some of my money in a lovely little Volkswagen cabriolet; white with a dark red hood, just as I had promised myself. I passed my driving test and got my licence and from then on, I made regular trips at the weekend, motoring ever further, exploring the countryside and visiting small towns and villages. My English friends wangled cheap petrol coupons for me and would often accompany me on my little outings.

One evening, I had walked round to the German cinema and saw a couple of British soldiers looking at the posters which were pretty saucy, it was apparent that they couldn't understand the captions below them.

I translated for them. They thanked me and said they would give it a miss and go to the AKC (Army Kinema Corporation. The Cinemas were all called "The Globe") instead. I stood, unable to make up my mind, bored.

Suddenly, a very cultured English voice enquired,

"Are you going to see it?"

I turned to see a distinguished looking man, in his early fifties, dressed immaculately in civilian clothes and I replied,

"No, I don't think so. I think I'll go for a drink instead."

"I hope you won't think me forward, but I should be delighted if you would care to join me, it's not much fun drinking alone, is it?" he said.

I accepted his offer and we went to the cocktail bar in the Four Seasons.

He introduced himself saying, "Dr Hans Joachim Lement, I'm very pleased to make your acquaintance, Miss?"

He raised his eyebrows enquiringly.

"Janni Kowalski," I supplied and continued, "You surprise me, I thought you were English."

He laughed and said,

"I only addressed you in English because I heard you speaking to those soldiers. When I heard you, I thought you must be English. You have no trace of an accent and although I speak it well myself, I can tell the real thing when I hear it."

"Don't be fooled," I said in German and continued speaking in that language, watching the surprise on his face.

He smiled and said,

"My word, you are a very accomplished linguist aren't you."

We shared a bottle of Sekt and he said,

"No strings attached, I only live a short distance from here and I should deem it an honour if you would take supper with me. We can listen to some music, have another drink or two and then I'll escort you safely to your doorstep. Would you like to do that?"

With only a moment's hesitation I smiled and said,

"That sounds delightful. How could I possibly refuse so gracious an invitation."

We took a taxi the short distance to his splendid first floor flat, which was lavishly furnished. Valuable artefacts stood in little alcoves and expensive paintings adorned the walls. I wondered how it was that so many of these Germans appeared to have been totally unaffected by the war and oozed opulence and self-confidence while others, who had no doubt served their country, as evidenced by the fact that a great many still wore their old army jackets or overcoats, struggled to make a livelihood.

He produced typical German Abendbrot, a supper of mixed salads, prawns, meat, sausage, unsalted butter and apart from the main loaf, packets of pumpernickel and vollkornbrot and a carton of quark, cottage cheese. We drank tea without milk from beautiful, shallow, china cups with Beethoven's Pastoral as background music. It was very civilised.

He cleared the table and from a cabinet, collected two monstrous, crystal brandy balloons into which he poured two equally monstrous measures of Asbach Uralt, setting one on an occasional table beside an armchair and indicating that I should sit there. He offered me an English cigarette and, when I declined, courteously sought my permission to smoke.

The brandy was fairly good, just a little rough round the edges and in the comfortable surroundings, suitably replete, I foolishly accepted a refill. If anything, it was very much larger than the first and although, under normal circumstances I have a very good tolerance to alcohol, on this occasion, it was going to my head very quickly.

He got up, went over to a bureau and brought back a photograph album then he handed it to me to look through. The photos started off innocently enough. First, there were a number of shots, obviously pre-war, of groups of friends. In them, he always appeared in civilian clothes while many of his colleagues were in uniform, mostly high-ranking officers, among them, well known SS generals. It came as a great shock to me when, among this notorious hierarchy and obviously on intimate terms with all of them was the unmistakable figure of a well known member of the royal family of a European country, who happened to be our allies during the war and when I commented on this, he confirmed that they had been friends for many years. I wondered if, when he was head of their government in exile in London, the British government had known of these connections. The mind boggles.

The rest of the photos were of an obscene nature, involving boys and girls. Boys together or with men, girls together or with men, individual couples having intercourse or group orgies. He was taking part in most of the activities as were many of the members in the earlier photos and it was immediately apparent that all of them had been filmed in this very room.

I was speechless and quite frightened, but determined not to show it, I mustered enough courage, laughed and said,

"My word, you do believe in enjoyment on a grand scale, don't you?"

He chuckled and said,

"Yes, I do and I have a confession to make. I was sure it was you when I saw you earlier this evening. You used to play the piano and sing in the Monocle bar, didn't you and you're not really a girl either, are you?"

I was shocked, but he didn't even appear to notice as he continued,

"The prince is coming to stay with me over the weekend and it would be perfect if you and one of your young friends could come and join us."

My head was spinning but I managed to say,

"You haven't given me much notice. I'm not sure whether I can organise a friend in time, but write down your telephone number for me, I'll see what I can arrange and give you a ring."

"Splendid. Splendid," he repeated.

I stood up, glad that my unsteady feeling had not yet found its way to my legs and said,

"You really will have to excuse me now. I'm very tired and I've an early start in the morning. You've been a wonderful host and it's been a very enjoyable evening. Next time promises to be even more interesting." I added with a lazy smile.

To my relief, he didn't argue. He donned his overcoat, escorted me down to the street with one steadying hand on my elbow and hailed a passing taxi. He was about to climb in with me when I said,

"You don't have to come with me, it only means a double journey for you." I closed the door firmly, opened the window and said,

"I'll ring you tomorrow and thanks again for a lovely evening."

I wound up the window before giving the driver his instructions.

By the time I'd climbed the stairs to my little flat, I was almost peeing myself with relief and laughter and barely made it to the loo.

Several strong, black coffees later, I fell asleep in the chair and awoke the next morning with a stiff neck, one arm completely devoid of feeling, a foul taste in my mouth and a thumping headache.

I cleaned my teeth for a long time then stood under the shower for ages, feeling dirty, and gradually reduced the temperature until I was shivering. I wrapped myself in a big bath sheet, lovely and warm, straight from the airing cupboard, slid my feet into my slippers and headed for the kitchen, clutching a bottle of aspirins.

Tea, the saviour of mankind! In no time at all, I was ready to face the world again!

I didn't tell Hilde what had happened, not because she was prudish or anything like that, on the contrary, she'd have found the whole thing hilarious, but because I was incensed that this horrible bastard had honestly imagined that I should welcome the chance to take part in his filthy games with his illustrious friends and I intended to teach him a lesson. The fewer people who knew about it, the better.

At lunchtime, I drove out to the Hamburg Transit Camp, an enormous barracks used to accommodate vast numbers of soldiers on their way to other destinations or waiting for postings. Among the contingents temporarily stationed there were a number of semi permanent staff, both English and Canadian. Amongst the latter contingent was an enormous guy of Polish origin. A very hard, lumberjack type who really had a severe crush on me, the other good side was that he absolutely detested Germans and sought any excuse to beat the hell out of them. I managed to get a message through to him and he came to meet me at the gate. Once in his company, he took me to his mess and he was highly amused when I declined his offer of a drink and in stitches after I had related the events of the previous night.

"What do you want me to do?" he asked.

"Come with me as my friend on Saturday, in civvies of course, and we'll speak Polish and German only, I don't want them to know you are Canadian. We'll drink their booze and then it's up to you to do your usual demolition act," I replied.

"Great. Can't wait," he enthused.

I rang the Doktor that evening and told him I could bring a friend on Saturday, prepared to stay the weekend, but we shouldn't be able to get there until about nine-thirty in the evening.

He was very excited, asked what my friend liked to drink and could my friend please bring a pair of tight fitting, brief shorts!

As arranged, we arrived at the Doktor's flat just after nine-thirty. There were vases of white carnations everywhere and the heady, clove-like scent filled the air.

I won't go into too much detail, but after several very large drinks while we watched a disgusting blue film, my friend suddenly stood up, picked up the nearest valuable artefact and threw it straight through the window, without bothering to open it first, following up quickly with several more such items. Then, he turned his attention to the paintings, tearing them off the walls, putting his foot right through the middles and hurling them into the street below. Everything portable went the same way, including most of the furniture through the completely shattered window frame.

Because the Doktor knew me, we had arranged that I should shout at my friend to stop, try to restrain him and be brushed aside. I acted my part very well so did my friend, too well, and I sustained a black eye. Finally, my friend (I've deliberately refrained from mentioning his name for obvious reasons) grabbed the Doktor by the throat and for one awful moment, I thought he was going to follow his possessions through the window. Instead, he held him at arm's length with one hand, shouted a stream of abuse at him in a mixture of Polish and German and proceeded to flatten him with a single blow, so powerful that I expected to see his head fly from his shoulders.

He turned to the other guest and said,

"You. Piss off back to your own country you bloody pervert and don't ever cross my path again or I'll kill you." As an afterthought he added,

"And you Janni, I thought more highly of you. You can piss off too before I beat the shit out of you." I ran out of the building to a prearranged spot where he joined me some ten minutes later.

We laughed like hell and went, arm in arm into a Bierstube for a drink.

Inside, he saw my rapidly swelling eye and his face changed dramatically.

"Oh shit Janni, I'm so very sorry. I didn't mean to hurt you," he said, looking terribly worried.

"It's O.K, you couldn't help it, I just got in the way. Besides, it adds authenticity to my claim, should it become necessary, that I tried to stop you but couldn't prevent it." I reassured him and for fun, I added, "You're so strong, you big brute. Now come and kiss it better."

He rolled about laughing and said,

"You really are an absolute bastard to me and you know that I would do anything for you." I heard nothing more about this incident, which was hardly surprising considering the identity of the guest. To prosecute would have meant calling him as a witness and the attendant publicity would have ruined him.

CHAPTER FIFTY-EIGHT

On the Sunday, I drove out to Glckstadt to have lunch with a couple of friends from the Monocle Bar.

We sat, overlooking the Elbe, the warm sun wonderfully relaxing as I hid my black eye behind enormous sunglasses and heavier than usual make-up.

Sitting back sipping my wine and watching the ships in the river, I hadn't a care in the world.

Suddenly, very tentatively, Uschi, one of my friends said,

"I hope you are not going to be cross with us, but Jutta and I have invited a friend." She turned and waved as Emil appeared and walked rather shamefacedly and hesitantly towards us.

He looked suntanned and very fit and my heart skipped several beats. To spare his obvious embarrassment, I stood up, walked over to him and linked my arm through his, announcing to everyone,

"What a wonderful surprise. How can I ever thank you."

Everyone relaxed and Jutta said,

"Before we have lunch, Uschi and I have to do a little shopping. We shan't be long. You will excuse us won't you." and without waiting for a reply, they got up and left.

"God Emil, this was all so obvious. All you had to do was telephone," I said, brushing my hand over his.

"I wanted to but I was afraid you would put the 'phone down and that would have hurt so much. I couldn't face the probability of rejection," he replied honestly and continued,

"I'm desperately in love with you Janni, you must know that and I'm sorry I let my feelings get out of control. Will you please forgive me and come out with me again. Please Janni."

"Yes Emil, I can't think of anything that I'd like better, but it will have to be on my terms. I'm not going to go through any more abuse, distrust, name-calling, mental torment or anything else for that matter. Love is about more than just sex. Love is not about owning the other person. Love is about trust and respect and never doing anything to harm the other either mentally or physically. Love is about tolerance, caring, listening to the other's point of view. It is not about raised voices, tempers and threats of violence. It's about lots of things, but that is enough to be going on with and if you let me down on any of them. It will be finished for good this time. Is that clear?"

I think he wondered if my list of conditions was ever going to stop. In a very subdued manner, he answered,

"Yes, that's clear enough and I fully understand why you want these reassurances. I did behave abominably and I promise to make it up to you."

"I don't play at the club any more, the girls probably told you that, although from time to time I do a spot at the Kaskade to help out in an emergency. This means that all my evenings are entirely my own. However, this doesn't mean that I shall go out with you every night. Initially, we should have a few dates and if you come back to the flat, you can't stay the night. You'll have to go home. Saturdays may be the exception, but you will have to go home on Sunday. I hate imposing these conditions, but I have to be sure. We don't want to hurt each other like that again, do we?"

"I'll agree to any conditions, anything at all. I'd almost convinced myself that I couldn't live without you and one of my pals became so worried about me that he took me away sailing for a couple of weeks, hence the suntan."

He looked at me with such obvious longing and said,

"For God's sake Janni, I can't wait. May I kiss you now? Please."

I thought, "I need my head examining" as I went and sat on his knee, put my arms round his neck and set about some serious kissing.

I'd taken my sunglasses off and he noticed my swollen and discoloured eye. There was nothing for it but to explain. I didn't tell him that in the first instance I had agreed to go home with a man who had virtually picked me up in the street and how naive and trusting I had been. Instead, I implied that I knew of the Herr Doktor's SS connections and engineered the meeting myself.

Emil was both alarmed and amused, particularly when I described the part where my friend had ripped a washbasin from the bathroom wall and hurled it through the shattered window, leaving hot and cold water spraying from the ruptured pipes.

We all had lunch in good spirits after I had told the girls they were forgiven for their duplicity. In fact it was a very enjoyable afternoon and with the tension out of the way, everyone was very witty and we laughed a lot. As evening approached, Jutta asked Emil how he had travelled here to which he replied that he had come by train and wasn't too sure of the return train times.

"Its not far down the coast road. I'll take you home to Blankenese," I volunteered.

He hadn't known about my little car and was suitably impressed with the car and the fact that I had obtained my driving licence.

"You never cease to amaze me," He said as he climbed in beside me, "You really are quite wonderful."

We said our farewells to Jutta and Uschi who were going on elsewhere and I drove slowly, hood down, enjoying the evening air.

On arrival at his home, he invited me in.

"Just for a few minutes," I responded

His mother said," Hello dear, how lovely to see you again. We have missed you haven't we Klaus. His father stood up and I went over and offered him my cheek which he kissed saying,

"My, it's so good to see you again Liebchen, I swear you're prettier than when we saw you last."

I did a little curtsy and said,

"Thank you kind Sir and may I say that you are looking as handsome as ever."

"You know just the right things to say to the silly old fool," Emil's mother chortled.

We all laughed and Emil, almost pleadingly said,

"Can you stay long enough for a drink?"

"I'd love a cup of coffee if it's not too much trouble, nothing stronger."

Eventually, I stood, thanked Emil's parents for their hospitality and with their sincere invitations to 'come again soon' following me, Emil escorted me to the car.

We kissed for a few minutes, then I started the motor, said, "Ring me tomorrow evening after six", let in the clutch and drove home very thoughtfully, wondering all the time if I had done the right thing.

The following morning, I went to the boutique as usual still harbouring a few misgivings about Emil, but excited at the same time.

Hilde commented on my excitement and I told her what had transpired. She exploded, "Mein Gott Kindchen, bist du verrckt oder wass!" (My God child, are you mad or what!). She threw her hands up in despair and continued,

"Just look at you. You've only seen him again for a couple of hours and already you've got a black eye!" She must have thought her suspicions as to my mental state were confirmed when I burst into hoots of laughter and once again I had to explain. So much for my intended secrecy!

She laughed along with me but cautioned,

"I hope you know what you are doing Liebchen but please, tread very carefully. I know how much you were hurt last time and I can't bear the thought of it happening again. You're far too nice and you deserve to be treated better." She hugged me to her in a very motherly way and said, "Let's go and have a drink."

CHAPTER FIFTY-NINE

Emil must have been impatiently counting the hours because he rang me a few seconds after six o'clock. I arranged to meet him at eight o'clock in a nice bar near Planten und Blumen, the Botanical Gardens which was only a short distance away. It had the additional advantage of being a couple of minutes walk from Dammtor Bahnhof from whence he could take the train home. He implored me not to eat too much since he wanted to treat me to supper at any place of my choice. I agreed, hung up and set about making myself look as devastating as possible.

I hated nail varnish and spent hours buffing my nails and shaping them with emery boards. They were not too long and I never shaped them to a point, or even rounded them since it was easier playing the piano to have them square. My hands had always been small and my wrists very slim. Anything but the tiniest of watches looked ridiculous and I hated chunky bracelets or bangles. I had bought a delicate little cocktail watch, three fine gold bracelets, a fine chain necklace with an opal and diamond pendant and an opal ring. Nothing looked ostentatious.

The current fashions were either dresses with very full skirts and narrow waists or with very slim, pencil line skirts. I wore the latter in cream, sleeveless, with a coffee coloured belt, a silk scarf in autumn colours and a loose, buttonless camel jacket with deep, sloping pockets. Cream and tan stilettos a matching shoulder bag and gloves finished the whole ensemble. My hair always lightened in the summer and since I liked it like that, I'd knocked off work early and had some blonde streaks and highlights added. I looked at my reflection in the long mirror, the offending eye was no longer swollen and some stage make-up had done an excellent job of covering the discolouration.

Satisfied, I stuffed my bag with the usual collection of unnecessary rubbish, locked the flat and walked the short distance to the bar. I arrived at about five past eight and Emil was pacing up and down impatiently outside. Through my sunglasses, he looked even more suntanned and he was immaculately turned out in a beautifully cut beige suit, which set off his athletic figure to perfection. He looked very handsome indeed.

His eyes lit up when he saw me and he said,

"Wow! You look like a million dollars and you're surely the sexiest thing on two legs."

We gave each other a brief peck and he escorted me inside.

We sat in a little, intimate alcove and Emil ordered my favourite Deinhard Sekt, Brut.

He poured for us and after returning the bottle to the ice bucket, he held my hand and kept telling me how beautiful I was. He was in raptures over my outfit and regarded my mop of hair in wonder. I loved every minute of it!

I had decided to get something out of the way right at the start because I knew that sooner or later he was bound to ask me, knowing him, he wouldn't be able to stop himself, so I said,

"There's something I want you to know before we go any further. Two things actually."

I had his undivided attention and I continued,

"First, I've been on my own ever since you left. There has been no one else; I haven't so much as gone out on a date with another man during all the time I have known you. (It wasn't strictly true. I had gone out a number of times with Michael, the staff sergeant but I hadn't gone beyond kissing with him although I have to confess, I almost let the situation get out of hand.).

Second, apart from Alex, there has never been anyone else but you and that sergeant who provoked such jealousy was instrumental in getting us together again. I had told him everything about you and our relationship and how I owed my life to you. But for his intervention and machinations, I'd still be in the MSLO doing guard duties. If you had waited for a few seconds before flying off the handle, you would have found yourself being thanked, congratulated on your just release from internment and you'd have made a very good friend. Instead, your behaviour on that occasion negated all that I had said in praise of you. I'd been so proud of you and loved you and I wanted you to share my friend's admiration and respect. When and if I introduce you to any more of my friends, and you have to accept that they will probably give me a hug and a kiss, you must not start imagining all sorts of wild goings on. Once again I repeat, apart from Alex, there has not only never been anyone else, I've never wanted anyone else and I hope that in future you'll not let your wild imagination run riot. That is all I intend to say on the subject. Where are you going to take me for supper?"

He had remained silent throughout my diatribe, his face, half grin, half hangdog, nodding his head in agreement.

He looked up and smiled that smile which always got to me and said,

"I said I'd let you choose but I know a little place along the river where we can have wonderful lobsters and all the trimmings, what is more, they have an amazing cellar. What do you think?"

"Sounds great so long as I can have a very large napkin. This dress shows up every little blemish," I agreed

"It also shows off every little curve of your figure too. I'll swear you are not wearing a bra. Christ, I could forget the lobster and eat you." he said, adopting a deliberately menacing pose and growling like an animal.

This was not going as I had planned. It had been my intention to keep the sex bit at bay and here I was thinking,

"To hell with the bloody lobster, let's go home to bed. Now!"

To regain control of my wandering mind, I excused myself and headed for the toilet, you may tell how confused I was, for although I had lived as a girl ever since leaving Osnabrck, I walked into the gent's toilet, said "Oh! Sorry. Wrong door," to the line of men, peeing into the urinals, heads bowed as though awaiting execution, and beat a hasty retreat.

We finished the bottle of Sekt and headed out onto the street hand in hand. I knew I was being a fool, but here I was going all potty over him again.

He hailed a cab, gave directions to the driver and we drove for about fifteen minutes to his quaint little riverside lobster bar.

The atmosphere was fantastic and it was apparent from the happiness of other couples and the undivided attention they were giving to their lobsters with an assortment of special tools, that the food was every bit as good as Emil had promised. A cheerful, fat man played an accordion French style and the delicate smell of herbs and a hint of garlic pervaded the air. Lautrec posters were pasted on the walls at odd angles, strings of large, brown onions hung from the rafters and although the place was spotlessly clean, nothing had seen a coat of paint in years. It was brilliant.

As Emil had enthused, the wine list was very impressive and he chose for both of us, a fabulous, chilled, crisp Chablis which must have cost an arm and a leg.

With his confidence returning in leaps and bounds, he proceeded to order for both of us. Crevettes in garlic, butter and parsley with a hint of Pernod, served in little cast-iron pannikins on heavy wooden boards, chunks of lemon and bread for dunking. Emil didn't mess about. He tucked his large napkin into his collar and set about them with gusto. I hadn't a suitable collar on my dress so the waiter came over with a little clip and fastened my napkin at the back of my neck.

Conversation came to a halt except for expressions of pure pleasure as we devoured the superb fare. A dip in the finger bowl, blot the lips and guzzle some of the excellent Chablis. I complimented Emil on his choice, reached across the table and held his hand.

He was completely relaxed, very happy and his conversation was witty and entertaining.

"If only it could be like this for ever", I thought.

A whole lobster each and another bottle of wine, the pair of us cracking, tugging, poking in total abandon until even a flock of ravenous, well trained vultures could not have found a solitary edible morsel. After a lengthy pause, there was the most wicked, coffee, chocolate and walnut torte over which Emil poured a full measure of Tia Maria and passed the bowl of whipped cream for my attention. I felt indecently gluttonous, savouring every delicious forkful, finally sitting back, barely able to move. Bliss!

The place was extremely popular and people were waiting for tables so we took our coffee and brandies into a delightful little, glassed-in terrace and contentedly looked out over the sparkling reflections of the river.

I broke the silence, although I could just as easily have broken wind, by saying,

"Thank you Emil, that was the most wonderful meal I have ever eaten and I must say it's a great improvement on the scraps of bread and sausage you used to fob me off with in return for my favours."

He roared with laughter, said,

"Hell yes, you were much cheaper then."

We both laughed and felt extremely close in our shared memories.

He settled the bill, held my coat for me and said,

"Come on, it's getting late. I'd better take you home."

I hadn't intended it to happen but when we got to my flat, I didn't want the night to end. I invited him in, one thing led to another and he stayed the whole night. So much for my resolve!

CHAPTER SIXTY

Over the next few months we saw each other nearly every day and he usually stayed Wednesday nights and weekends. As the winter set in, he took me to Bavaria, we shared the driving with snow chains on the wheels of my little car, stayed in a lovely chalet hotel which looked like an oversized cuckoo clock, ate rich food and drank gallons of Glhwein.

He taught me to ski, which was very exciting, and on the specially prepared frozen area near the village centre he introduced me to ice-skating. I never was very good at it and left to my own devices, fell frequently. But, with arms crossed behind us, holding hands, it was brilliant and I could be guided round the crackling surface to the Viennese music blaring from the strategically placed loudspeakers. We would return from these exertions, faces glowing, to an enormous fire where we stood, warming our bottoms while drinking the spiced, hot wine.

I took to the life very easily.

Emil was a man transformed. All the previous petulance, anger and jealousy were nowhere in evidence, as if they had never existed., even when I danced with fellow guests, often being held so tightly that my tits nearly popped out of my dress. He was caring, attentive and solicitous without overdoing it and he made me laugh a lot. One night I persuaded him to play a duet with me and he was surprisingly good. After that, we played regularly together, frequently accompanied by members of the little village band. The most memorable evening was when some of the village men turned up, all appropriately attired and did some 'Knuppel' dancing, fighting mock battles with short sticks and slapping their 'lederhosen' and the sides of their boots as they danced. Then there was some amazing yodelling. I never knew it was possible to yodel in harmony!

They followed up by blowing in glorious, rich harmonies on Alpen horns, varying in length from two to five metres. It was obviously pre-arranged, but as our horn players finished, another group across the valley struck up, filling the intervening valley with sounds so beautiful they brought a lump to the throat.

Emil held me very close as I listened in awe and afterwards told me that I looked just like a little child who had just been to fairyland. If at first, he was the one who had been besotted, now, it was my turn, I was madly in love with him.

His parents and sisters loved me too and I spent a lot of time at their house, the only trouble was, they kept hinting that we ought to think about getting married!!

Emil was very conscious of the fact that in some situations I was still very claustrophobic and never argued if I said I needed to be on my own for a day or two. He knew that he wasn't even to 'phone me on these occasions and it was left to me to make the first call.

I was quite well off by now and through my army connections and being almost accepted as English, while still in Osnabrck, Michael, the English staff sergeant had wangled a NAAFI pass for me and had arranged for me to be able to exchange some of my marks into BAFSVs, a special currency for the British servicemen and their families. I think it stood for British Armed Forces Special Vouchers. Armed with these, I bought most of my luxury foods, spirits, coffee and cigarettes, at ridiculously low prices and although I preferred to buy coffee beans and grind them freshly each time, there was a great demand for tins of Lyons Ground coffee, Nescafe and cigarettes. German cigarettes were appalling, foul-smelling things and I have to confess to doing a roaring trade in cigarettes, cigars and tinned coffee which netted a very nice income. Several people were caught by the Military Police Special Investigation Branch and prosecuted, but somehow or other my activities went undetected.

I still worked with Hilde and loved it. She was delighted with the way things had worked out and became very fond of Emil. One day she confessed to me that if she had been a bit, actually she meant a whole lot, younger, she would not have minded having her slippers under his bed.

My hunting activities had trailed off, not through lack of determination, but because the authorities persisted in avoiding any issues other than those directly involving British Nationals on the grounds that they had no recourse in law to prosecute foreign nationals for crimes committed against other foreign nationals outside the United Kingdom and it's dominions. It was a very convenient way of avoiding contentious issues.

I still handed over the results of my searches to the appropriate authorities while simultaneously passing the same information to my Jewish friend. Needless to say, some 'accidents' continued to occur and after one particularly nasty 'accident,' I finally ceased my campaign. I liked far too many German people to maintain this hatred.

By the summer of nineteen forty-eight, as far as I knew, I had just turned twenty-two, but felt as though I had lived for a hundred years. Emil was thirty-three, he'd passed all his exams and was becoming quite successful. He still lived at home with his parents and had bought himself a smart DKW Sonderklasse, (Auto Union, later to become Audi) which he used to travel to and from his office each day. When he stayed with me, he parked it in our underground garage. It was more economical than mine, it purred along and was a pleasure to drive.

We had a fortnight's holiday, not staying in any one particular place, but travelling somewhere different each day, staying some nights in quaint little hotels, other nights in more opulent establishments. It was a very happy time except for the last three days when I contracted a throat infection and caught a tummy bug, which seemed to cause the dreaded dysentery to recur. I became very ill and Emil insisted on taking me straight home.

Fortunately, we had been on a circular tour and were not too far from Hamburg. Once in the flat, he put me to bed and because I had shivering fits, he collected some hot water bottles and tucked them in with me. He stayed to look after me, making me hot drinks. I couldn't manage any food. If I tried, within seconds I was vomiting. He was so tender, so caring and so worried, I think he hardly slept. The doctor called twice a day and despite all his ministrations and potions, my throat wouldn't clear up and I was becoming weak through my inability to take food. I could just about manage the thinnest of broths and Hilde, fussing like an old hen, came in morning and night to give Emil a break. Sometimes, to give him a full night's sleep, she would pack him off home and stay the night herself.

I wasn't improving and was losing weight at an alarming rate, the doctor became so concerned that he had me transferred to hospital by ambulance. By now, I was convinced that I had cancer. My colour was awful, a greyish-yellow, reminiscent of those hopeless wraiths in Belsen and my bones were showing through everywhere. In hospital, they pumped me full of antibiotics and a whole cocktail of other drugs for a period of about eight weeks. They fed me through a drip and I had tubes firmly implanted in arms and ankles. Gradually, they got everything under control and I was able to eat in the normal way. They kept me in for another month on a very strict, special diet and I had to take exercises every day to build up my strength again, all the time I was having a cocktail of tablets and injections twice per day. Finally, after three months in hospital, they allowed Emil to take me home.

His mother had insisted that he take me to Blankenese and I only agreed when Emil promised me that under no circumstances would he let his mother help me in the bath! Two weeks of his mother's cooking, morning walks with his father and evening walks with Emil and I was as good as new, or so I thought.

CHAPTER SIXTY-ONE

I had no more throat problems and I could eat like a horse, so much so in fact that imperceptibly at first, I began to put on weight and I was noticing other slight changes, the doctors had told me to keep on taking the medicines they had prescribed and that there could be possible side effects of weight gain but that I shouldn't worry about it. I didn't at first. After the party on New Year's Eve I had kicked off my shoes while dancing because they had begun to hurt my feet and many hours later I couldn't get them on again. I thought my feet were swollen from too much dancing and never gave it a second thought. After a good sleep and a shower, I found that whatever shoes I tried were so tight that it was impossible to walk in them and I could have sworn my hands were slightly larger. Concerned, I took my robe off and examined myself very critically in the mirror.

My breasts had shrunk considerably when I was in hospital and, while the rest of my body had put on weight, these had not returned to their former glory, if any thing, they had become smaller. Worse, my testicles had become larger and I was aware that the timbre of my voice was deeper but I had put this down to the seriousness of my throat infection. I dressed and quite inappropriately, put on a pair of open evening sandals to walk through the slush to the nearest shoe shop. The assistant measured my feet and I was nearly half a size larger. I bought two pairs of shoes and went to confide in Hilde.

In one of the changing cubicles, I stripped down to my knickers and Hilde set about measuring me. She confirmed my worst fears. I had gained over two and a half centimetres in height, nearly eight centimetres round the waist and about four centimetres round the hips and breasts. In the latter department, the overall increase was across my back whereas the cup size of my bra was considerably decreased. I was frantic. I had loved my body and now it appeared that some unwanted transformation was taking place.

Without telling Emil I made an appointment with the doctor to whom I expressed my concern and asked what, if anything, could be done about it. He admitted to being totally baffled and made an appointment for me with a specialist. I didn't have to wait too long and after examination, the specialist asked,

"I hope you don't mind, but I should like one of my colleagues to take a look at you with your permission?"

"I'll see anyone if they can help to put it right. I hate what is happening to me," I replied.

"Just sit there for a moment. I shan't be very long, " he said, indicating his examination couch.

After about ten minutes, he returned with his colleague, a female who turned out to specialise in paediatrics. She examined me from every angle and tapped me all over with a reflex mallet. She asked,

"Apart from feeling concerned, are you experiencing any other problems?"

I told her that I ached all over and my joints were often quite painful and worst of all, I was developing an Adam's apple. She just nodded and the two of them exchanged glances. She looked back at me and said,

"I've arranged for you to have a series of X-Rays, then we'll do it all again in two months time and I'll be able to give you a better idea of what is happening."

She took me to the X-Ray department, waited until they were completed and after I had dressed, she said,

"There is your card with your next appointment pencilled in. Between now and then, on this second card, keep a daily record of your weight, all your measurements and anything else about yourself that you may notice or feel."

I thanked her and asked,

"Have you any idea what is causing this?"

She thought hard for a minute and said,

"I'm not one hundred percent sure at the moment and until I have seen your X Rays and done a comparison with the next ones I'd rather not commit myself without confirmation of my suspicions."

"Can't you give me some inkling? I really am worried to death," I pleaded.

"Very well. But at this stage, it's only an educated guess, no more you understand. I think, and I stress that I only think, that what might have happened is that something in the treatment you received during your lengthy stay here last year has triggered your masculine growth metabolism which had somehow become arrested and lain dormant. Now, much later in life than is normal, you are suddenly starting to grow to your full potential. If I'm right, the whole growth process will take anywhere from two to four years. Your voice will become deeper, your genitals become larger, your breasts will disappear and your facial hair will grow.

To avoid these aches and pains, you'll have to do a special series of exercises on a regular basis and these will also help with the development of your muscles, which will have to keep pace with your overall growth rate. That is as much as I can tell you and I must emphasise that as of this moment, it is only a well educated guess."

I drove home very depressed. I didn't want to change. I hated the thought of becoming a man and all that it entailed. I wanted to stay as I had been, but knew that it was impossible. My idyllic life was coming to an end and I didn't know how I was going to cope with the lengthy transition, or even if I wanted to. Sooner or later, I was going to have to start dressing as a man; short hair, flat shoes, suit, collar and tie. I felt suicidal.

How many more times was my life and happiness going to crumble around me? I undressed, put on my robe and a pair of slippers, sat down and examined my hands. It was extremely difficult to take my ring off and once off, it was even more difficult to remove Becca's wedding ring to me, my beloved piece of string. I had never taken it off and always wore it under my other rings. Reluctantly, I worked it off, determined not to cut it and in doing so, made my finger very sore. I placed the string in a little locket and put it under my pillow.

I poured a large brandy and sat with my feet tucked under me considering a future as a full-blown man, without Emil or any of my lovely circle of friends. It was too distressing to contemplate and I just sat, staring out over the Alster without the will to do anything.

I heard the key in the lock and Emil came in. I had intended to 'phone him to tell him not to come this evening, but I had sat doing nothing unaware how quickly the time had passed and now it was too late.

He came over, kissed me and said

"Hi darling. What sort of day have you had?"

I started to cry.

He was so solicitous, so caring, so loving that it made everything worse. I hadn't wanted to tell him yet, without trying to think everything through but I knew that there wasn't any point in putting it off. His reactions to my awful disclosures should give me some idea of whether or not we would have any kind of future together.

I poured it all out, omitting nothing and when I had finished, I got up, poured him a large brandy and refilled my own glass.

He put the glass on the table, took mine from my hands and held both of my hands very firmly as he looked into my eyes and said,

"You poor, poor Darling. What a dreadful shock for you. I know how much you love being 'Janni', how much you love the way you have chosen to live and the lifestyle you have created for yourself. I can't say that it hasn't come as a shock to me, but I don't see why this should change things between us. I'll always love you, no matter what and after all, it's not going to happen overnight, is it?"

I thought hard, reluctant to question his belief in our future, because in doubting his sincerity, I would be confirming by own bleak view of the life that lay in store for me, but in an act of pure masochistic stupidity, I said,

"Emil, I know how much you love me, and have done for six years, but be honest, it was only because I was so different. You have always told me how beautiful I am, what a wonderful body I have and how delightfully feminine I am. But these are all physical characteristics and they are all about to change. You must have noticed that it's already begun. My whole body will change; I shall probably finish up almost as tall as you and I'll have to shave and speak with a deep voice. You won't stop loving me all at once, but as the changes become more pronounced, you'll try to find ways to let me down as lightly as possible as you bring our relationship to a close."

He hugged me to him and said,

"Janni. Oh Janni. You are far more than just a wonderful body and pretty face. I was in love with you from the first day, before I had even seen your body. I always thought you knew that. When you revealed your unusual body to me, it was just a fantastic bonus. I know that eventually, you'll have to stop wearing dresses and from then on our behaviour in public will have to be very restrained, but nothing else need change. Please believe me darling."

I had thought about the differences too and I hated the idea of us not being able to display spontaneous little acts of love, as we so frequently did, wherever we happened to be, from a quick kiss to a friendly, playful smack on the bum. We wouldn't even be able to hold hands or give each other a reassuring hug. The prospect was abysmal. I said,

"I know you believe it now and I hope, desperately, that it works out for us. I shall wear dresses for as long as possible, but the moment people can tell at a glance that I'm not what I appear, I'll ditch the lot and buy some men's clothes.

"When I first came to Hamburg, I could wear a size eight, then after we got together and you started fattening me up I started to wear size ten, now I'm struggling to get into those. From now on, I'm just going to wear full skirts and blouses or jumpers otherwise it will become very expensive with frequent changes to my wardrobe. Eventually I'll have to give up my job with Hilde and when that happens, we'll have to find a new flat where people will only know me in my new identity."

I was relieved to have told him and by the reactions that he had to the startling news, but deep down, I already knew that it wouldn't last but it didn't prevent me from clutching at straws.

The next set of X-Rays, together with my card full of notes, confirmed the doctor's diagnosis and although I had expected it, the confirmation was nevertheless devastating.

I commenced my course of exercises and at the doctor's suggestion joined one of the martial arts schools, which were becoming popular. There were quite a few 'butch' females attending these classes and although not yet in that same category myself, it would probably save a great deal of embarrassment in this period of transition if I practised with them. I was still growing, quite rapidly in fact and within a year, my 'tits' of which I had been so proud, had virtually disappeared and muscles were now clearly definable all over my body, my voice was lower, but, as yet, the facial hair hadn't sprouted for which I was very grateful.

The growing and the exercises made me quite tired and I slept a great deal. Sadly, as predicted, Emil, his visits becoming less and less frequent and unable to make further excuses, finally left. I was alone again.

CHAPTER SIXTY-TWO

It was time to move. The flat I settled for was only a couple of miles away at the other end of the Alster, convenient for my continuing hospital visits, and in my negotiations, I had said that it was for my twin brother. The owner never queried it and I had all my possessions brought round in a van. Hilde was the only person who knew of my new address and telephone number and on the night I was to metamorphose into my twin, she brought one of her hairdresser friends round to give me a more masculine haircut. It was all very sad.

Hilde had been an absolute brick. She had taken all my measurements and bought a jacket, trousers, ties, socks, shoes and shirts with the option to go back to the shop and change them if they were wrong in any way.

I needn't have worried; she had impeccable taste and a very good eye for detail. The whole outfit fitted to perfection. Attired in my new clothes, I looked at myself in the mirror and began to cry. I vowed I would never do it again. It was, after all, most unmanly!

When I'd left the old flat, since I had wanted to remain anonymous for a time, Hilde had suggested that I give hers as a forwarding address.

Months had passed in the new flat when one day Hilde rang to say there was a letter for me from England. I drove round to collect it and became very excited when I recognised the signature. It was from my old sergeant friend, Tim, from Osnabrck days. It seems he had been to every Member of Parliament he could gain access to, written to innumerable Ministries and finally found someone in the Foreign Ministry who could tell him of all the enquiries received about missing relatives in the aftermath of the invasion of Poland. He had narrowed the possibilities down to three families.

One of these families had all perished during the London Blitz and he judged from my accent that it was unlikely that I had been brought up in the centre of Birmingham. This left a pretty village located about three or four miles from the sea on the west coast. He had not been there as he felt that to start making enquiries might only raise false hopes for the family concerned and he hoped that I would be able to go over to England, meet him and together we could see if the surroundings struck any chord in my memory.

I was glad of something to get my teeth into and I wrote back, telling Tim how delighted I had been to receive his letter and that to make travelling easier in England, I would bring my car over on the ferry and telephone him on arrival.

As an afterthought, I told him about my change of appearance in case he was looking for a pretty girl!

CHAPTER SIXTY-THREE

The journey to England was uneventful although the motion of the ship left me feeling pretty queasy. Once through customs and having picked up my car, I drove out of the dock gates where I was immediately stopped by a policeman and advised that I was driving on the wrong side of the road. I started to apologise in German, apologised a second time and spoke in English.

He was very understanding and helpful, saying 'it happens to lots of people' and gave me directions. I stopped at a filling station, bought an up to date road map and headed off inland to the small country town where Tim lived. It was about a three-hour drive and I had no difficulty in locating the little hotel, which he had recommended.

Tim had made a provisional booking and everything went very smoothly, I wasn't even asked for my passport, which was a blessing because it was a very ambiguous, temporary, German Reisepass which left more questions unanswered than was normal.

To my surprise, the telephone held no fears and I operated it with such ease, without reading the instructions that, at some time in the past, I must have done this many times.

Tim came round within twenty minutes of my call and notwithstanding the very obvious change in my overall size and appearance, he couldn't resist saying,

"Hiya beautiful, you look great." He gave me a big hug ordered drinks and we sat in a corner where he offered me a cigarette and was greatly surprised when I accepted, lit up, took a long pull at it and inhaled the smoke.

"Christ, I never expected to see that. How long have you been smoking?"

"About six months I suppose. It all helps to create the new image," I said with a laugh.

"Honestly Janni, you look great, certainly you have changed, but you still look very much younger than your years. By the way, how old are you now?"

"Twenty three or four I think" I replied and added, "but you probably noticed that I haven't started shaving yet. I've still got that dubious pleasure to come."

I told him everything that had happened since the last time we met and in turn, he brought me up to date about himself,

He had been out of the army for a couple of years, had married and already had a daughter and another child on the way. He worked as an independent insurance agent, covering everything, vehicles, mortgages, life policies, commercial insurance, you name it and he could find a policy to suit you. He had an office in town and employed a junior clerk and a secretary. He and his family lived in a little semi on the outskirts of the town and I was told that his wife had insisted that I should move in with them tomorrow for the duration of my stay. I asked him about Michael and he said,

"He left the conventional services as such about two years ago and as far as I know, he went into one of the more covert intelligence branches. He spends lots of time abroad and we only meet up every once in a while. That was why he passed on all your papers to me. He no longer had the time or permission to pursue your case."

"I should love to see him again, he was so kind and thoughtful and great company too." I said, suddenly full of memories of the happy times the three of us had spent together.

Tim smiled and said,

"I suppose you know that he was madly in love with you and that he had himself posted away from Osnabrck deliberately. He confided to me that he would be incapable of sustaining his resolve to keep everything between you on a purely business basis. It was the only way he could put temptation out of the way. Poor Michael."

It was the first I had heard of Michael's efforts to avoid me. I knew that he had fallen in love with me and, had it not been for my love for Emil, I could quite easily have fallen for him, in fact, if I'm really honest with myself, I probably loved him too, but I had to find out whether Emil had survived the war and if he still loved me before embarking on another intense relationship.

I pulled myself back to the present and answered,

"Yes, of course I knew that he loved me and I know I probably hurt him, but you loved me too and I loved you. Michael got hurt and hurt me also because, unlike you, he couldn't control his emotions so well."

Tim laughed and said,

"Let's face it, you were a bit of a dish and yes, I loved you very much, but in a different way, just as I do now. That's how it should be between such long-time pals isn't it?"

I agreed and we drank our drinks in silence for a while.

We browsed through all the assorted paperwork he had collected over the years and I realised he had spent a great deal of time and money researching on my behalf. I made a mental note to reimburse him in a way that would cause the least offence.

The next day, he came round after breakfast. I settled my bill and we left in my car. His house was delightful and his pretty wife made me feel like an old friend. Their daughter was a real sweety and we took to each other instantly. I enjoyed it immensely when uninvited, she climbed onto my knee and sat down, making herself very comfortable. Tim and Jane looked at each other, smiling, and Jane said,

"Susan's already made a new friend"

"And so have I" I replied.

After showing me to my room, which was very comfortable, Tim and I left in the car. Tim had a motorcycle onto which he intended to fit a sidecar. He had said that it would be much quicker on the bike, but I insisted that my clothing was totally unsuitable, particularly if it should rain.

We drove for about and hour and a half and on the way, we passed by a Military establishment with high wire fencing and rows of wooden barracks which made me shudder involuntarily. I couldn't get away quickly enough.

I recognised the village the instant I saw it and after saying "Oh Shit!" I drove straight to where I remembered one of the two village pubs was situated. In the car park I said to Tim, "You're a bloody marvel. This is it. Come on. I'll buy you a drink while we're deciding what to do."

We entered the pub and went to the bar. Tim asked me what I would like to drink and since I didn't like English beer and they didn't sell wine, I asked for a large brandy. Tim settled for a pint of bitter and we hoisted ourselves onto the bar stools, lit cigarettes and began asking questions of the lady who had served us.

"I' haven't been here for more than ten years," I began and having secured her attention, I continued,

"I suppose there have been plenty of changes during that time?"

"Not so's you'd notice." she replied, eyeing me up and down.

"Do the same family still live at the old hall?" I enquired

"Oh yes, they've been there since the year dot but the sister and her son were lost at the beginning of the war, somewhere in foreign parts as I remember and the younger boy went missing with quite a few other young boys when a plane being chased by Spitfires jettisoned it's bombs and one of them scored a direct hit on the scout hut. There's only the older boy now and his mother and father of course"

I thought she had finished, but she said,

"Why do you ask, do you know them then?"

"I used to know them very well, but it's a long time ago now," I responded.

She looked at me, examining in acute detail and said,

"You would only have been a very little one then, in fact I was minded to ask you if you were old enough to drink."

I laughed and said,
"I can assure you that I am. I'm twenty- four. Appearances can be deceptive you know."
Tim started to laugh and said,
"I can vouch for that, you should have seen him when he was nineteen!"
I didn't want to be reminded of that period of my life, not because I was ashamed of it, but because my happiness ceased when it came to an end.

We had another drink and moved away from the bar to discuss the next move. From every point of view it was unthinkable to drive up to the house and announce myself, I didn't even recognise the name Tim had found for me and who knows what the effect would have been on the remainder of the family.

Tim suggested that he should write to them outlining the circumstances and omitting details of this visit, impress upon them that at this stage, it was only a possibility and that they should not raise their hopes too highly.

I agreed with the proviso that we should drive to the house on some pretext or other, I would remain in the car while Tim addressed the occupants and tried to bring them outside so that I should be able to get a look at them.

He spoke German reasonably well after his long spell in that country and since my car bore German registration plates, he didn't have much difficulty in using the worst broken English I have ever heard in asking for directions and getting the people to move right outside to give directions with much gesticulating and pointing.

I couldn't recognise any of them.

We drove back to Leominster very thoughtfully.

I spent the next ten days travelling back and forth to my 'home' village and finding out as much as I could about the family history. Back to London and Somerset House to obtain copies of birth certificates for my mother and myself then on to Hatton Garden where I sold a diamond and an emerald, the return was much better than I had received in Germany, which was very pleasing.

Armed with suitable funds, I approached a garage in Leominster, picked out a lovely little Austin car and agreed two prices. The first would be reduced by the value of Tim's motorbike if he agreed to part with it. The second would be for cash without part exchange.

Tim was furious when I told him of my intentions and wouldn't hear of any talk of reimbursement. He made a wonderful suggestion, pointing out that as currency regulations were in force in England and I should not be able to take much money out with me, it would be better if he opened an account for me and invested my money in England so that when I came over next time, funds would be readily available. We set it all up and after another day, I set off on my return to Hamburg.

CHAPTER SIXTY-FOUR

I didn't know what I wanted to do. Although in certain situations I was (and still am) very claustrophobic, I had become a city dweller and the tiny village which had apparently been my home, held no attraction for me whatsoever. As far as I could ascertain, the social life amounted to a dance in the miniscule Village Hall every Saturday, another dance every third Wednesday in the village school. In each case, the 'orchestra', comprised piano and drums, or if funds ran to it, a saxophone or accordion too.

In season, a few well meaning people would give garden parties or galas at which, there were such wonderful, skilful attractions to test one's prowess as 'throwing the wellington', sticking the tail on the donkey or throwing wooden balls into angled, galvanised buckets. It made the attractions of Hamburg pale into insignificance!!

My final instructions to Tim were not to do anything further until he had heard from me. I felt a tremendous sense of relief to be back home in my own flat and immediately 'phoned Hilde to let her know that I was back. We arranged to meet for lunch the next day.

In the morning, I 'phoned all my black market contacts to take orders and arrange supplies. I was instantly back in the swing.

During lunch, Hilde listened without interruption as I told her about the results of my visit to England and expressed her surprise when I told her that I had recognised the village instantly, but could not remember any names or anything else of significance. She, like Tim, had hoped that once the gate had been opened, everything else would come rushing back to me. It didn't happen. I'd even visited the schools I had attended and although there was a certain familiarity, the visits did little to help. Then, I recognised one name.

I'd driven directly to the house and there, on a brass plate, was the name of my music teacher, where I had toiled, legs too short to reach the pedals, practising my scales, struggling to keep in time with the metronome as my skills improved and eventually, becoming very accomplished. I knew that I had begun my piano lessons when I was very young and without going inside, I could remember every detail of the music room. I even recognised my teacher, but made no approach.

When I finished my tale, Hilde said,

"Janni, I don't know whether I should tell you or not, but Emil came into the boutique the other day. He said he was desperate to see you. I told him you were in England and I had no idea if or when you would be coming back. He was very shaken and pleaded with me to let him know if I heard from you. He asked for your number but I refused to disclose it. He became quite frantic, insisting that he had to see you and when I asked him what it was that was so urgent, he just said, "Hilde, I still love him and miss him dreadfully and I can't get him out of my mind. He was very dejected."

My mind was in turmoil. I'd put him out of my life forever, or thought I had and now, all the old excitement came rushing back and I knew that my heart would rule my brain and I would be a complete idiot all over again.

Would I never learn to control these emotions of mine?

At home, I gave the matter my full attention. I was no longer petite little Janni with all bar one of the female attributes. Now, I was only about five centimetres shorter than Emil, the breasts had disappeared to be replaced by muscles. My whole body had filled out, feet and hands were much larger and everything else had increased in proportion. My voice was much deeper but, as yet, I still didn't have to shave. I hated all of it. All that was left was the pretty face, which made me look about seventeen. Certain men still showed a great deal of interest in me, but they left me cold. There had still been no one since Emil.

He had only ever seen me dressed in prison garb or dresses and he would be horrified to see me smoking. In reality, I only started to enhance the masculine image and I didn't really like them anyway. Stopping would not present a problem since I only smoked when I was out having a drink with friends and never more than two or three on those occasions.

For the first meeting, I decided that it would be better somewhere reasonably public and the bar of the Hotel Alsterhaus seemed as good a place as any since it was within a convenient distance for both of us.

I dialled his office number and waited to be put through. A pause, a click and the familiar voice

"Von Schulenburg. Who is calling please?" He sounded so formal and competent and I would have loved to see the expression on his face as I answered,

"Hello Emil, it's me, Janni. Hilde told me about your visit."

I could almost feel him shaking as he struggled for words and when he finally managed, they were not the nicest words I'd ever heard.

"You sound so different, I wasn't sure it was you," he stammered.

"I have changed quite a lot Emil," I said, waiting for some response and when there was none forthcoming, I continued,

"I know what you said to Hilde, but you haven't seen me for a long time so I thought it would be better if we meet, have a drink, get to know each other all over again and then see how we both feel. Does that make sense to you?"

"Sounds very sensible to me. Where had you in mind for this drink and at what time?" Emil asked excitedly.

"Well, you finish at about five-thirty so if you are not doing anything this evening, I'll see you in the bar of the Hotel Alsterhaus at six and by the way, you don't have to wait outside for me, I walk into bars on my own these days." I said jokingly.

"Oh that's great Janni, I'm really looking forward to seeing you. Sorry, I'm with a client and I must get on. Till six then. Bye."

I liked the cut of English men's clothes very much better than the German stuff, which, unless one paid the earth for it, was pretty shapeless, uninspiring and loaded with ghastly pleats in the backs of the jackets, more like a cross between a safari jacket and a two man tent than a serious fashion statement.

In England I had bought a beautiful mid grey suit with tapered trousers, single breasted hacking style jacket with slanting pockets, skirted waist, single vent in the back and hand stitching round the lapels and pocket flaps. I laid this out on the bed with a pink and white striped shirt, silver and darker pink tie and matching handkerchief and pale grey socks. The only concession to German fashion was a pair of soft grey casuals.

I spent ages in the shower, washed and dried my hair, which was probably a little too long. I hadn't been able to relinquish some last vestige of my former glory. I sat polishing my nails. It was still important and I liked them to look good.

Dressing took some time as I fiddled with my tie to get the knot exactly right and struggled with the cufflinks. Finally I spent ages obtaining the desired effect with the handkerchief in the top pocket, made sure that the right amount of cuff was showing and stood back and examined my reflection in the mirror. It looked like a very expensive, upper crust rent boy.

I was delighted with the result!!

CHAPTER SIXTY-FIVE

Emil was already there when I arrived and judging by the state of his glass, he'd been there some time. He stood up, broke into a huge smile and looked me up and down with a mixture of admiration and amazement. I almost forgot myself. Damn him. He always provoked this same reaction in me whenever he smiled like that.

Public place or not, I wanted to wrap myself around him. Instinctively, I knew that his thoughts were precisely the same.

Common sense prevailed and I ordered a glass of beer and a refill for Emil. We adjourned to a corner table and the moment we were seated, Emil reached out for my hands, thought better of it and said,

"You are still as beautiful as ever Janni. O.K., so you have changed quite a lot but your are still unmistakably Janni and I'll bet you turn heads wherever you go."

This sounded like a promising start and I responded, saying,

"I'm glad you like what you see, and although I have changed a great deal, I haven't been able to lose all my feminine mannerisms or my love of jewellery and if these things are going to cause you embarrassment in the future, it's as well if you say so now. They are so ingrained, so much a part of me that I doubt if I'll ever get rid of them entirely. Will that trouble you if we are in company?"

"Not at all, they add to your desirability." he said, with that damned smile again.

"You're sure they won't bring back too many reminders of how I used to be and leave you feeling cheated?" I asked, looking for reassurance.

"Don't be silly. Can't you tell that I'm having great difficulty in keeping my hands off you at this very minute?" he said and once again reached over to take my hands.

There was nobody paying attention so I took his outstretched hands in mine for a brief moment before relinquishing them and saying,

"Behave yourself and get me another drink please."

He called the waiter, and was about to order a bottle of Sekt when I stopped him. I'd already made up my mind on a course of action and I said,

"No Emil, let's leave the champagne till later and just have another beer for now."

"Fine by me," he said, with a quizzical look.

As soon as the waiter had left, I plunged straight in,

"Emil, let's eat here, have our champagne and then I'm going to break all my own rules."

"What rules are they?" he queried, one eyebrow raised.

"I had decided that I was not going to invite you to my flat until I was sure of you, but, how can I possibly be sure of anything until you've seen me with my clothes off. Just like I did all those years ago in your quarters, quite brazenly I might add, I want to take my clothes off in front of you and just as I could then, I shall be able to judge our chances from your reactions."

I didn't give him a chance to make any comment before continuing,

"There hasn't been anyone else in my life since you and I don't know what to expect now that I have changed so drastically. Everything is different now. Before, I never considered myself as a man, but now, I'll be a man, going to bed with another man and I'm not even sure what effect this will have on me, let alone you. You couldn't handle it before when I was changing before you eyes and this time, we both need to be one hundred percent sure before we embark on anything that is going to end in tears and acrimony. Does that make sense?"

He looked at me for quite a long time before replying,

"You've obviously given this a great deal of thought and I'm very encouraged because it's apparent that you really want it to work. So do I, more than you'll ever know and if we do as you say I'm sure it will work out."

"O.K. then, let's go and eat." I suggested.

The meal was nothing to write home about but we hardly noticed. I suppose we were both thinking about the forthcoming strip show and what the outcome would be. Even the Sekt tasted bland although it was my favourite brand and was properly chilled.

We left the hotel and I led the way while Emil followed in his car.

I'd rented this flat unfurnished and everything in it was of my own choice. Emil fell in love with it on sight, told me I was very talented and ought to take up interior design. It was all very flattering and helped tremendously, because now that the moment had arrived, I was procrastinating. Not only had I suddenly become shy, but I was afraid that his reaction might be unfavourable. Although I hated my masculine body, I had worked very hard on it, what with my exercises, twice weekly sessions in the gymnasium with weights and my martial arts classes, I had a very finely tuned physique.

I couldn't put it off any longer and I said,

"I suddenly feel very self conscious and nervous. Will you pour us both a large brandy then, so that I don't feel like an animal being appraised in a cattle market, will you take your clothes off with me please?"

I didn't wait for an answer. First, the jacket; undo the cufflinks, remove watch then sit on the bed and remove shoes and socks (there is nothing looks more ridiculous than a man wearing only wristwatch and socks), unbutton the shirt, slide it off, next the trousers and finally the underpants, never once looking at Emil. Finally, turn and walk towards him and wait.

He didn't wait. He came straight over to me and held me in his arms and said,

"My Janni. You're still the most beautiful person in the world and I still love you very much."

I had promised myself I would never do it again, but it was beyond my control, tears welled up in my eyes and I gave a couple of involuntary sobs.

"Whatever is the matter?" Emil asked anxiously,

"Nothing", I replied, laughing through my tears. "I'm just so happy. I've never stopped loving you and I've missed you so much."

We stayed together for another three years and Emil came to England with me on a number of occasions when I eventually established contact with the remaining members of my family.

In the finish, it was not Emil who ended the relationship but me. He was coming up to thirty-nine, I was approaching twenty-eight was only fifteen millimetres shorter than him and only a fraction lighter. I'd been shaving for three months. For the first time since Becca died, I had begun to take an interest in girls and at first, Emil thought I was just playing games to make him jealous and it came as something of a shock to him when he realised that my games were becoming serious.

We didn't argue or fight, he was very reasonable and if he was totally honest, I think he was probably glad that it was over, because he was a rising star in his profession and having a very pretty young man as an inseparable companion was narrowing his social circle and causing quite a few raised eyebrows.

We remained very good friends, and kept in touch.

CHAPTER SIXTY-SIX

Finally, in September, nineteen fifty-four, almost exactly fifteen years after I had first left England, I returned for good, still claustrophobic, still suffering the occasional nightmares but the proud possessor of restored British nationality. I was fairly well off but pretty useless in terms of employability.

Of my childhood, I only knew what people had told me, although there were the odd, tantalising half-recollections, just as I recognised the village when I first saw it. My family were all complete strangers and if I'm honest, they have felt like that ever since.

My first real memory is of regaining consciousness in the rubble of the Warsaw Blitzkrieg and I still carry a small dent in my skull, above my forehead, under the hairline as a memento.

Throughout all the intervening years, through many different agencies, I had continued my quest to find Hedwig and Alex without success and when it became easier to travel to Poland, I could not find the courage to return to Warsaw or to revisit Auschwitz as so many managed to do. Indeed, Bergen Belsen was only a relatively short drive from Hamburg and I had never revisited the accursed place even though I had often passed within five kilometres of the site during my trips with Emil.

When I look at the remainder of Rebecca's and my precious stones, I wonder how many remained undetected and how many people went to the gas chambers and were cremated with their jewels still inside their stomachs. The Germans probably had people sifting the ashes for this purpose. They took everything else from them in life and in death, even their hair and the fat from their bodies for industrial use. I know nothing of whether the stones would have survived the intense heat intact.

For the most part I have managed to retain all the good memories, and I have been able to blot out the bad ones. Perhaps one day, I shall pluck up the courage to return but for now, I'll be too busy trying to create a new life.

I have seen Michael and Tim on a number of occasions and we are still good friends and keep in touch regularly. Michael's old boss, Arthur has been an absolute brick in helping me to re-establish my life, even arranging interviews for me with potential employers. They have all been so caring and constant with their unqualified friendship, concern for my well-being and are so unstinting in their kindness and generosity that I feel humbled, undeserving of such loyalty but eternally grateful to them all for helping me through the most difficult times of my life.

I know, because they still persist in calling me by my old name that to all of them, I'm still Janni, the waif and as such, I still love them all just as I used to do.

Arthur and I spent many hours recording this story and in the retelling, the old hatreds and fears returned and with them came a resurgence of the nightmares. I recalled with a dreadful guilt, how callous I had become, how, with the exception of those closest to me, I became indifferent to death and suffering. I remember the faces, the voices even, of those I loved but can recall only a few names of others and cannot no matter how hard I try, put faces to those names even though I had shared bunks with them for months on end, watched some of them die and seen others, no longer fit enough to work, being 'selected' and marched off to KANADA and the gas chambers. I felt no pity. I was thoroughly selfish and had sunk to the level of those I had condemned earlier in the ghetto for the same disregard for all forms of human decency.

Emil and I still correspond and we both live alone. My relationships with girls don't last very long and in all the years since Emil and I parted, I've only had one brief fling with another guy. His name was David. That lasted for about ten days, was very unsatisfactory and I haven't bothered since. In fact, I lead a very celibate existence and people, if they bother to think about it, probably regard me as a cold fish, often distant and frequently disdainful of those I do not like. I do not make friends very easily and I am often very lonely, since, like so many of the other survivors, my experiences set me apart from other men and women. I have undergone mental and physical changes. I am a freak. I have been, with all the others, to Bedlam and back, returning outwardly unscathed, but inwardly, changed beyond all recognition, frequently intolerant and often sarcastic except with my few treasured friends, with whom, because of our shared experiences and our shared love, I behave like a normal individual and thankfully, can allow my emotions to have free rein.

CHAPTER SIXTY-SEVEN
(Final questions to Janni)

That then was Janni's story and one evening, some weeks after we had finished the recordings, I said to him,

"There is something which I have been reluctant to ask you but I need to know, otherwise, your story won't be complete."

"Ask away, I have no secrets from you," he replied.

I gave it a few moments thought and asked,

"Bearing in mind that you only lived a relatively short period of your life as a girl and more than fifty years as a man, can you state, quite categorically, which existence you preferred?"

His reply came without hesitation,

"There is no question about it. My life and lifestyle as a girl was the happiest period of my life and I was on the brink of suicide when it came to an end."

I probed deeper,

"If all the modern drugs and gender re-assignment surgery had been available at the time, would you have taken advantage of them to retain your femininity?"

He lit a cigarette and took his time before answering,

"It's a very difficult question to answer, but bear with me and I'll do my best."

He took a long pull at is cigarette and continued,

"Firstly, I was extremely happy with my body the way it was and so were my two lovers. Even if the surgical skills had been available, I should neither have wanted to nor was it necessary to have my genitals converted.

Apart from which, by all accounts it's quite an excruciatingly painful procedure and therefore something I would not have undergone voluntarily."

He gave a mock shudder at the thought and laughed before continuing,

"If, on the other hand, there had been a 'one-off' course of injections or tablets which would have enabled me to retain all my female characteristics, I should have jumped at the chance but I couldn't have coped with the need to succumb to a lifetime routine of injections and tablets to keep the changes at bay.

"Imagine for one moment, if, convinced that I should remain the same for ever, I had undergone surgery before my male hormones kicked in and, then, when they did and I began to change physically into a man, I'd wantonly interfered with nature and had my dick and testicles removed. As far as I know, there is no way of restoring the complete 'balls and all' tackle and I'd have been left neither one thing nor the other and would, without a doubt have committed suicide. To be honest, I think that trying to alter what Mother Nature has in store for each of us in our individual genetic make-up, is fraught with danger and should only be resorted to in extreme, life-threatening circumstances."

He lit another cigarette, poured us both a drink and said,

"I hope I've answered your question satisfactorily."

I nodded, saying nothing as I pictured him in my mind as I had seen him on that first memorable occasion fifty-five years ago. He was and will always remain, the most beautiful human being I have ever seen. I cannot begin to imagine the depths of despair to which he sank, the sheer desolation at the end of what had been for him, his true life and the years of turmoil, which must have followed. He has suffered more heartbreak, anguish, deprivation, sheer terror, loss and indescribable horrors than anyone I have ever met.

But, the one thing he has never lacked is courage. He faced every setback with great determination and dignity and has never taken refuge in, nor sought pity from others.

In a nutshell, he was and still is a truly remarkable person and I consider myself very lucky to have known him and to have had him as a loyal friend for all these years.

CHAPTER SIXTY-EIGHT
(The homecoming as described by Janni)

England, September, nineteen fifty-four. Apart from a couple of short visits to Tim, it is just over fifteen years since I was here, since England was my home and since I had parents, even if one of them was remote, only seen for a couple of months out of each year. Now it was to be my permanent home again and as I drove from Tilbury Docks on that beautiful sunny day, on the wrong side of the road (for me), I felt like a foreigner, a total alien.

The 'home' that I was going to, was in fact my house, left in trust for me by my absent father and which, should I have pre-deceased my mother, would have passed on to her and upon her death, then, through my mother's will, to her younger sister, my aunt, who now lived there with her husband and one son. She had also inherited quite a large sum of money, again left in trust for me under the same conditions. I will leave you to draw your own conclusions when I tell you that my aunt failed to apply for a death certificate for her younger son who happened to be at a meeting of the Boy Scouts in the local Scout hut when a German bomber being chased by fighters, jettisoned its bombs with the purpose of losing weight and gaining speed. At least one of those bombs scored a direct hit on the scout hut and killed all the Scouts, Guides, Cubs and Brownies who were busily 'Dib Dib Dibbing' away that fateful night. I blame Lord Baden Powell!! My young cousin was literally blown to pieces and none of his remains were ever identified. He was therefore declared 'Missing. Presumed Dead'. In the case of my mother and myself, although we too were both declared 'Missing and presumed Dead', Aunty wasted no time in having us both pronounced dead. She had no problem in obtaining all the appropriate papers, since, in nineteen forty-nine, mother and I had not been heard from in ten years and the circumstances surrounding our supposed deaths left very little room for doubt as to our fate.

As you can well imagine, my 'resurrection' came not only as a surprise, but an unwelcome one at that.

In the short time since obtaining title to the house, the farm and my money, in fact my total inheritance, they had made great inroads into the capital, made a mess of running the farm, having sacked the manager to save money and renting his house out for further income. They knew absolutely nothing about farming, were losing money hand over fist and had mortgaged several of the properties to obtain yet more cash, which they then proceeded to spend with indecent haste and no clear plans.

To compound their wanton behaviour, they had continued to carry on in this vein even after they had been advised of my deliverance and the fact that I would be returning to take up my inheritance. They had known of this since Tim first advised them after my visit in nineteen fifty. Through Tim, they had known that it was my ultimate intention to return home. Without a thought for my father's feelings and what must have been (as he later told me) one of the most joyous moments of his life, they did not inform him of the fact that I had survived until shortly before I was due to arrive home for good and one can draw one's own conclusions for this 'omission'.

The first meeting with my family was going to be extremely fraught to say the least and I can well imagine that in anticipation of the discovery of the full extent of their reprehensible behaviour, sphincter muscles were at the point of losing control.

CHAPTER SIXTY-NINE

I have always hated confrontation in any form and I had already made up my mind that for my part, the first meeting was to be in the form of a 'joyous re-union'. I hoped that they would go along with this line until we had become well enough re-acquainted to get down to the more recriminatory, abusive meetings, which would surely follow. I had no wish for the situation to descend to these levels, but it would depend very much upon the attitude of my family as to which way negotiations would proceed. Their deliberate squandering of my assets despite their knowledge of my impending return gave me little hope of a smooth passage when making my decisions known to them.

Already, the antagonism must have started and must have been well on the way to festering because, upon hearing from my father about all the provisions he had made for me, on Tim's advice (he had been managing my finances for over five years), I had obtained injunctions preventing them having any further access to the funds still in their accounts and prohibiting them from raising money on any of the properties. This action had seriously impaired my uncle's full time occupation, which appeared to be dedicated to drinking the nation dry of every known alcoholic beverage, all at someone else's expense of course.

My surviving cousin and his wife, who were both gainfully employed, were living rent and rates free with his parents in my house. They knew that this arrangement was about to come to an end.

All in all, I did not expect to be popular, or to be greeted with open arms.

CHAPTER SEVENTY

I arrived at the gates to the main house, opened them, drove through and, hoping that I was adopting the appropriate 'country code', closed them after driving through to prevent any livestock from going astray. Always assuming that there was any livestock left to stray. When I had been here before with Tim, we had approached the house from a side road with a side gate leading directly to the house. I had chosen this way simply to get an idea of the extent of the place.

The drive was quite long and impressive although the verges required some attention and a few potholes were in urgent need of repair.

I pulled up at the main door which was quite imposing and took a tentative step towards it. I hesitated for a few seconds before returning to my trusty Volkswagen to lock it. From now on, I should have to think in terms of prevention being better than cure for I had no idea of the extent of their penchant for pilfering my possessions.

Before I could ring the bell, a lady whom I assumed to be my aunt opened the door. She confirmed this by stepping forward rather stiffly because of the need to clench the cheeks of her bottom together and opened her arms, expecting me to rush into them for a welcoming hug as she said,

"I am your Aunt Helen and I suppose that for now, we must call you Janni."

I played along, allowed myself to be enfolded and responded by giving the old bat a peck on the cheek saying,

"What a lovely welcome Aunt Helen and yes, for the time being I should prefer it if you all called me Janni because that has been my name for over fifteen years and I might not respond if I'm addressed differently. That might convey the impression that I was being very rude. The last thing I want to do."

We entered the large hall and if I was hoping for any burst of recognition from an inanimate object, particularly as 'old clenched cheeks' had failed to register in my memory, I was disappointed. Nothing. No illuminating flashbacks or spontaneous sense of direction. I was a total stranger as was the house and all of the family as I met them in turn. This, considering the situation and out of necessity, how ruthless I was going be, was probably for the best. I would have hated to treat 'family' in the way that I proposed to treat this diabolical bunch.

We made small talk and as was my uncle's wont, he seized upon the opportunity to invite us all to help him drink copious amounts of alcohol. I made sure that from my polite refusal and expression he was aware of my total contempt, but lessened the effect by saying that I would prefer to be shown my room, settle in and have a shower before dinner when there would be plenty of time for drinks.

I unpacked in what I had been told was my old room, which was very spacious with lots of windows making it light and airy. There were excellent views from each of the windows and it was comfortably furnished.

I took my time arranging the few of my belongings I had brought with me. The rest of my things, including my piano would be arriving within the next day or two, courtesy of Pickfords.

Satisfied with the appearance of the room and myself, I took two bottles of Deinhardt Sekt down to the kitchen and placed them in the fridge. I made another trip to my car to fetch a bottle of good Armagnac, and a litre bottle each of Scotch and Gin. I placed these on the sideboard in the dining room.

In the sitting room, Uncle Robert, cousin Charles and his wife Jean, were sitting comfortably with the doors to the terrace open letting in the sounds of birdsong and I hoped that the evening would remain as peaceful as it was right at this moment. I noticed that

Uncle had a glass near at hand and from his general demeanour I could tell that this was not his first drink of the evening. He had obviously been fortifying himself for what he must have imagined to be the outbreak of hostilities and this did not bode well for the rest of the evening, because I tend to lose patience with people who, through drink, become pompous, stupid, aggressive or a combination of all three and I also tend to let them know how I feel.

At the moment however, he was giving the impression of being the perfect host, inviting me to drink and virtually ordering me to make myself comfortable. If he remembered that it was in fact my house, he gave no sign of it and behaved very much as though he was 'Lord of the Manor'.

I must have smiled at my own thoughts, but Uncle took this as a good sign and after pouring a small scotch with water for me, he helped himself to a monumental 'only the second today'? and seated himself in what had come to be known as 'his chair'.

Aunt Helen entered the room and I stood up as she did so. She smiled, told me I didn't need to get up and went and poured herself a large sherry.

Once they had all settled down, they all looked at me as though waiting for the start of a concert, recital, or something similar and I wondered if they were expecting me to start ranting and raving. If so, they were in for a surprise.

I offered cigarettes and when everyone had lit up and settled again, I said that they must have so many questions to ask me about what had happened in September 1939 and what I had been doing in all the intervening years. So, to make matters easy for them and to avoid areas about which I was still extremely sensitive, I would give them a brief rundown on the whole thing.

They all seemed to think that this was a very good idea and left me to get on with it. I told them the full story, only omitting the extent of my involvement with Alex and Emil.

During my narration, Uncle helped himself to a couple more 'large ones' and as we headed for the dining room, he had to place his feet very deliberately and make sure that one was firmly secured to the floor before advancing the other. I knew that before the evening was through, he was going to turn belligerent.

Sure enough, the moment came earlier than expected.

I had been making small talk with my cousin and, since everything about England was of great importance to me, I had enquired about the state of the economy and the levels of unemployment. After all, sooner or later, I would have to see about getting a job.

My Uncle seized upon this to open hostilities by assuming that my mention of unemployment was a direct criticism of him and the fact that as far as anyone knew, he had never been gainfully employed or done anything useful for the most part of his life.

He commenced his assault by saying, in a sneering voice, that it was alright for people like me who had money to burn handed down to them on a plate.

I thought this a bit rich and answered by saying that all the money in my bank account I had earned myself and on the contrary, he was the one who had my money handed to him on a plate and had made it his business to 'burn' as much of it as he possibly could.

He started to bluster and call me a cheeky young whippersnapper and other uncomplimentary things. I let him continue in this vein until he ran out of steam.

At this point, I asked him if he had quite finished and before he could respond, I said that at least we now knew where we stood and that his resentment at my survival was not only apparent, but a disgraceful attitude, extremely hurtful and showed him up for the thoroughly nasty piece of work that he was. I said that it had not been my intention to tackle any of the problems surrounding their behaviour until much later when I had hoped to be able to sort things out in such a way that we would all be able to remain on friendly terms.

However, I was not going to accept this sort of behaviour from a stupid, unprincipled oaf, a drunken, thieving ne'er-do-well and without an instant apology from him, he would be packing his bags and leaving MY house within the hour.

There was a hushed silence which they were all afraid to break and I think that, up until that moment, they had thought that because I still looked very feminine and smiled a lot, that I was going to be fairly easy to deal with, a pushover.

I stared hard at my Uncle and kept staring at him as I prompted him by demanding, "Well?"

He could not meet my gaze and he stood up unsteadily. If he hadn't had so much to drink, he would probably have stormed out of the room.

My Aunt went over to his side and after remonstrating with him about his behaviour, told him to apologise to me forthwith and then to go to bed and sleep it off.

He shambled from the room, bumping into things and muttering under his breath then everywhere went quiet. This time, I was not going to be the one who broke the silence.

My cousin was the first to attempt to excuse his father's behaviour by saying that he had been under a lot of strain.

I laughed out loud and said that in the circumstances, it was hardly surprising and added that I didn't object to people drinking and could drink large quantities of it myself, but I could not stand people who could not control themselves. Its one redeeming feature was that people under the influence of drink invariably told the truth because their addled brains could not cope with inventing a convincing lie. Uncle Robert had shown precious little in the way of contrition and even after hearing of the appalling time I had lived through in Warsaw, Auschwitz and Bergen- Belsen, he had not once said, "How dreadful for you" or "We are so glad you survived and got home safely, even if it was after a long time." On the contrary, he made it quite clear that he was totally resentful of my survival that in fact, he wished that I had not. I said that I found it totally unbelievable and that as far as future negotiations were concerned, his presence would not be needed nor tolerated since, in any event, he had not been a beneficiary under my Mother's will.

I shall not bore you with all the nastiness and recriminations which took place after that first 'homecoming', except to say, that apart from issuing direct instructions to my Uncle and my cousin, I never spoke to either of them again. My Uncle died a few years later, the result of a lifetime's heavy drinking and pneumonia. I became quite fond of my Aunt and supported her up until her death in the late nineties. She came to stay with me on many occasions, particularly over Christmas and New Year. My cousin Charles and I have hardly exchanged a word since nineteen fifty-five.

I used all the money that I had accumulated from my 'work' in Germany and the proceeds of the sale of some of my remaining stones (I still have all of Rebecca's) to redeem all the loans my 'family' had obtained on the property and bit by bit, I broke it all up into individual parcels of land, houses etc., and sold them off over a period of a few years.

In hindsight, I would have been a multimillionaire if I were selling them at today's prices. As it was, I recouped my money and made a very reasonable profit, moved back to city life, took a flat in London and finally set about finding employment and a new set of friends.

POSTCRIPT

I never recovered my early memory and the details on my Birth Certificate only served to open up an extremely unpleasant can of worms.

It turned out that my Mother had been housekeeper to a very well known titled family of landowners. She had an affair with the 'master', became pregnant and I was the result.

He, my Father, was a very honourable gentleman and made many provisions for me, and, to conceal the 'awful deed' My mother was transferred to his Scottish estate for the delivery of the offending article….Me!

I was brought up on that estate, hence the slight Scottish accent, long since gone, and to improve my education, I was sent with my Mother to friends in the German part of Poland for extended summer holidays and from there, we would visit other friends and relatives of my Father in Poland itself. These holidays gave my father the opportunity to get away from England and spend some time with his mistress and their son.

Normally, or so I have been told, he could only manage about two or three weeks out of every year whereas Mother and I stayed for several months. By all accounts, we had been doing these rounds since I was two or three, which explained my linguistic skills.

Nothing is certain, but it must have been during a visit to friends in the Polish capital that everything went disastrously wrong and, from what I have been able to glean, being of noble descent and therefore thinking that no one dare harm them or their offspring, the relations and friends of my father, with whom we were staying, thought that since they were German, no member of the family would suffer.

Obviously, their confidence was misplaced!

I still have no logical explanation for the failure of either parent to appreciate the seriousness of the situation at this crucial time, although later decisions of my own tended to prove that I had inherited this same inability to ignore my head and follow my heart instead!

I did catch up with my real Father in the late fifties; he was delighted at my survival, did everything in his power to make life easy for me, which was difficult for him since he had married and had children. We remained very close, having clandestine meetings, dinners and fun times in various locations right up until his death.

I have never betrayed his trust and my half-brothers and half-sisters know nothing of my existence.

Although, in effect, I was his eldest child, illegitimacy would have prevented me making any claim to his title or estates. Not that I ever harboured any desires in that direction.

In so far as inheritance is concerned, I am entitled to all the properties, monies and valuables of the Lipschitz family as set out in Julius' will. However, all such papers were taken from us on the first day in Auschwitz and even if I wanted to lay claim, I have nothing to prove my claim. As it happens, I never had any intention of benefiting from the deaths of that incredibly wonderful family and my only hope is that the present 'owners' of the properties and those who continue to use his fortune for their own ends realise that in a way, they are continuing the persecution and should not rest easily with their consciences.

The words 'It must never be allowed to happen again', have been bandied about by statesmen from many countries, while, at the same time, these same statesmen and their successors have tried everything in their power, by fair means and foul, to retain the fortunes of the Jews murdered in the Holocaust. The British, Swiss, American, German and French governments, amongst others, have fought tooth and nail to deny relatives of those who perished their just inheritance and it is a sad reflection on all concerned that only now, over fifty years too late, only miniscule, token amounts have been released to their rightful owners. This applies too to art collectors, who, despite all the evidence to the contrary, deny that some of the items in their collections are the rightful property of the descendants of many who had also perished in the gas chambers. They too are perpetuating the persecution of the Jews although, being the good, upright citizens they profess to be, they probably expressed outrage at the time when all those reports where coming out of Germany and Poland and the extent of the Nazi excesses was shown on cinemas throughout the civilised world.

The world is full of hypocrites!

For the Jews, the words mean 'It will never happen to us again'. For them, their exiles and persecution should have ended with the recognition, first by the United States of America, of the state of Israel. Up to that point in their history, they had suffered at the hands of so many for thousands of years. Unlike many others, they have never tried to impose, by force or any other methods, their religious views on others. They have maintained strong family loyalties and family life where love and respect are apparent for all to see and they have lived, harmoniously and inoffensively among us, their moderate, principled behaviour an example to us all and one only has to scan the newspapers or listen to the TV news broadcasts to see that by comparison with the rest of us, the incidence of crime involving members of their race is virtually non-existent which says a great deal more about their respect for family values and the property of others than it does of those who would deride them.

With the birth of Israel, the wish to be left in peace and to live in harmony with everyone else, the resolve did not weaken, indeed, as those who have waged war against them have found to their cost.

Such is the determination to ensure that it 'Never happens again', that it would be total folly of the greatest magnitude for any nation, led by fanatics, even to contemplate an attempt to invade Israel.

It is my belief that such is the resolve of that nation, that, regardless of the size of the forces massed against them, all restraints would be removed, they would fight to the last man, woman or child and use all the devastating, up-to-the-minute technology at their disposal to ensure that they are never enslaved again. The result would be the Holocaust to end all Holocausts and the effects would be felt, not only in the Middle East, but also throughout the world for many thousands of years to come.

Despite all the well-intentioned protestations, we have learned nothing from the experiences of the 'death camps '. Genocide is still rampant, from the excesses of Pol Pot, numerous African, Arab, Asian and South American dictators to Americans and Europeans endeavouring to ethnically 'cleanse' their nations. The death toll from these activities since the end of the second world war must run into countless millions and usually, as in the case of Adolf Hitler, these terrible campaigns are the result of one man's twisted, insane visions of a perfect future. In every case, those who had the power and the means to stop them sat back and allowed it to happen.

Alas, they did not have the resolve of the Jews.

Sadly, during the time it has taken to present this story in acceptable form, two of our original 'gang of four' have died within a few months of each other. Arthur and I are the only two left. Tim, the Pay Corps sergeant, who, from the very first day I did guard duty at his place of work, befriended me and did so much over the years to make my return to England not only possible, but far less traumatic than it would otherwise have been and Michael, the Intelligence Corps staff sergeant, Tim's best friend, who like Tim did everything possible to help me through times good and bad. We never exchanged a cross word and enjoyed many memorable times together which will live in my heart forever.

We had all been friends for over fifty-five years and were in regular communication. I loved them both very dearly and have to admit that I almost fell in love with Michael in the early days of our friendship.

One person's death cannot be worse than that of anyone else, but when Emil died just before Christmas last year, a part of me died too. We had loved each other for over sixty years.

Their passing leaves a great void in my heart though they will live on in my mind until my time comes. I shall miss their good-natured banter, their protectiveness towards me and their unstinting love, generosity and friendship.

How lucky I was to have known them.

CHAPTER SEVENTY-ONE

RETURN TO AUSCHWITZ-BIRKENAU

I had spotted the guard towers of that hideous place minutes before the train arrived at Oswiecim station from a southerly direction. It was an overwhelming feeling, something approaching dread which made me look to my left, and there, about a mile distant, although the camp was barely visible through the trees, the watch towers were clearly silhouetted against the late afternoon sky. I could not suppress the involuntary shudder and feeling of nausea, which overcame me, but I continued to search avidly for other evidence that my instinct had not betrayed me. We were past in a matter of seconds, but not before I had seen the rows of brick-built, barrack blocks which had formed the women's camp and the hospital.

The train, which had been travelling very slowly because of repair and maintenance works, in fact, at about the same speed as the train which had first taken me there all those years ago, ground to a halt and there, the bold, fear-inducing name, OSWIECIM (Auschwitz), stood out, defiantly, as though proud of itself, proclaiming to the world "I am Famous".

In that other lifetime, I had arrived from the same direction and the train did not pass though this station but branched off down that now infamous line which took it straight through the entrance, now familiar to millions and under its central tower, ever onward, to the 'Selektion Ramp'.

It was only a brief halt and then we were moving again to pass through another station whose name was also instantly recognisable: BRZEZINKA (Birkenau). Then we were past, heading towards Krakow where I had made my hotel reservations.

The train journey had left me tired and drained so the moment I was in my room, I showered, washed my hair and put on a complete set of clean clothes. These tasks completed, I went to the bar and fortified myself for the days to come.

CHAPTER SEVENTY-TWO

After a good night's sleep and an excellent breakfast, but afraid that I should be unable to enter the place alone, I elected to join a party on a paid tour which went by coach and had excellent, well-informed guides.

The journey took about forty-five minutes in the comfortable coach and we chatted about ourselves to one another, making many new friends. No one else on the coach was an ex-inmate and therefore could not have imagined what I was feeling as we arrived at the vast car park of 'Auschwitz One' and began to disembark.

I experienced a sort of abject terror mixed with a ghastly, ghoulish nostalgia and an overwhelming desire to run back to the coach and hide from the awful, almost palpable aura of this vile place. I felt very sick in my stomach and my hands were shaking as I dragged my feet, following the others through the reception area.

We stopped and looked at a few exhibits and photographs before being ushered into a small but comfortable cinema where an introductory film, giving a good background in preparation for the rest of the tour was shown. It lasted about fifteen minutes.

We left the cinema through a pair of side doors which opened directly onto a path that led straight towards those much-photographed gates bearing those words, carefully, cynically chosen to convey hope: "ARBEIT MACHT FREI" (Work sets you Free).

Reluctantly, I ambled forward, holding back at the rear of our party and almost instinctively adopting the subservient, eyes down shuffling gait which was the accepted method of walking by the parties going to and from work, avoiding all eye contact with anyone in uniform. I passed through those gates, trying to recall how many times before I had trodden this very path and as I left them behind me, very slowly, I raised my eyes and to my right, I saw immediately the small area where the camp orchestra had played nearly every morning as the inmates marched to work. Thoughts and clear mental pictures of Rebecca flooded into my mind and I could not suppress the sobs, which shook me nor prevent the tears, which streamed down my cheeks. I cried unashamedly.

A delightful Australian lady and her husband (Margaret and Brian), who was about the same age as myself, stopped to comfort me and from then on accompanied me for the rest of the visit together with an extremely kind Scottish gentleman called Neville. I cannot thank them enough for their support, sympathy and compassion.

We went into several of the blocks where there were photographs and further exhibitions. I had been in some of these blocks on many an occasion; where there were reconstructions of original sleeping quarters, they were very accurate and I felt the old intense claustrophobia and dread seeping inexorably over me. I had to go out and have a cigarette, which raised a few eyebrows. Then, they all understood and left me to compose myself with the comforting smoke.

Now, we approached a thoroughly evil place. Blocks ten and eleven. Block eleven turned out to be far worse than I had ever realised because I should point out that since leaving at the end of nineteen forty four, I have never wanted to read a book, have any discussions, or see any film about the Holocaust. Indeed, I never wanted to meet any other survivors or become part of an 'elite' clique who would be preyed upon by ghouls in search of lurid details to satisfy their sick minds. The atrocities, sadistic cruelty and downright brutality that took place in these two blocks made me realise how very lucky I had been. The courtyard between the two was where the executions took place. The end of the enclosed yard, at the other end from the Iron Gate had a structure in front of it known as 'The Black Wall'. Here, those sentenced to death would be stripped naked, made to face the wall and an SS Officer would walk up behind them, one at a time and shoot them in the back of the head. Those awaiting execution would see this happening. One SS man alone, Obersturmfhrer

Palitsch was said to have shot several thousand prisoners here. Estimates of the overall number whom he shot in cold blood vary from twenty to twenty-five thousand. Whatever the figure, one was one too many. What sort of mentality must it take to relish such a task and carry it out with pride?

Mercifully towards the end of nineteen forty three Rudolf Höss was replaced by Arthur Liebehenschel as commandant (I hope I got the spelling right) and he put an end to these endless, early hours of the morning executions. He was later replaced by yet another new commandant, Richard Baer and then finally Höss the 'Odious little shit' as 'Emil' called him, returned to take up the post once again.

In the main part of the book, I made it clear from the outset that it was not my intention to dwell on the horrors of Auschwitz-Birkenau, but now, I realise that perhaps I should have given them some space.

By comparison with the feelings I was experiencing now, my life, as I reported it then seems shameful and trivial and I felt terribly guilty, as though I had actually betrayed all those who had loved and trusted me. I was extremely upset and thoughtful as we left this block and walked through to where the roll calls and hangings took place. It was exactly as I had remembered it and as I had sketched it in the sanctuary of 'Emil's' quarters. I had witnessed multiple hangings here as had many of us for these were meant to be an 'example' to us.

From here, we walked to the surviving gas chamber and 'Krema' (crematorium), sited only sixty - seventy metres from the Commandant's house where Höss had lived with his wife and children!! Between his house and the gas chamber stood the specially constructed gallows on which Höss had been hanged as a war criminal.The Gas chamber and 'Krema' were truly awful and despite being one of the longest surviving former inmates of Auschwitz, it was the first time I had seen inside one of these truly evil places. I had never seen any of the activities going on there which was all the more surprising because 'Emil's' office was directly opposite this site in the Administration Block. I rang Emil when I returned home and asked him about this and he said that it was the practise to form 'Sonderkommandos' (special groups made up from the inmates) to remove the bodies from the gas chambers and take them to the 'Krema' where they would also have to place them on trolleys and put the corpses into the ovens. Similar groups did identical work in Birkenau. Because of what they had witnessed, they were to be given no chance of testifying and as a result, every so often, all these Sonderkommandos were, in turn, gassed and cremated and new groups formed. Emil pointed out that despite my relatively privileged position as his orderly, the same fate would have awaited me if I had witnessed these mass murders. For this reason, he always made sure that we were somewhere else when these 'special actions' took place. Indeed, for this same reason, he elected to carry out all his duties from an office in the SS Barracks, pleading the excuse that the distance was too far for him to travel to Auschwitz One every morning and afternoon, bearing in mind the extent of his injuries. This way, we were both at the point of the camp furthest away from the Gas chambers and 'Krema' adjoining 'Kanada' and no longer went to the Admin block overlooking the original chamber in Auschwitz One.

As we were leaving this part and heading once again for the infamous gate, something had been niggling away at the back of my mind and I wondered why, despite all my feelings, the place no longer looked as intimidating as it once had. It was not the absence of guards or dogs or the sound of shots, screams from beatings being administered by savage 'Kapos' or SS Men, nor the absence of prisoners shuffling round in their rags and poorly shod feet. Then it dawned on me: All the wire, barbed and electrified had been removed, with the exception of a few strands here and there. Although the fence posts with their porcelain insulators were still in evidence, the removal of the wire had also removed one of the very many elements which had the effect of inducing real fear.

We left through THE GATE. I did not turn to look back. I had returned to lay ghosts and demons but had only succeeded in resurrecting many more. They will continue to haunt me for the rest of my days.

CHAPTER SEVENTY-THREE

It was a relief to get back to the main reception area, drink a cup of coffee and smoke another cigarette.

Before leaving the main reception building, I had scanned the photos lining the walls, desperately searching for a glimpse of Rachel or Rebecca or any other member of my 'family'. Again, scanning the names on the piles of suitcases on display behind the plate glass windows hoping to see a familiar name.

In retrospect, it was perhaps more merciful that I found none. In all probability, my emotions would not have been able to cope with any such discoveries.

We re-boarded our coach for the short trip to Birkenau arriving at the car park by that now, much photographed, equally infamous entry building with the railway passing through it, directly below its squat tower.

Once inside and despite the continuous, dead straight run of the railway line, straight to the Selektion Ramp, I lost my bearings. I couldn't understand why at first and then, the reason was all too apparent, I was looking for something, which no longer existed, and this confused me. Where literally two to three hundred wooden 'blocks' had stood, now, there remained only part of a row, which had been the men's 'quarantine' camp. As far as the eye could see, all that remained were the chimney stacks of those once, filthy, lice infested, over-populated ex -stables. Even the two rows which had stood behind this first part-row, which had been the 'Family Camp' and had been euphemistically called Theresienstadt (if my memory serves me correctly) had disappeared except for a latrine block.

There were lots of Jewish students, the boys wearing prayer shawls and yarmulkes and the girls carrying Israeli flags much in evidence, groups of them saying Kaddish and other Jewish prayers and occupying most of the remaining buildings. We managed to enter a reconstructed 'block' made from the timbers of the few surviving buildings and I have to admit that it was a very faithful copy. So powerful was it's impact that almost at once, I felt the need to start scratching.

People from our group were asking questions of our extremely competent, young guide and he asked me if I would mind answering some of their questions.

I agreed.

The guide, pointing to the tiers of ramshackle bunks in which we often slept eight in a row, asked if I would mind telling them which was the better place to sleep, bearing in mind the inadequacies of the heating system, the fact that the walls and roof were only the thickness of one plank and the walls, in places had small gaps under them through which the wind howled and the snow blew. Everyone expected the answer to be 'The Middle' tier. When I said "The Top" people automatically responded, "Of course, warm air rises!" Partially true, but the main reason was that nearly everyone had either typhus or dysentery or both and since the bed boards had many gaps in them and mattresses were virtually non-existent, lice, scabs, dry-powdered excrement, urine and the contents of people's bowels would fall through onto those below. It paid to be young and fit so that each night, one could climb as fast as a squirrel in the race for the top bunks.

I think it was then that some of the horror began to make its impact felt upon the visitors.

On to the latrine block where three rows of concrete WCs still stood, in each, double rows of holes in the cast concrete. The washing facilities had gone except for the concrete floor.

Continuing the theme of dysentery, and typhus, the guide pointed out that the water had never flowed properly for the washing facility and the underground supplies were often frozen solid for months on end. The filthy and, insanitary conditions led to massive outbreaks of typhus. The guide mentioned that even one of the camp doctors had died of typhus and one of the ladies, bless her, asked why the people were not vaccinated or inoculated against it. Again, the guide asked if I would be kind enough to answer.

Once again, I agreed and answered without pulling any punches:

"You must appreciate that the whole purpose of the camp was ultimately to kill all the inmates when they were no longer capable of work. Indeed, immediately after 'Selektion', mothers with very young children, the old and infirm and others who were unfit for work would be marched directly from the ramp to the showers (Gas Chambers) and then be cremated. They had been reduced to ashes within an hour of arrival at Birkenau. There was no way that they would waste time and money on people who were going to die anyway especially as there were replacements coming in by trainloads every day. To make matters worse, the latrines had no running water and no proper drainage system and these had to be emptied by hand and, I mean that quite literally. Without any means of cleaning oneself properly following such work, it requires very little imagination to realise that typhus would spread even quicker and do the job of the gas chambers, not as efficiently, but, just as effectively and the guards had squeezed every last ounce of work out of them to the bitter end."

We left the latrine block, glad of the fresh air and together with Brian and Neville and a couple of others, we started to walk down the long road which ran beside the railway to the 'Ramp', the brick buildings of the women's camp, still in very good order to our left. The blocks, which stood closer to the rail track together with the buildings closest to the main gate in which, medical experiments were carried out were dark reminders of other terrifying aspects of this awesomely evil place. In their final days, the SS had certainly made every attempt to destroy the most incriminating of sites but this was still there, a testament to Mengele and his ilk whose use of human guinea pigs in pursuit of his badly flawed theories involved extremes of pain, unendurable suffering and cruelty beyond the bounds of human comprehension.

At this point our guide informed us that the time of our tour was up and that we must return to the coach. This came as something of a surprise and a disappointment to my newfound friends because they were eager for me to give them all the details of the other parts of the camp towards which we had been heading and there were still so many places which I wished to visit alone. I made up my mind to return under my own arrangements the following day.

There was nothing for it but to follow our guide back to the bus.

On the way back, I was asked many more questions and I pointed out that I had written a book, which would now be completed with details of this return visit. All of them asked what the book would be called, when it would be published (to which I could give no answer) and we all exchanged email addresses with them eliciting the promise from me to advise them the moment it was to be published and them promising in return to buy it. Indeed, Brian and Margaret asked me to visit them in Australia if I was doing a promotional tour there.

The coach dropped us off at our various hotels and my first stop was at the hotel bar where I 'tried' several large vodkas before going to my room to stretch out for an hour or so before dinner.

To say that I was still somewhat shaken and disturbed by my innermost thoughts would be something of an understatement. I made no attempt to register my immediate thoughts on paper because a lot of them were irrational and would have come out as a jumble of confused impressions rather than fair, clinically analyzed comment.

I slept a little and when I awoke feeling very jaded and un-refreshed, I had a shower, put on some clean clothes and, feeling much better, dined excellently yet again in the hotel's first class restaurant.

It had been my intention to take the morning train back to Prague and spend the night there. Instead, I went to the station and altered my booking to take the night train with a couchette (the journey takes something approaching nine hours) and took the next train to Oswiecim.

I hired a taxi for several hours and returned to Auschwitz One alone.

At the spot where Rebecca had played with the camp orchestra and in the 'Block' where Julius, Aaron and Isaac had lived, I stood quietly, not so much in prayer, because I had ceased to believe in a God over sixty years ago, but in my heart, wishing them all well, hoping that they, together with Rachel, were all re-united and assuring them of my continued and undying love.

I returned to my taxi and drove on quickly to Birkenau.

Here, unhampered by being part of a group, I walked round the ruins of the main camp, noticing that 'Mexico', the new extension, which had been under construction on the eastern side of the men's barracks, was also virtually non-existent. Having established this location, I realised that the SS Barracks, where I had done all 'Emil's' cleaning and ironing, had been allowed to bathe and use his toilet and had indulged in all sorts of other 'activities', had actually been outside the camp, and, looking from inside, to the left of the main entrance. A busy road now passed through this spot and I could not identify any of the remaining buildings.

I continued walking along the eastern boundary to the junction with the northern boundary of the men's barracks, turned left and walked to 'Kanada'.

Past the site of the temporary gas chamber and the disrobing barracks, where those about to die were told to remember where they put their clothes so that they could find them easily after they had showered! It was drizzling slightly as it had been the day before and I refrained from walking into the wooded area in which were situated the pits where the bodies of executed Russian POWs had been burned. On, past the first part of 'Kanada' compound at the north end of which had stood Gas chambers and 'Kremas' IV and V. Now, past the main area of 'Kanada' where the sorting of all the clothing, shoes, jewellery, spectacles etc took place and where all the bundles of human hair were stored prior to transportation back to Germany and where Rachel and Rebecca had first been employed. At the top end of these blocks was the place where new inmates were disinfected, after having our heads shaved. Then, issued with our striped suits and being tattooed, we were allocated to our new 'homes'. To the south side of 'Kanada', between the fence and the Gypsy camp, were the ash pits. Whether or not it was the rain or just my imagination, I cannot say, but I was acutely aware of the pungent, acrid smell of ashes. I shuddered and moved on quickly past the old sewage plant to the shattered remains of Gas chambers and 'Kremas' II and III. Back now, following the railway line down towards the 'Ramp' once more. The Medical Barracks to my right, the Gypsy camp, followed by the Men's camp to my left. Now, the women's camp to my right, where poor, dear Rachel had been executed in reprisal for some other's attempts to commit suicide by hurling themselves onto the electrified fencing. I stood there a long time remembering her, so beautiful, so thoughtful, so caring and so generous with her love and affection for me. I bade her a long, loving, very tearful farewell and carried on past what had been the Hungarian women's camp to my left, followed by 'Theresienstadt' (the family camp) and finally past the men's quarantine blocks. I turned to look back. It was calm and quite peaceful in the light drizzle as I stood, running my finger over the slight dent in my skull, just above the hairline on the left of my forehead, eyes closed, picturing the scene as it had been all those years ago. A hive of activity, continuous construction work going on to make the camp ever larger, trains arriving at regular intervals disgorging their terrified 'passengers' onto the ramp, some with only a matter of minutes left of their lives. Black oily smoke belching forth from the chimneys and with it, the all-pervading sickly sweet smell which seemed to find its way, not only into one's clothing, but right inside one's body so that the smell was permanently in one's nostrils and we could actually taste it.

I opened my eyes, the vision left me and still rubbing the dent in my head where the chunk of masonry which had caused it and had brought about my amnesia, left its permanent reminder. I wondered for a brief moment if somehow, it could all have been just a terrible dream, a continuous, wild hallucination. But no, it wasn't any temporary insanity of mine that had created this place only in my mind, but the totally evil, barbaric plotting and scheming of a collection of mentally deranged fanatics.

I headed for the car park and took my taxi back to Oswiecim.

I had been astonished during the last two days by the very large numbers of people arriving by the coach load to visit these places, old and young alike. I wondered for what diversity of reasons they all came. It would be a difficult and complex path to follow and would need a better trained mind than mine to answer the question.

I knew why I had returned.

Before leaving Birkenau and before I sum up the overall effect this return visit has had upon me, I should like to make an number of observations about the behaviour of the many visitors who were there in Auschwitz One and Birkenau on both days that I was there.

Many may find my views very controversial and may well feel that in some ways, the views that I am about to express are in some way insulting. Let me make it clear from the outset that I have no intention of insulting the Jewish race nor the memory of all those who perished here for there were many thousands of Non-Jews who suffered an identical fate here at the hands of the same persecutors.

My main complaint was the arrogance of these young Jews, so young in fact that I doubt if their parents were old enough to have been born when all the dreadful events which took place here had occurred.

They assumed a sort of proprietorial right to behave exactly as they pleased, to be intolerant of other visitors and on occasions to be downright rude towards people whom they clearly thought had no right to be in 'Their Place'. One Jewish girl, who couldn't have been more than eighteen or twenty years old, without politely asking or even waiting her turn walked up behind an aging gentleman and saying nothing, pushed him aside in a quite peremptory manner just so that she could take a photograph. There was no hint of an apology and it was clear from her expression that her attitude was, 'I am Jewish and that means that we have greater rights than anyone else in this place.'

This brings me to the unpalatable thoughts, which have been plaguing me of recent years:

Immediately after the war and on through the trials and tribulations of the infant state of Israel, one could find many reasons to excuse the behaviour of that nation towards the rest of the world, foremost among these was the 'Holocaust'. After sixty years, there can be few survivors of that terrible period in their history and I think that, as an excuse for their own, recent questionable actions, it is time they jumped off the 'Holocaust' bandwagon. It is well past its sell by date.

In contrast, some of the Jewish youths were noisy, laughing, climbing in the tower of the Main Gate at Birkenau leaning out of the windows, shouting and joking. I found their behaviour insensitive and insufferable.

The other, non-Jewish visitors on the other hand, who made up the vast majority, were quiet, subdued and behaved more appropriately and with a greater degree of dignified solemnity as opposed to the overt, in-your-face, theatrically staged services which prevented many of the visitors access to many of the places which they had paid to see.

I preferred to do my remembering and grieving alone and in silence.

Before recording the overall effect upon me of this traumatic visit I should like to make an observation on the official estimate of the number of people who died in Auschwitz-Birkenau. This figure is currently estimated to have been in the region of one and a half million. At his trial, Rudolf Hss boasted that, under his control, the combined camps had 'disposed' of, 'or, in his own words, 'processed' close to three point four million. The exact total will never be known, but I am inclined to believe that a more accurate figure would be somewhere between the two.

What are my reasons for this assumption?

They are many.

Firstly, the numbering (tattooing) system was changed three times during my period of occupancy, making continuity of records very difficult.

No accurate numbers were kept of the Russian POWs who were executed then incinerated in those vast pits, nor of the total number executed in the medical blocks or Block eleven where they died from starvation, suffocation and death by shooting.

No accurate records exist of the numbers who died from typhus, dysentery or any other illnesses.

The people who went directly from the 'Selektion Ramp' to their deaths often outnumbered the people who were declared 'fit for work' and these poor souls were not tattooed so no accurate figures exist for these 'disposals'.

In addition, many died on the working parties, particularly those who were sent to work in Auschwitz III (Monowice) and in many of the other Auschwitz sub-camps which were dotted around the area.

Add to this the deaths by hanging, suicides, individual or mass shootings as reprisals and brutal beatings, again, of which no records were kept and the figure continues to multiply.

Finally, it has been stated that the average daily 'capacity' for the Gas Chambers and 'Krema' was from four to six thousand and bearing in mind that in the autumn of nineteen forty-four, it was claimed that with the whole process continuing for twenty-four hours per day, seven days per week, they were 'disposing' of fourteen thousand Hungarian Jews per day. With this in mind, if you take just one period of three months and allowing for gross exaggeration, put the figure at three thousand five hundred per day, you arrive at a figure of around three hundred thousand. On this basis and even adjusting for the fact that in it's early years, it was far less efficient, 'Kremas' II, III, IV and V only becoming operational over a period of three years, it is inconceivable that in the other four and a half years of its existence, they only killed one point one million.

CHAPTER SEVENTY-FOUR

The first and possibly the most important thing that I should say about the impact upon me of this dreadful place is, that apart from an overwhelming sadness there is also a profound sense of despair.

Despair for what has happened in the world since this place flourished. I use the word 'flourished' because that is what it was allowed to do by people who would describe themselves as normal, average, decent people.

How was it possible for these 'decent' people to allow themselves to become so indoctrinated that they turned their backs on every known form of civilised behaviour? When any citizens of any country become the subjects of a dictatorship which has no scruples, only the motivation of hate and envy and determined to right the wrongs, real or imagined, the people become subservient to the will, often imposed by force and severe penalties, of the dictator and his lackeys.

This holds true for either political or religious fanatics or a combination of both.

I shall not pursue this line of thought because to do so would require another book of much greater length than this one.

Suffice to say, for those who still believe in the existence of an all-powerful, omnipotent being,

"God preserve us all from political and religious fanatics, whatever their faith or political persuasion."

To address my own, deeper, personal feelings and reactions, I must start with the feeling of guilt at my own survival while so many, many others died.

It is no consolation to me that I have been assured by those 'counsellors' who purport to know and understand these matters, that this guilt complex is a common phenomenon of all survivors of tragedies, no matter how large or small. This gives me no comfort.

I try to find excuses and yet, only a few paragraphs earlier, I was criticising the Jews for 'riding on the back of the Holocaust'. I am no better.

My excuse for my behaviour is, always has been and will probably continue to be, that my life began the moment I was dragged from the rubble in Warsaw in 1939. My 'childhood' began at that precise moment. For this reason, I was impressed by many things, which, had I been aware of my existence before that time, would no longer have held such significance, nor had quite so much impact upon me as they did. In retrospect, I apologise to all you readers who might have thought that in the main narrative, I was obsessed with trivia, my own appearance and childish pride and observations about those things which gave me pleasure and tended to make me appear a better person than I was. I was certainly vain and proud of my strange physical characteristics, but in the end, it was these self same 'abnormalities', which saved me.

Hindsight becomes a great leveller!!

I have been asked by my biographer if, on my first day on the 'Ramp' at Auschwitz, I had been confronted by a very ugly, brute of an officer, who, nevertheless, had shown more than a passing interest in me, would I have behaved in exactly the same way as I did?

It is a question I have asked myself many, many times. I would hope that my answer would have been a definite NO.

Because of the way I looked, I quickly became accustomed to the unwelcome approaches of soldiers and civilians alike and, of necessity, learned how to handle the situations. I also learned how to be a good scrounger and provide for my 'family'. To use the modern vernacular, I became exceedingly 'streetwise', but in all other matters, I was very, very naïve. After all, I was only thirteen and a half or fourteen and my life had literally begun in 1939. I had to learn very quickly and there was no room in this learning curriculum for anything which did not produce immediate and profitable rewards.

When I was bundled out of that cattle truck at Oswiecim, I was just as stunned, terrified and confused as everyone else and did not have, nor could have made any plans for my survival.

Fate, and that is what it must have been, intervened on my behalf that day.

'Emil' had never been to the 'Selektion Ramp' on any previous occasion and was only there to inform another officer that his brother had been killed in action. He had sent the officer to his quarters and told him that he would be sent home on leave immediately to his grieving parents. 'Emil' was still on the ramp moments later as 'our' train arrived.

When Aaron shouted, "He's a boy, not a girl", Emil turned to look in our direction.

He told me later that he was extremely 'intrigued'!!

Because of his very senior rank, no one questioned him when he called me to "Come up here and drop your trousers".

He told me he was very impressed by my air of defiance. In actual fact, I was almost peeing myself with fright. But, being street wise, I recognised more than interest in his look and after I had dropped my underpants, I slowly raised my eyes and stared directly at him and into his eyes. I liked what I saw as a man and what I saw in his eyes. Something told me that this man would be my saviour. I make no bones about it, I let him know, just with my eyes that I would be a willing participant in whatever he had in mind. If that sounds shameful and like the behaviour of a common tart, my only defence is to say that until any of my critics has been in the position where their life or death would be decided in a matter of seconds, particularly if they were only sixteen and a half or seventeen and that they had the means to survive handed to them on a plate, they would have taken that option.

Many people, male and female, much older than me, made the same decision and a great number of the SS Officers had long-running affairs with inmates, including Rudolf Hss himself.

In addition, up until the dramatic physical changes which happened to me from the very end of 1949, to all intents and purposes, I considered myself a girl.

Certainly I was selfish, indifferent to the suffering of many others, but so was everyone else, thinking only of oneself. At least I tried to do as much for my family as I could because I felt that I owed nothing to anyone else, only those who had loved me and had taken me into their home and their hearts. Even that was a very risky business and I could not have accomplished what I did without the support and connivance of Emil. That in the end it all proved to be of no avail was heart-breaking. I didn't need another visit to Auschwitz to remind me of them, or to make me weep for them. I have done that over the past fifty-eight years on many an occasion.

One has to start to forgive and forget somewhere. I chose to start by forgiving all the people amongst us who, before we went into the Ghetto, during our time in the Ghetto and our time in the Camps, betrayed members of their own race and those of other races for their own gains and to save their own skins. Who knows whether or not they would do the same under such extremes of pressure? I am confident that no act of mine harmed another living soul and should not be considered by any of my critics in the same breath as those misdeeds.

I forgive some of the guards who, very bravely declined, even under threat of severe punishment, possibly death, to carry out the gruesome tasks they were ordered to perform. A lot of the guards 'did their duty' under great duress and some, in fact many, were not brave enough to stand up to the power of 'The Third Reich' and thus betray the oath they had taken to the 'Fuhrer'.

Some were beyond forgiveness. It is impossible to forgive and forget that which is truly evil.

Having said that, I cannot harbour hatreds. To do so is, in it's turn, a way of perpetuating that evil.

Whole nations and by contrast, small communities or, whole families have been torn apart for years, sometimes even centuries, by grievances so old that it is doubtful whether the protagonists could state with any degree of accuracy, the original cause or causes for the long-running feud or hatred. But one thing is very certain, their children, who are born totally innocent and trusting, will be taught by their parents and their elders to hate, just as they had learnt from their parents and so it will continue until someone has the courage to say 'Enough is Enough'. There will never be peace anywhere on earth until people have learned to forgive and not to taint the minds of their children with bitterness.

I hope that my experience in those dreadful places has made me a better person, more tolerant, more ready to forgive, more ready to listen to the other person's point of view and to try to accept some of the unpleasant changes which have now become 'normal' in this modern age.

One last thought: Despite all the hardships which we all endured in Warsaw, it's Ghetto and the Camps, apart from the very nasty form of German which was spoken and the mishmash of abusive terms which became an integral part of the inmates' vocabulary, truly foul language was seldom heard except from some of the viler 'Kapos' and their criminal associates. By contrast with the language used in films and on the television and indeed, in everyday conversation by both men and women, boys and girls, ours was virtually angelic. It seems to go hand in glove with totally boorish behaviour, lack of good manners, respect for one's elders and those in positions of authority. Downright, aggressive rudeness is par for the course and people resort to violence all too frequently. We live in an avaricious, greedy, grasping society where the number one priority is oneself with little or no care for others.

Where will it all end? Sooner or later someone will come into power and bring in drastic measures, which we will all approve initially because we are fed up with what is happening around us. Next, as a deterrent, will come the re-introduction of capital punishment. This in turn will be abused by those in power, who now brook no opposition, to rid the land of dissidents (for this read opposition or ordinary people who don't agree with all the 'government's' policies). For 'government' read dictatorship. From there, it is only a short step to eliminating alleged troublemakers, ethnic groups and all other political parties.

Does this have a familiar and terrifying ring about it?

I had better stop here lest people think that I am not as tolerant as I profess to be!

A BRIEF MEDICAL NOTE

I am not qualified to make any particular observations about Janni's unusual physical characteristics, but in discussions I have had with a number of members of the medical profession, the general consensus of opinion was that Janni was born with what is known as XXY chromosomes.

In that period covering Janni's 'problems' not very much was known about this syndrome although the Nazis, through the likes of Mengele and other medical colleagues, had a long-established genetic research programme which had been operating since the mid thirties and was linked to their quest for racial purity. Apparently they had synthesized male growth hormone - testosterone quite some time before the war.

My understanding is thatonce a course of this has been initiated, the results are irreversible as opposed to the female growth hormones of oestrogen and progesterone, the effects of which stop with the termination of the treatment and the patient reverts to his/her former condition.

Greater study and research has now been carried out into the sort of condition from which Janni suffered. It must be emphasised that in those early days, the life expectancy of anyone suffering this unusual complaint was not very high and few, if any, made it much beyond thirty years. It affected the sufferers in many different ways, some grew very tall with large feet and hands, other, like Janni remained small and acquired all the female characteristics, some with both male and female genitalia. Many suffered learning difficulties and Janni admits to having definite problems in this area and great difficulty in reading.

These days, a lot more is known about this abnormal condition and it is referred to as Klinefelders Syndrome. Caught early enough the treatment is relatively straightforward; a lengthy course of treatment with injections of male growth hormone.

Janni is convinced that without seeking his permission, the doctors in the Hamburg hospital who looked after him during his long illness and who had undoubtedly benefited from the results of those dreadful research programmes, put im on a very lengthy course of this treatment. Janni reluctantly admits that although they changed his life forever, it was ironic that in the end, he benefited from the worst excesses of the Nazi regime and that they most assuredly saved his life!!